ELEMENTARY NUMBER THEORY

BY

EDMUND LANDAU

TRANSLATED BY

JACOB E. GOODMAN
Columbia University

WITH EXERCISES BY

PAUL T. BATEMAN
Professor of Mathematics
University of Illinois

AND

EUGENE E. KOHLBECKER
Assoc. Professor of Mathematics
University of Utah

CHELSEA PUBLISHING COMPANY
NEW YORK

The present work is a translation into English, by Jacob E. Goodman,
of the German-language work ELEMENTARE ZAHLEN-
THEORIE (Vol. I_1 of Vorlesungen ueber Zahlentheorie), by
Edmund Landau, with added exercises by Paul T. Bateman and
E. E. Kohlbecker

SECOND EDITION

Library of Congress Catalogue Card No. 57-8494

Printed in the United States of America

PUBLISHER'S PREFACE

THE READER may be interested in having more bibliographical detail than can be found on the title page of the present work or on the verso of the title page.

To begin with: Professor Landau gave a six-semester course on Number Theory at the University of Göttingen, which was published in three volumes as *Vorlesungen über Zahlentheorie* (Leipzig, 1927), each volume being in two sections. The titles of these six sections are *Aus der Elementaren Zahlentheorie* and *Aus der Additiven Zahlentheorie* (Vol. I), *Aus der Analytischen Zahlentheorie* and *Aus der Geometrischen Zahlentheorie* (Vol. II), and *Aus der Algebraischen Zahlentheorie* and *Über die Fermatsche Vermutung* (Vol. III).

When *Vorlesungen über Zahlentheorie* was reprinted in 1947, the part on Elementary Number Theory was issued separately as *Elementare Zahlentheorie*, with a German-English vocabulary. This made the book somewhat more accessible to students; but it was hoped that the book would ultimately become available in English, and this hope is now realized.

The present work, then, is a translation of *Elementare Zahlentheorie*, to which has been added exercises for the reader by Professor Paul T. Bateman of the University of Illinois and Professor Eugene E. Kohlbecker of the University of Utah. It is thus the textbook equivalent of the first semester of Professor Landau's course on Number Theory.

3

PREFACE

IN EACH OF THE SIX SEMESTERS from the Fall Semester of 1921 through the Spring Semester of 1924, I gave a four-hour course on Number Theory at the University of Göttingen. The content of the courses was so very different from the material presented in the standard textbooks that I decided to follow numerous suggestions to publish the material of my lectures. [See Publisher's Preface.]

Among the topics from the theory of integral rational numbers that I have included over and above the basic classical results are the beautiful results of modern number theory that we owe to such leading scholars as van der Corput, Hardy, Littlewood, and Siegel.

As to the theory of algebraic number fields, my one and only fixed goal was to present, after an exposition of the elements, the two most important results that have been obtained concerning the so-called Last Theorem of Fermat, as well as the proofs of those results. Thus, I first give an exposition of Kummer's Theorem to the effect that for every so-called regular prime number $p>2$, the equation $\xi^p+\eta^p+\zeta^p=0$ cannot be solved in algebraic (non-zero) integers of the field of the p-th roots of unity, and thus in particular cannot be solved in rational integers none of which is zero. The proof of this theorem of Kummer's is so difficult that even, for example, in Bachmann's book on the Fermat problem the main lemma (which contains the whole difficulty and which itself can be proved only as the last link of a long chain) is stated without proof. Thus, the only exposition of the matter in the entire literature is Hilbert's *Zahlbericht*; however, everything is presented there in the framework of more general ideas. From this source, I extracted, simplifying as far as possible, the arrangement of the proof in the present work. The second result that I prove concerning Fermat's Theorem is the Theorem of Wieferich, which is as follows: If $x^p+y^p+z^p=0$ has a solution in integers none of which is divisible by p, then $2^{p-1}\equiv1 \pmod{p^2}$; I also prove Mirimanoff's supplementary result to the effect that $3^{p-1}\equiv1 \pmod{p^2}$ as well.

As for the rest, my lectures are concerned primarily with the theory of the rational integers. I attach great value throughout to a presentation of the new theories concerning the—for the most part—old complexes of problems which does not stress the greatest generality obtainable but, rather,

4

goes just so far that the most characteristic form of a result applies, but applies to problems with as few parameters as possible. Since each section of the work is prefaced by a more-or-less lengthy introduction, I will mention here only a few details.

1. I do not speak of the Waring-Kamke problem but of the Waring-Hilbert problem and I prove, following Hardy and Littlewood, that all large numbers can be written as a sum of 19 fourth powers, and almost all of them (this notion will be defined) as a sum of 15 fourth powers; similarly, for all exponents k other than 4.

2. I prove Thue's theorem, and Siegel's sharpening of it, only for ordinary diophantine equations, not for equations with algebraic coefficients and unknowns. Thus, the reader can find in this book Thue's famous theorem as a special case, to wit: Every diophantine equation $g(x, y) = a$, where $g(x, y)$ is an irreducible homogeneous polynomial of degree higher than second with integer coefficients, has only a finite number of solutions.

3. In the theory of lattice points, I include, to be sure, van der Corput's main theorem from his Thesis, but otherwise I treat in the main the very special problem of the number $A(x)$ of lattice points in the circular disk $u^2 + v^2 \leq x$, because all the essential ideas of the theory show up in this problem. The reader will be astonished to see how little depth is involved in the theorem by Hardy and myself (1915) and in the theorem of van der Corput (1923) to the effect that the (as yet unknown) lower bound ϑ of all a for which $A(x) - \pi x = O(x^a)$ is on the one hand $\geq \frac{1}{4}$, and on the other hand $< \frac{1}{3}$. True, it was a labor of some years to reduce things to this simplicity. I did not find my new proof of the theorem $\vartheta \geq \frac{1}{4}$ until toward the end of the sixth semester. Also, the proof given later in this book for $\vartheta \leq \frac{37}{112} < \frac{1}{3}$ is the union of three new proof arrangements by Littlewood, Walfisz, and myself.

Needless to say, in working out the lectures for publication, I have changed the order of the topics somewhat. On the other hand, I have made hardly any additions or omissions.

I will mention a few more details concerning the content. First, this work is not intended to compete with my two published volumes on Prime Numbers nor with my book on the Theory of Ideals. There are relatively few points of contact. Nor was it my intention to give a comprehensive treatment of all of number theory. A comparison with the content of the relevant encyclopedia articles or with Dickson's *History of the Theory of Numbers* shows how big is the world of number theory and with how small a part of this world the reader will become acquainted in these many pages. But I shall lead him to the classical regions and to the most beautiful of the hitherto hardly accessible regions; some preference has been shown for places the roads to which it was my privilege to help build, a preference, that is, for the analytic part of the theory of rational integers.

For the convenience of the reader, there are no footnotes and only few bibliographical references. From the above-mentioned excellently arranged historical sources (the encyclopedia and Dickson) the reader can ascertain with little trouble where the original papers are to be found.

Following the wishes of my friends, I have retained the lively and sometimes jocular style of my lectures as far as possible and have not completely replaced it with a dry textbook style.

My thanks go first of all to the authors of the beautiful works (especially those from the most recent decades) whose fruits I was able to harvest. Most especially, I thank my assistant of many years past, and present colleague, Privatdozent Dr. K. Grandjot, who knows the entire field thoroughly, gave me the most valuable help during the preparations of the lecture, and finally, checked through the manuscript. In reading proofs, I also enjoyed, in addition to Dr. Grandjot's help, the collaboration of an outstanding expert in the field of analytic and geometric number theory, my student Dr. A. Walfisz. Furthermore, Miss L. Kirchhoff (stud. math.) not only rendered valuable and understanding assistance with the proofs but also went to the great trouble of producing a fair copy of my entire manuscript. I most heartily thank these three faithful collaborators.

I also wish to express my thanks to the firm of S. Hirzel, who undertook the publication of this work and thus made possible its appearance in book form.

Göttingen, February 23, 1927

EDMUND LANDAU

CONTENTS

PART ONE

Foundations of Number Theory

PART TWO

Brun's Theorem and Dirichlet's Theorem

PART THREE

Decomposition into Two, Three, and Four Squares

PART FOUR

The Class Number of Binary Quadratic Forms

APPENDIX

Exercises

PART ONE

FOUNDATIONS OF NUMBER THEORY

CHAPTER I

THE GREATEST COMMON DIVISOR OF TWO NUMBERS

Until further notice, lower case italic letters will always represent integers, i.e.

$$1, \quad 2, \quad 3, \dots \text{ (positive integers or natural numbers)},$$
$$0 \qquad\qquad \text{(zero)},$$
$$-1, -2, -3, \dots \text{ (negative integers)}.$$

The following facts will be used constantly: If a is an integer, then so are $-a$ and $|a|$; if a and b are integers, then so are $a+b$, $a-b$, and ab; if $a>b$, then $a \geq b+1$; and if $a<b$, then $a \leq b-1$.

DEFINITION 1: *Let $a \neq 0$; let b be arbitrary. Then b is said to be divisible by a if there exists a number q such that*

$$b = qa.$$

This q, namely $q = \dfrac{b}{a}$, is then uniquely determined.

We also say that: b is a multiple of a, a is a divisor of b, a divides b, or a goes into b. In symbols,

$$a|b$$

If $a \neq 0$ and b is not divisible by a, then we write

$$a \nmid b.$$

Examples: $2|6$, $4 \nmid 6$, $3 \nmid 4$, $2|-4$,

$a|0$ for every $a \neq 0$,

$1|a$ and $-1|a$ for every a,

$a|a$ and $a|-a$ for every $a \neq 0$.

THEOREM 1: *If $a|b$, then*

$$a|-b, \quad -a|b, \quad -a|-b, \quad |a| \big/ |b|.$$

Proof: By hypothesis we have $b=qa$; furthermore $a \neq 0$, and therefore $-a \neq 0$ and $|a| \neq 0$. It follows that

$$-b=(-q)a, \quad b=(-q)(-a), \quad -b=q(-a), \quad |b|=|q||a|.$$

11

THEOREM 2:   *If $a|b$ and $b|c$, then $a|c$.*

This is also expressed as follows: Divisibility is transitive.

Proof: By hypothesis $a \neq 0$, and there exist two numbers q_1, q_2 for which

$$b = q_1 a, \quad c = q_2 b.$$

From this it follows that

$$c = q_2 q_1 \cdot a.$$

THEOREM 3:   1) *If $ac|bc$, then $a|b$.*
2) *If $a|b$ and $c \neq 0$, then $ac|bc$.*

Proof: 1) Since $ac \neq 0$, we have $a \neq 0$ and $c \neq 0$. Moreover, $bc = qac$; hence $b = qa$.

2) Since $a \neq 0$, we have $ac \neq 0$. Moreover $b = qa$; hence $bc = qac$.

THEOREM 4:   *If $a|b$, then $a|bx$ for every x.*

Proof: $b = qa$, $bx = qx \cdot a$.

THEOREM 5:   *If $a|b$ and $a|c$, then $a|(b+c)$ and $a|(b-c)$.*

Proof: $b = q_1 a$, $c = q_2 a$, $b \pm c = (q_1 \pm q_2) a$.

THEOREM 6:   *If $a|b$ and $a|c$, then $a|(bx+cy)$ for any x and y.*

Proof: By Theorem 4,

$$a|bx, \quad a|cy;$$

therefore, by Theorem 5,

$$a|bx+cy.$$

THEOREM 7:   *If $a>0$ and b is arbitrary, then there is exactly one pair of numbers q and r such that*

(1) $$b = qa+r, \quad 0 \leq r < a.$$

($r=0$ corresponds to the case $a|b$.)

"Dividend = (incomplete) quotient times the divisor + remainder,
$0 \leq$ remainder < divisor."

Proof: 1) I first show that (1) has at least one solution.

Among all the numbers of the form $b-ua$ there occur negative and positive ones (namely, for sufficiently large positive u and for negative u having sufficiently large absolute value, respectively). The smallest non-negative number $b-ua$ occurs for $u=q$. If I set

$$b-qa=r,$$

then
$$r=b-qa\geq0,\ r-a=b-(q+1)\,a<0,$$

so that (1) is satisfied.

2) The proof of uniqueness goes as follows: If (1) holds and if $u<q$, then
$$u\leq q-1,\ b-ua\geq b-(q-1)\,a=r+a\geq a;$$

if (1) holds and if $u>q$, then
$$u\geq q+1,\ b-ua\leq b-(q+1)\,a=r-a<0.$$

The desired relations
$$0\leq b-ua<a$$

thus hold only when $u=q$.

THEOREM 8 (for $g=10$ this is the familiar representation of a in the decimal system): *Let $g>1$. Then any number $a>0$ can be expressed in one and only one way in the form:*
$$a=c_0+c_1g+\cdots+c_ng^n,\ n\geq0,\ c_n>0,\ 0\leq c_m<g\ \text{ for }\ 0\leq m\leq n.$$

Proof: 1) I first prove the *existence* of such a representation (using mathematical induction).

For $a=1$, the existence is obvious ($n=0$, $c_0=1$, $0<c_0<g$).

Let $a>1$, and assume the assertion true for $1, 2, \ldots, a-1$. a belongs to one of the intervals $1\leq a<g$, $g\leq a<g^2$, $g^2\leq a<g^3$, ... (ad infinitum). Hence there is some $n\geq0$ for which $g^n\leq a<g^{n+1}$. By Theorem 7, we have
$$a=c_ng^n+r,\ 0\leq r<g^n.$$

c_n must be >0, since $c_ng^n=a-r>g^n-g^n=0$; in addition, $c_n<g$, since $c_ng^n\leq a<g^{n+1}$.

If $r=0$, we are finished ($a=0+0\cdot g+\cdots+0\cdot g^{n-1}+c_ng^n$, $0<c_n<g$).

If $r>0$, then, since $r<g^n\leq a$, we have
$$r=b_0+b_1g+\cdots+b_tg^t,\ t\geq0,\ b_t>0,\ 0\leq b_m<g\ \text{ for }\ 0\leq m\leq t.$$

t must be $<n$, since $g^n>r\geq b_tg^t\geq g^t$; therefore
$$a=b_0+b_1g+\cdots+b_tg^t+0\cdot g^{t+1}+\cdots+0\cdot g^{n-1}+c_ng^n.$$

2) The proof of *uniqueness* goes as follows: Let
$$a=c_0+c_1g+\cdots+c_ng^n=d_0+d_1g+\cdots+d_rg^r,\ n\geq0,\ c_n>0,\ 0\leq c_m<g$$
$$(\text{for }\ 0\leq m\leq n),\ r\geq0,\ d_r>0,\ 0\leq d_m<g\ (\text{for }\ 0\leq m\leq r).$$

The assertion is that $n=r$ and that $c_m=d_n$ for $0\leq m\leq n$. If this were not so, then, by subtraction, we would have

$$0=e_0+\cdots+e_s g^s,\ s>0,\ e_s\neq 0,\ -g<e_m<g\ \text{for}\ 0\leq m\leq s;$$

hence

$$g^s\leq|e_s g^s|=|e_0+\cdots+e_{s-1}g^{s-1}|\leq(g-1)(1+\cdots+g^{s-1})=g^s-1.$$

THEOREM 9: *Let* $a>0$ *and* $b>0$. *Of all the common multiples of* a *and* b (there are such multiples, and even positive ones: for example, ab and $3ab$), *let* m *be the smallest positive one and let* n *be any of them* $\left(n\gtreqless 0\right)$. *Then*

$$m|n.$$

In words: Every common multiple is divisible by the smallest positive one.

Proof: By Theorem 7, the numbers q and r can be chosen such that

$$n=qm+r,\ 0\leq r<m.$$

From

$$r=n-qm=n\cdot 1+m(-q)$$

and

$$a|n,\ a|m,\ b|n,\ b|m,$$

it follows by Theorem 6 that

$$a|r,\ b|r.$$

Hence, by the definition of m, r cannot be >0. Therefore

$$r=0,\ n=qm,\ m|n.$$

THEOREM 10: *If* $a\neq 0$ *and* $b|a$, *then*

$$|b|\leq|a|,$$

so that every $a\neq 0$ *has only a finite number of divisors.*

Proof: $\qquad a=qb$ and $q\neq 0$;
therefore

$$|q|\geq 1,\ |a|=|q||b|\geq|b|.$$

THEOREM 11: *Let* a *and* b *not both be* 0. *Let* d *be the greatest common divisor of* a *and* b. (d exists and is >0; for at least one of the numbers a, b is $\neq 0$ and hence, according to Theorem 10, has only finitely many divisors; and the number 1 is certainly a common divisor of a and b.)

1) *If* f *is any common divisor of* a *and* b, *then*

$$f|d.$$

In words: Every common divisor goes into the greatest common divisor.

2) *If $a>0$, $b>0$, and m is the smallest positive common multiple of a and b, then*

$$md=ab.$$

In particular, then: If $a>0$, $b>0$, and $d=1$, then $m=ab$.

Proof: Case I: Let $a>0$ and $b>0$. Since ab is a common multiple of a and b, then by Theorem 9,

$$m/a\,b,$$

$$\frac{a\,b}{m} \text{ is an integer.}$$

Setting

$$\frac{a\,b}{m}=g,$$

we shall prove the following:

a) that if f/a and f/b, then

$$f/g,$$

b) that

$$g=d$$

(which will prove all our assertions in Case I).

In fact,

a) If f/a and f/b, then

$$a/a\,\frac{b}{f}, \quad b/b\,\frac{a}{f}\,.$$

$\dfrac{a\,b}{f}$ is thus a common multiple of a and b; hence by Theorem 9,

$$m/\frac{a\,b}{f},$$

$$\frac{a\,b}{g}\Big/\frac{a\,b}{f},$$

so that the quotient

$$\frac{a\,b}{f}:\frac{a\,b}{g}=\frac{g}{f}$$

is an integer, and consequently

$$f/g.$$

b) Since

$$\frac{a}{g}=\frac{m}{b}, \quad \frac{b}{g}=\frac{m}{a}$$

are integers, we have

$$g/a, \quad g/b;$$

g is thus a common divisor of a and b. Since, by a), every common divisor f of a and b goes into g, and $g>0$, we have by Theorem 10,

$$f \leqq g,$$

so that g is the greatest common divisor of a and b.

Case II: Suppose that the assumption $a>0$, $b>0$ is not satisfied but that a and b are still both $\neq 0$. Then 1) follows from Case I, since a has the same divisors as $|a|$ and b the same divisors as $|b|$. In fact, d is the greatest common divisor not only of a and b but of $|a|$ and $|b|$ as well.

Case III: Let one of the two numbers be 0, say $a=0$, so that $b \neq 0$. Then obviously $d=|b|$, and from $f|0$ and $f|b$ it follows that $f|d$.

Notation: *For any a and b which do not both vanish, the greatest common divisor of a and b is denoted by (a, b).*

Examples: $(4, 6)=2$; $(0, -3)=3$; $(-4, -6)=2$; $(1, 0)=1$.

Theorem 12: *If a and b are not both 0, then*

$$(a, b)=(b, a)$$

Proof: The definition of (a, b) is obviously symmetrical in a and b.

Definition 2: *If $(a, b)=1$, that is, if 1 is the only positive common divisor of a and b, then a and b are called relatively prime.*

We also say: a is relatively prime to b. 1 and -1 are then the only common divisors of a and b.

Examples: 1) $(6, 35)=1$, since 6 has $1, 2, 3,$ and 6 as its only positive divisors, and none of the numbers $2, 3,$ and 6 goes into 35.

2) $(a, 0)=1$ for $a=1$ and for $a=-1$, but for no other a.

Theorem 13: *If $(a, b)=d$, then $\left(\dfrac{a}{d}, \dfrac{b}{d}\right)=1$.*

Proof: If $f>0$, $f\left|\dfrac{a}{d}\right.$, $f\left|\dfrac{b}{d}\right.$, then by Theorem 3, 2) we have

$$f\,d|a, \quad f\,d|b,$$

and therefore by Theorem 11

$$f\,d|d,$$

so that by Theorem 3, 1)

$$f|1, \quad f=1.$$

Theorem 14: *If $c>0$, $c|a$, $c|b$, $\left(\dfrac{a}{c}, \dfrac{b}{c}\right)=1$, then $c=(a, b)$.*

Proof: Since $\dfrac{a}{c}$ and $\dfrac{b}{c}$ do not both vanish, a and b are not both 0. If we set $(a, b)=d$, then $c|d$ by Theorem 11, so that $\dfrac{d}{c}$ is an integer. From

$$\frac{d}{c}\frac{a}{d}=\frac{a}{c}, \quad \frac{d}{c}\frac{b}{d}=\frac{b}{c}$$

it follows that

$$\frac{d}{c}\Big/\frac{a}{c}, \quad \frac{d}{c}\Big/\frac{b}{c},$$

and therefore, since $\left(\dfrac{a}{c}, \dfrac{b}{c}\right)=1$, $d>0$, $c>0$,

$$\frac{d}{c}=1, \quad c=d.$$

THEOREM 15: *If $a|bc$ and $(a, b)=1$, then $a|c$.*

In words: If a number divides the product of two numbers and is relatively prime to one of them, then it divides the other.

Proof: By assumption, $a\neq0$.

1) If $b=0$, then $a=\pm1$, since $(a, 0)=1$; and hence $a|c$.

2) If $b\neq0$, let m be the smallest positive common multiple of the relatively prime positive numbers $|a|$ and $|b|$. By Theorem 11,

$$m=|a||b|.$$

Since, by hypothesis, bc is a common multiple of $|a|$ and $|b|$, we have, by Theorem 9,

$$|a||b||bc,$$
$$ab|bc \quad \text{(Theorem 1)},$$
$$a|c \quad \text{(Theorem 3, 1))}.$$

THEOREM 16: *If $a\big|\prod\limits_{n=1}^{v} a_n$, $v\geq2$, $(a, a_n)=1$ for $1\leq n<v$, then*

$$a|a_v.$$

Proof: For $v=2$, this is shown by Theorem 15. For $v>2$, Theorem 15 yields, successively,

$$a\Big|\prod_{n=2}^{v} a_n, \quad a\Big|\prod_{n=3}^{v} a_n, \quad \ldots, \quad a\Big|\prod_{n=v-1}^{v} a_n, \quad a|a_v.$$

CHAPTER II

PRIME NUMBERS AND FACTORIZATION INTO PRIME FACTORS

The number 1 has only one positive divisor, namely 1; every number $a>1$ has at least two positive divisors, namely 1 and a.

DEFINITION 3: *A number $a>1$ is called a prime number (or simply a prime) if it has only two positive divisors* (namely 1 and a).

Examples: The first few primes are 2, 3, 5, 7, 11.

The letter p will be reserved for prime numbers only; likewise, symbols such as $p_1, p_2, \ldots, p', p'', \ldots$ will always represent primes.

Our next aim will be to prove that every number $a>1$ can be represented as a product of primes (this will be easy) and that this representation is unique apart from the order of the factors (this is somewhat deeper).

THEOREM 17: *Every $a>1$ can be represented as a product of prime numbers:*

$$(2) \qquad a=\prod_{n=1}^{r}p_n, \ r\geq 1.$$

(For primes $a=p$, this is obvious, and the product reduces to $p=\prod_{n=1}^{1}p_n$.)

Proof (by mathematical induction): 1) For $a=2$ the assertion is true, since 2 is a prime.

2) Let $a>2$ and assume the theorem true for 2, 3, ..., $a-1$.

21) If a is prime, the assertion is true.

22) Otherwise, by Definition 3, there exists a factorization

$$a=a_1a_2, \ 1<a_1<a, \ 1<a_2<a.$$

Thus a_1 and a_2, and therefore a also, are representable as products of primes.

Theorem 17 justifies the following definition:

DEFINITION 4: *Every number >1 which is not a prime is called a composite number.*

The natural numbers thus fall into three classes:

1) The number 1;
2) The primes;
3) The composite numbers.

There are, of course, infinitely many composite numbers; for example, all numbers of the form 2^n, $n \geq 2$.

Theorem 18: *There are infinitely many primes.*

Proof: We must show that to any finite set of primes there can be adjoined yet another prime.

Let $p_1, \ldots, p_v$ be distinct prime numbers. Then

$$a = 1 + \prod_{n=1}^{v} p_n$$

is, to begin with, >1 and, in addition, is not divisible by any of the prime numbers $p_1, \ldots, p_v$, so that by Theorem 17 it is divisible by a prime number different from $p_1, \ldots, p_v$.

Theorem 18 can be expressed as follows: For any $\xi > 0$, let $\pi(\xi)$ represent the number of primes $\leq \xi$. Then as ξ approaches infinity, so does $\pi(\xi)$; i.e., given $\omega > 0$ there exists $\eta = \eta(\omega)$ such that

$$\pi(\xi) > \omega \quad \text{if} \quad \xi > \eta = \eta(\omega).$$

The question as to whether, and with what degree of accuracy, $\pi(\xi)$ can be approximated by the functions of analysis, can be answered only later on. In Part 7, Chapter 2, § 3 of my *Vorlesungen über Zahlentheorie,* the reader will find a very accurate result, the methods used being those of complex function theory. This result contains as a special case the "Prime Number Theorem"

$$\lim_{\xi = \infty} \frac{\pi(\xi)}{\dfrac{\xi}{\log \xi}} = 1;$$

this theorem can be found in Part 7, Chapter 1, § 2 of the work cited.

Let us also note here that the question, for example, of whether there exist infinitely many primes whose decimal representations end in the digit 7 will be answered (in the affirmative) in Part Two, Chapter III; specifically, the answer will appear as a special case of Dirichlet's well-known Theorem on Arithmetic Progressions (Theorem 155).

None of this will be made use of, however, until it has first been proved.

Theorem 19: *If $p \nmid a$, then $(p, a) = 1$.*

Proof: p has as positive divisors only 1 and p. Hence $(p, a) = 1$ or p and, since $p \nmid a$, the latter is impossible.

Theorem 20: *If*

$$p \Big| \prod_{n=1}^{v} a_n,$$

then for at least one n we have

$$p | a_n.$$

Proof: If, for all n, $p \nmid a_n$, then by Theorem 19 we would always have $(p, a_n) = 1$, so that, by Theorem 16,

$$p \nmid \prod_{n=1}^{v} a_n.$$

Theorem 21: *If*

$$p \Big| \prod_{n=1}^{v} p_n,$$

then for at least one n we have

$$p = p_n.$$

Proof: By Theorem 20,

$$p | p_n$$

for at least one n; but since the prime p_n has 1 and p_n as its only positive divisors, and since $p \neq 1$, it follows that $p = p_n$.

Theorem 22: *The representation (2) of any number $a > 1$ is unique up to the order of its factors.*

In words: Every prime number appearing in a decomposition into "prime factors" of a given number appears equally often in every such decomposition.

Every $a > 1$ is therefore of the form

$$a = \prod_{p|a} p^l,$$

where p runs through the various primes that divide a; and where every $l = l_{a,p} > 0$ and is uniquely determined by a and p. (This is the so-called canonical decomposition of a.)

Example: $12 = 2 \cdot 2 \cdot 3 = 2 \cdot 3 \cdot 2 = 3 \cdot 2 \cdot 2 = 2^2 \cdot 3 = 3 \cdot 2^2$.

Proof: It is obviously sufficient to prove the following: If

$$a = \prod_{n=1}^{v} p_n = \prod_{n=1}^{v'} p_n', \quad p_1 \leq p_2 \leq \cdots \leq p_v, \quad p_1' \leq p_2' \leq \cdots \leq p_{v'}',$$

then

$$v = v', \quad p_n = p_n' \text{ for } 1 \leq n \leq v.$$

1) For $a=2$ the assertion is true, since we merely have

$$v=v'=1, \quad p_1=p_1'=2.$$

2) Let $a>2$ and suppose that the assertion has been proved for 2, 3, 4, ..., $a-1$.

21) If a is a prime, then

$$v=v'=1, \quad p_1=p_1'=a.$$

22) Otherwise, we have $v>1$ and $v'>1$. Since

$$p_1' \,\Big|\, \prod_{n=1}^{v} p_n, \quad p_1 \,\Big|\, \prod_{n=1}^{v'} p_n',$$

it follows by Theorem 21 that

$$p_1'=p_n, \quad p_1=p_m'.$$

for at least one n and at least one m. Since

$$p_1 \leq p_n = p_1' \leq p_m' = p_1,$$

we have

$$p_1=p_1'.$$

Now (since $1<p_1<a$, $p_1|a$) we have

$$1<\frac{a}{p_1}= \prod_{n=2}^{v} p_n= \prod_{n=2}^{v'} p_n'<a,$$

and hence (by the induction hypothesis)

$$v-1=v'-1, \quad v=v'$$

and

$$p_n=p_n' \text{ for } 2\leq n\leq v.$$

THEOREM 23: *Let $a>1$, let $T(a)$ be the number of positive divisors of a, and let*

$$a= \prod_{n=1}^{r} p_n^{l_n}$$

be the canonical decomposition of a (i.e., p_1, ..., p_r are distinct and every $l_n>0$). Then a has for its positive divisors the numbers

(3) $$\prod_{n=1}^{r} p_n^{m_n}, \quad 0\leq m_n\leq l_n \text{ for } 1\leq n\leq r$$

and no others. Hence

$$T(a)= \prod_{n=1}^{r} (l_n+1).$$

(That the numbers (3) are distinct follows from Theorem 22.)

Proof: 1) Each number of the form (3) obviously divides a.

2) If $d>0$ and $d|a$, then $a=qd$, so that d cannot contain any prime factor that does not divide a, nor can d contain any prime factor of a a greater number of times than that factor appears in a itself.

Definition 5: *For any real number ξ, let $[\xi]$ denote the largest integer $\leq\xi$, that is, the integer g for which*

$$g\leq\xi<g+1.$$

Obviously

$$\xi-1<[\xi]\leq\xi,$$

and if

$$a\leq\xi$$

then

$$a\leq[\xi],$$

and if

$$a>\xi$$

then

$$a\geq[\xi]+1>[\xi].$$

Theorem 24: *The number q of Theorem 7 is equal to $\left[\dfrac{b}{a}\right]$.*

Proof:
$$qa\leq b=qa+r<(q+1)a,$$
$$q\leq\frac{b}{a}<q+1.$$

Theorem 25: *If $k>0$ and $\eta>0$, then the number of positive multiples of k which are $\leq\eta$ is*

$$\left[\frac{\eta}{k}\right].$$

Proof: Since $h>0$ and $hk\leq\eta$, it follows that

$$0<h\leq\frac{\eta}{k}$$

and conversely; but the number of natural numbers $\leq\xi$ is $[\xi]$ for every $\xi>0$.

Theorem 26: *If $k>0$ and $\eta\gtreqless 0$, then*

$$\left[\frac{\eta}{k}\right]=\left[\frac{[\eta]}{k}\right].$$

(For $\eta>0$ this also follows from Theorem 25, for there are just as many positive multiples of k up to η as there are up to $[\eta]$.)

Proof: From

$$g \leq \frac{\eta}{k} < g+1$$

it follows that

$$kg \leq \eta < k(g+1),$$
$$kg \leq [\eta] < k(g+1),$$
$$g \leq \frac{[\eta]}{k} < g+1.$$

THEOREM 27: *Let $n > 0$, and let p be any prime. Then p divides $n!$* exactly

$$\sum_{m=1}^{\infty} \left[\frac{n}{p^m} \right]$$

times.

(This infinite series converges, since the general term vanishes for sufficiently large m, and in particular for $m > \dfrac{\log n}{\log p}$, since we then have $p^m > n$, $0 < \dfrac{n}{p^m} < 1$. The series can therefore also be written as $\displaystyle\sum_{1 \leq m \leq \frac{\log n}{\log p}} \left[\frac{n}{p^m} \right]$, where, in case $p > n$, the sum stands for zero—as shall every empty sum henceforth.)

In other words: We have

(4)
$$n! = \prod_{p \leq n} p^{\sum\limits_{m=1}^{\infty} \left[\frac{n}{p^m} \right]}$$

(where, in case $n=1$, the product represents the number 1—as shall every empty product henceforth) ; for the primes $p > n$ do not divide $n!$. We can equally well write

$$n! = \prod_{p} p^{\sum\limits_{m=1}^{\infty} \left[\frac{n}{p^m} \right]}$$

where the product is taken over all primes arranged in increasing order of magnitude, for every factor is 1 for $p > n$.

Proof: In preparation for later on, I present two proofs.

1) The number of positive multiples of the number p up to n is, by Theorem 25, $\left[\dfrac{n}{p} \right]$; the number of positive multiples of p^2 up to n is $\left[\dfrac{n}{p^2} \right]$; etc.

The multiplicity with which p divides $n!$ therefore

$$= \sum_{m=1}^{\infty} \text{ number of positive multiples of } p^m \text{ up to } n$$

$$= \sum_{m=1}^{\infty} \left[\frac{n}{p^m} \right];$$

for each of the numbers $1, \ldots, n$ is counted l times (and so not at all if $l=0$) as a multiple of p^m for $m=1, 2, \ldots, l$, if p divides it exactly l times ($l \geq 0$).

2) (This proof is longer than the former, and introduces the logarithmic function—which can, of course, be eliminated by the use of exponents—but the proof is otherwise useful.)   Let us henceforth set

(5) $$\Lambda(a) = \begin{cases} \log p & \text{for } a=p^c,\ c\geq 1, \\ 0 & \text{for all other } a>0. \end{cases}$$

(thus $\Lambda(1)=0$, $\Lambda(2)=\log 2$, $\Lambda(3)=\log 3$, $\Lambda(4)=\log 2$, $\Lambda(5)=\log 5$, $\Lambda(6)=0, \ldots$).   Let the symbol

$$\sum_{d|a} f(d)$$

mean, on principle, for $a>0$, that the sum is taken over all positive divisors d of a.

Then we have

(6) $$\log a = \sum_{d|a} \Lambda(d).$$

For (6) is obvious if $a=1$ ($0=0$), and if

$$a = \prod_{p|a} p^r \quad (r=r_{a,\,p})$$

is the canonical decomposition of $a>1$, then

$$\log a = \sum_{p|a} r \log p = \sum_{p|a} (\Lambda(p)+\Lambda(p^2)+\cdots+\Lambda(p^r)) = \sum_{d|a} \Lambda(d).$$

From (6) it now follows that

(7) $$\log([\xi]!) = \sum_{a=1}^{[\xi]} \log a = \sum_{a=1}^{[\xi]} \sum_{d|a} \Lambda(d) = \sum_{d=1}^{[\xi]} \Lambda(d) \left[\frac{\xi}{d}\right].$$

(I am generalizing the result somewhat, in that I replace n by any real $\xi>0$); for $\Lambda(d)$ appears only for $1\leq d\leq[\xi]$, and for each such d it appears as many times as there are positive multiples of d up to ξ, that is, $\left[\dfrac{\xi}{d}\right]$ times, by Theorem 25. By the definition (5) of Λ we have, by (7),

$$\log([\xi]!) = \sum_{p\leq\xi} \log p \left[\frac{\xi}{p}\right] + \sum_{p\leq\xi} \log p \left[\frac{\xi}{p^2}\right] + \cdots \text{ ad inf.} = \sum_{p\leq\xi} \log p \sum_{m=1}^{\infty} \left[\frac{\xi}{p^m}\right],$$

so that the assertion (4) is proved if we set $\xi=n$.

If we wish to apply Theorem 27, we should note that for every $n > 0$ and every p, the terms of

$$\sum_{m=1}^{\infty} \left[\frac{n}{p^m} \right]$$

can be most expeditiously computed one after the other by use of the result

$$\left[\frac{n}{p^{m+1}} \right] = \left[\frac{\left[\frac{n}{p^m} \right]}{p} \right],$$

which follows from Theorem 26.

Example: $n = 1000$, $p = 3$; the calculations should not proceed as follows (every ϑ is > 0 and < 1)

$$\frac{1000}{3} = 333 + \vartheta_1, \quad \frac{1000}{9} = 111 + \vartheta_2, \quad \frac{1000}{27} = 37 + \vartheta_3, \quad \frac{1000}{81} = 12 + \vartheta_4,$$

$$\frac{1000}{243} = 4 + \vartheta_5, \quad \frac{1000}{729} = 1 + \vartheta_6;$$

but rather

$$\frac{1000}{3} = 333 + \vartheta_7, \quad \frac{333}{3} = 111, \quad \frac{111}{3} = 37, \quad \frac{37}{3} = 12 + \vartheta_8, \quad \frac{12}{3} = 4,$$

$$\frac{4}{3} = 1 + \vartheta_9,$$

in order to compute the terms 333, 111, 37, 12, 4, 1, and the final result of 498.

CHAPTER III

THE GREATEST COMMON DIVISOR OF SEVERAL NUMBERS

THEOREM 28: *Let $a \geq 1$ and $b \geq 1$. Let their canonical decompositions be written*

$$a = \prod_{p|a} p^l, \quad b = \prod_{p|b} p^m \qquad (l = l_{a,p} > 0, \; m = m_{b,p} > 0)$$

(where, in case a or $b=1$, the empty product shall mean 1). *If l and m are allowed to assume the value 0, then a and b may be written in uniform notation as*

$$a = \prod_{p|ab} p^l, \qquad b = \prod_{p|ab} p^m.$$

Then

(8) $$(a, b) = \prod_{p|ab} p^{\text{Min}\,(l, m)}.$$

If $\gamma_1, \ldots, \gamma_r$ are real numbers, then Min $(\gamma_1, \ldots, \gamma_r)$ represents here— as it shall from now on—the smallest and Max $(\gamma_1, \ldots, \gamma_r)$ the largest, of the numbers $\gamma_1, \ldots, \gamma_r$.

Examples: Min $(-3, 0, -3) = -3$; Max $(1, 0) = 1$.

Proof: The positive divisors of a are (by Theorem 23) the numbers $\prod_{p|ab} p^t$, $0 \leq t \leq l$; those of b are the numbers $\prod_{p|ab} p^u$, $0 \leq u \leq m$; the common positive divisors are therefore the numbers $\prod_{p|ab} p^v$, $0 \leq v \leq$ Min (l, m) and the right-hand side of (8) is the largest of them.

NOTATION: *If the numbers $a_1, \ldots, a_r$ ($r \geq 2$) are not all 0, then their greatest common divisor* (which of course exists) *is denoted by* $(a_1, \ldots, a_r)$ (in agreement with our former notation for $r=2$).

Examples: $(6, 10, 15) = 1$, $(2, 0, -4) = 2$.

DEFINITION 6: *If $r \geq 2$ and $(a_1, \ldots, a_r) = 1$, then $a_1, \ldots, a_r$ are called relatively prime.* (For $r=2$ this is our old definition.)

THEOREM 29: *If $r \geq 2$ and if $a_1, \ldots, a_r$ are not all 0, then $(a_1, \ldots, a_r)$ is divisible by every common divisor of $a_1, \ldots, a_r$.*

Proof: If only one of the numbers $a_1, \ldots, a_r$ is different from 0, then the assertion is trivial.

Otherwise, without loss of generality, let $a_1, \ldots, a_r$ all be >0; for if they are not, then we merely discard those that equal zero and change the sign of those that are negative.

1) For $r=2$ the assertion is true by Theorem 11.

2) For $r>2$, I give two proofs.

21) Set

$$a_1 = \prod_{p/a_1 \cdots a_r} p^{l_1}, \ldots, a_r = \prod_{p/a_1 \cdots a_r} p^{l_r} \quad (l_1 \geq 0, \ldots, l_r \geq 0).$$

Then (compare the proof of Theorem 28), we obviously have

$$(a_1, \ldots, a_r) = \prod_{p/a_1 \cdots a_r} p^{\text{Min } (l_1, \ldots, l_r)},$$

and every common divisor is

$$\pm \prod_{p/a_1 \cdots a_r} p^v, \quad 0 \leq v \leq \text{Min } (l_1, \ldots, l_r),$$

and hence goes into $(a_1, \ldots, a_r)$.

22) Let the assertion be already proved for $r-1$. Every common divisor of $a_1, \ldots, a_r$ divides $a_1, \ldots, a_{r-1}$ and hence $(a_1, \ldots, a_{r-1})$; it also divides a_r, and hence $((a_1, \ldots, a_{r-1}), a_r)$. This number divides $(a_1, \ldots, a_{r-1})$ and a_r, and hence $a_1, a_2, \ldots, a_{r-1}, a_r$; it is therefore equal to $(a_1, \ldots, a_r)$.

We should make note of the relation

(9) $(a_1, \ldots, a_r) = ((a_1, \ldots, a_{r-1}), a_r)$

for $r>2$, $a_1>0, \ldots, a_r>0$, which we found during the second proof.

THEOREM 30: *Let $r \geq 2$, $a_1 > 0, \ldots,$ and $a_r > 0$. Then every common multiple n of $a_1, \ldots, a_r$ is divisible by their smallest positive common multiple v (which obviously exists).*

Proof: 1) For $r=2$, we know this by Theorem 9.

2) For $r>2$, I give two proofs (as for Theorem 29).

21) In the notation of the previous proof, we clearly have

$$v = \prod_{p/a_1 \cdots a_r} p^{\text{Max } (l_1, \ldots, l_r)}.$$

Either $n=0$ (so that it is certainly divisible by v), or $|n|$ contains every $p|a_1 \ldots a_r$ at least l_1 times, $\ldots$, at least l_r times, and therefore at least Max $(l_1, \ldots, l_r)$ times.

22) Let the assertion already be proved for $r-1$. Let w represent the smallest positive common multiple of $a_1, \ldots, a_{r-1}$, so that n is divisible by $a_1, \ldots, a_{r-1}$ and hence by w; but it is also divisible by a_r and hence by the smallest positive common multiple of w and a_r. Since this number is itself a positive common multiple of $a_1, \ldots, a_{r-1}, a_r$, it must equal v.

CHAPTER IV

NUMBER-THEORETIC FUNCTIONS

DEFINITION 7: *A function $F(a)$ which is defined for every $a>0$ is called a number-theoretic function.*

The value of the function is not required to be a positive integer, nor an integer, a rational number, or even a real number.

Examples: $F(a)=a!$, $F(a)=\sin a$, $F(a)=(a+2)^{-1}$, $F(a)=T(a)$ (the number of positive divisors of Theorem 23), $F(a)=\Lambda(a)$ (Formula (5)), $F(a)=\underset{d|a}{\Sigma}d=S(a)$ (the sum of the positive divisors of a).

THEOREM 31: *If $a>1$ and $a=\underset{p|a}{\Pi p^l}$ is its canonical decomposition, then*

$$S(a)=\underset{p|a}{\Pi}\frac{p^{l+1}-1}{p-1}.$$

Proof: If we add the positive divisors $p_1{}^{m_1}p_2{}^{m_2}\cdots p_r{}^{m_r}$ of a enumerated in (3), and use the fact that

$$\sum_{m=0}^{l}p^m=\frac{p^{l+1}-1}{p-1},$$

then the result follows.

DEFINITION 8: *Any divisor of a other than a itself is called a proper divisor of a.*

DEFINITION 9: *a is called even if $2|a$; odd, if $2\nmid a$.*

Examples: 0 is even; of two successive numbers a and $a+1$, exactly one is always even, the other odd; every $p>2$ is odd.

DEFINITION 10: *$a>0$ is called a perfect number if a equals the sum of its proper divisors, that is, if*

$$S(a)=2a.$$

Examples: $6=1+2+3$, $28=1+2+4+7+14$.

This old-fashioned concept of perfect number, and the questions associated with it, are not especially important; we consider them only because, in so doing, we will encounter two questions that remain unanswered to this day: Are there infinitely many perfect numbers? Is there an odd perfect number? Modern mathematics has solved many (apparently) difficult problems, even in number theory; but we stand powerless in the face of such (apparently) simple problems as these. Of course, the fact that they have never been solved is irrelevant to the rest of this work. We will leave no gaps; when we come to a bypath which leads to an insurmountable barrier, we will turn around, rather than—as is so often done—continue on beyond the barrier.

THEOREM 32: *If* $p=2^n-1$ (so that $n>1$; for example, $n=2$, $p=3$; $n=3$, $p=7$), *then*

$$\frac{p+1}{2}p=2^{n-1}(2^n-1)$$

is a (necessarily even) *perfect number, and there are no other even perfect numbers.*

Proof: 1) For

$$a=2^{n-1}(2^n-1),\ 2^n-1=p$$

we have, by Theorem 31,

$$S(a)=\frac{2^n-1}{2-1}\frac{p^2-1}{p-1}=(2^n-1)(p+1)=(2^n-1)2^n=2a.$$

2) If a is an even perfect number, then

$$a=2^{n-1}u,\ n>1,\ u>0\ \text{and odd},$$

so that, by Theorem 31,

$$2^nu=2a=S(a)=\frac{2^n-1}{2-1}S(u)=(2^n-1)S(u)$$

and

$$S(u)=\frac{2^nu}{2^n-1}=u+\frac{u}{2^n-1}.$$

In this formula, $\frac{u}{2^n-1}$ ($=S(u)-u$) is an integer, and hence (since $n>1$) it is a proper divisor of u. The sum $S(u)$ of all the divisors of u is therefore equal to the sum of u and a certain proper divisor. Hence u is a prime, and the proper divisor $\frac{u}{2^n-1}=1$, so that $u=2^n-1$. This proves the theorem.

Now, are there infinitely many perfect numbers? I do not know. It was already mentioned above that 2^n-1 is prime for $n=2$ and $n=3$. For $n=4$, $2^n-1=15$ is composite. More generally, 2^n-1 is always composite if n is composite; for if $n=bc$, with $b>1$ and $c>1$, then

$$2^n-1=2^{bc}-1=(2^b-1)(2^{b(c-1)}+2^{b(c-2)}+\cdots+2^b+1),$$

where both factors are >1.

For $n=5$, $2^n-1=2^5-1=31$ is a prime that yields the perfect number $16\cdot31=496$; for $n=7$, $2^n-1=2^7-1=127$ is a prime that yields the perfect number $64\cdot127=8128$; for $n=11$, $2^n-1=2^{11}-1=2047=23\cdot89$ is composite. The question is, therefore, whether there are infinitely many primes p for which 2^p-1 is a prime. Even this is not known.

Are there infinitely many odd perfect numbers? I do not even know whether there is a single one.

However, I should like to ask the reader not to meditate too long over these two questions; he will meet with many more promising and gratifying problems in his study of this work.

The analogous problem of finding all the numbers $a>1$ which are equal to the product of their factors, i.e., for which

$$(10) \qquad\qquad \prod_{d|a} d=a^2,\ a>1$$

is trivial. For the following simple theorem holds:

THEOREM 33: (10) *holds if and only if*

$$a=p^3\ or\ a=p_1p_2,\ p_1\neq p_2.$$

Proof: 1) As d runs through all the positive divisors of a, so, obviously, does $\dfrac{a}{d}$. It therefore follows from (10) that

$$a^4=a^2a^2=\prod_{d|a} d\cdot\prod_{d|a}\frac{a}{d}=\prod_{d|a}\Big(d\cdot\frac{a}{d}\Big)=\prod_{d|a}a=a^{T(a)},$$

$$T(a)=4;$$

and hence, by Theorem 23,

$$(l_1+1)\ldots(l_r+1)=4$$

in the canonical decomposition $a=p_1^{l_1}\cdots p_r^{l_r}$, so that either $r=1$ and $l_1=3$, or $r=2$ and $l_1=l_2=1$.

2) Conversely, in these cases,

$$\prod_{d|p_1^3} d = 1 \cdot p_1 \cdot p_1^2 \cdot p_1^3 = p_1^6 = (p_1^3)^2 \text{ and } \prod_{d|p_1p_2} d = 1 \cdot p_1 \cdot p_2 \cdot p_1p_2 = (p_1p_2)^2,$$

respectively.

DEFINITION 11: *The number-theoretic function $\mu(a)$* (the Möbius Function) *is defined by*

$$\mu(a) = \begin{cases} 1 \text{ if } a=1, \\ (-1)^r \text{ if } a \text{ is the product of } r \ (\geq 1) \text{ distinct primes,} \\ 0 \text{ otherwise, i.e., if the square of at least one prime divides } a. \end{cases}$$

The numbers $a \geq 1$ that are not divisible by the square of any prime (or, equivalently, by any perfect square >1) are also called square-free numbers; this quite customary terminology is just as logical as saying that two numbers are prime to each other when they have exactly one positive common divisor (namely, 1). In this sense of square-free, we say: $\mu(a) = \pm 1$ if a is square-free, and $\mu(a) = 0$ otherwise.

Examples: $\mu(1)=1, \mu(2)=-1, \ \mu(3)=-1 \ (\mu(p)$ is always $=-1)$, $\mu(4)=0, \ \mu(5)=-1, \ \mu(6)=1, \ \mu(7)=-1, \ \mu(8)=0, \ \mu(9)=0, \ \mu(10)=1.$

THEOREM 34: *If $a>0$, $b>0$, and $(a, b)=1$, then*

$$\mu(ab) = \mu(a)\mu(b).$$

Proof: 1) If a or b is not square-free, then neither is ab, so that

$$\mu(ab) = 0 = \mu(a)\mu(b).$$

2) If a and b are square-free, then since $(a, b)=1$, ab is also square-free. If $a=1$ or $b=1$, then the statement is obviously true; otherwise the number of prime factors of ab equals the sum of the number of prime factors of a and of b.

THEOREM 35: $\sum_{d|a} \mu(d) = \begin{cases} 1 \ \text{for} \ a=1, \\ 0 \ \text{for} \ a>1. \end{cases}$

Proof: 1) $\sum_{d|1} \mu(d) = \mu(1) = 1.$

2) If $a>1$ and if $a = p_1^{l_1} \cdots p_r^{l_r}$ is the canonical decomposition of a, then obviously

$$\sum_{d|a} \mu(d) = \sum_{d|p_1 \cdots p_r} \mu(d) = 1 + \binom{r}{1}(-1) + \binom{r}{2} + \cdots + \binom{r}{r}(-1)^r$$

$$= \sum_{s=0}^{r} \binom{r}{s}(-1)^s = (1-1)^r = 0;$$

for if $s=1, 2, \ldots, r$, then there are exactly $\binom{r}{s}$ divisors of $p_1 \ldots p_r$ which consist of exactly s prime factors, and for these we have $\mu(d)=(-1)^s$.

THEOREM 36: *If $\xi \geqq 1$, then*

$$\sum_{n=1}^{[\xi]} \mu(n) \left[\frac{\xi}{n}\right] = 1.$$

Proof: Let the formula of Theorem 35 be summed over $a=1, 2, \ldots, [\xi]$. This gives

$$1 = \sum_{a=1}^{[\xi]} \sum_{d|a} \mu(d) = \sum_{d=1}^{[\xi]} \mu(d) \left[\frac{\xi}{d}\right];$$

for, by Theorem 25, the number of positive multiples of d up to ξ is $\left[\frac{\xi}{d}\right]$.

THEOREM 37: *If $x \geqq 1$, then*

$$\left| \sum_{n=1}^{x} \frac{\mu(n)}{n} \right| \leqq 1.$$

Remark: The infinite series

$$\sum_{n=1}^{\infty} \frac{\mu(n)}{n}$$

therefore either converges, or else it oscillates between finite limits. The question as to which of these two alternatives holds does not interest us at the moment; the reader can learn the answer in Part Seven, Chapter 12, § 1 of my *Vorlesungen über Zahlentheorie*.

Gordan used to say something to the effect that "Number Theory is useful since one can, after all, use it to get a doctorate with." In 1899 I received my doctorate by answering this question.

Proof: We have

$$0 \leqq \frac{x}{n} - \left[\frac{x}{n}\right] \begin{cases} <1 & \text{for } 1 \leqq n < x, \\ =0 & \text{for } n=x. \end{cases}$$

Hence, by Theorem 36,

$$\left| x \sum_{n=1}^{x} \frac{\mu(n)}{n} - 1 \right| = \left| \sum_{n=1}^{x} \mu(n) \left(\frac{x}{n} - \left[\frac{x}{n}\right]\right) \right| \leqq \sum_{n=1}^{x} \left(\frac{x}{n} - \left[\frac{x}{n}\right]\right) \leqq x-1,$$

$$\left| x \sum_{n=1}^{x} \frac{\mu(n)}{n} \right| \leqq 1 + (x-1) = x.$$

Theorem 38: *Let $F(a)$ be any number-theoretic function whatever.*
Let $G(a)$ be the number-theoretic function

$$G(a) = \sum_{d \mid a} F(d).$$

Then

$$F(a) = \sum_{d \mid a} \mu(d) G\left(\frac{a}{d}\right).$$

(This is the so-called Möbius Inversion.)

Remark: The fact that $F(a)$ is uniquely determined at all, in reverse, by $G(a)$ is clear to start with; for from

$$G(1) = F(1), \ G(2) = F(2) + \cdots, \ G(3) = F(3) + \cdots, \ \ldots$$

we can successively compute $F(1), F(2), F(3), \ldots$.

Proof: For every positive $d \mid a$ we have

$$G\left(\frac{a}{d}\right) = \sum_{b \mid \frac{a}{d}} F(b),$$

$$\mu(d) G\left(\frac{a}{d}\right) = \sum_{b \mid \frac{a}{d}} \mu(d) F(b),$$

$$\sum_{d \mid a} \mu(d) G\left(\frac{a}{d}\right) = \sum_{d \mid a} \sum_{b \mid \frac{a}{d}} \mu(d) F(b) = \sum_{b \mid a} \sum_{d \mid \frac{a}{b}} \mu(d) F(b)$$

(for b only runs through positive divisors of a, and to every such b there correspond exactly those d for which $d \mid a$ and also $db \mid a$, that is, for which $d \mid \frac{a}{b}$)

$$= \sum_{b \mid a} F(b) \sum_{d \mid \frac{a}{b}} \mu(d) = F(a),$$

since, by Theorem 35,

$$\sum_{d \mid \frac{a}{b}} \mu(d) = \begin{cases} 1 & \text{for } b = a, \\ 0 & \text{for } b \mid a, \ b < a. \end{cases}$$

Definition 12: *The number-theoretic function $\varphi(a)$* (Euler's Function) *represents the number of numbers n in the sequence $1, 2, \ldots, a$ for which $(n, a) = 1$.*

Examples: $\varphi(1) = 1 \, (n = 1)$, $\varphi(2) = 1 \, (n = 1)$, $\varphi(3) = 2 \, (n = 1, 2)$, $\varphi(4) = 2$ $(n = 1, 3)$, $\varphi(5) = 4 \, (n = 1, 2, 3, 4)$, $\varphi(6) = 2 \, (n = 1, 5)$, $\varphi(p) = p - 1 \, (n = 1, 2, \ldots, p - 1)$.

THEOREM 39: $\sum_{d|a} \varphi(d) = a.$

Proof: Divide all the a numbers $n=1,\ldots,a$ into classes according to the value of $d=(n,a)$. Only those numbers $d>0$ that divide a enter into consideration. To each $d|a$ let there belong the $n=kd$ for which $(kd,a)=d$, i.e. (by Theorems 13 and 14), $\left(k,\dfrac{a}{d}\right)=1$ and moreover for which $0<kd\leq a$, i.e., $0<k\leq\dfrac{a}{d}$. But by Definition 12 there are exactly $\varphi\left(\dfrac{a}{d}\right)$ such numbers. Hence

$$a=\sum_{d|a}\varphi\left(\frac{a}{d}\right)=\sum_{d|a}\varphi(d),$$

since $\dfrac{a}{d}$ runs through all the positive divisors of a when d does.

THEOREM 40: $\varphi(a)=a\sum_{d|a}\dfrac{\mu(d)}{d}.$

Proof: By Theorems 39 and 38 (with $F(a)=\varphi(a)$ and $G(a)=a$), we have

$$\varphi(a)=\sum_{d|a}\mu(d)\frac{a}{d}=a\sum_{d|a}\frac{\mu(d)}{d}:$$

THEOREM 41: $\varphi(a)=a\prod_{p|a}\left(1-\dfrac{1}{p}\right).$

Proof: 1) For $a=1$ we have $\varphi(1)=1$ (the product in the statement of the theorem is empty).

2) For $a>1$ let $a=p_1^{l_1}\cdots p_r^{l_r}$ be its canonical decomposition. Then by Theorem 40 we have

$$\varphi(a)=a\sum_{d|p_1\cdots p_r}\frac{\mu(d)}{d}=a\prod_{n=1}^{r}\left(1-\frac{1}{p_n}\right),$$

as is seen by calculating the 2^r terms of the product.

THEOREM 42: *For $a>1$ we have, in the canonical notation,*

$$\varphi(a)=\prod_{n=1}^{r}p_n^{l_n-1}(p_n-1).$$

Proof: By Theorem 41,

$$\varphi(a)=\prod_{n=1}^{r}p_n^{l_n}\cdot\prod_{n=1}^{r}\left(1-\frac{1}{p_n}\right)=\prod_{n=1}^{r}p_n^{l_n}\left(1-\frac{1}{p_n}\right).$$

THEOREM 43: *For $l>0$ we have*

$$\varphi(p^l)=p^{l-1}(p-1).$$

Two proofs: 1) Special case of Theorem 42.

2) (Direct proof.) Of the numbers $1, 2, \ldots, p^l$, those not relatively prime to p^l are precisely all the multiples of p; their number is p^{l-1}; hence

$$\varphi(p^l)=p^l-p^{l-1}.$$

All of Theorem 42 itself can be proven directly by counting the numbers n which are not relatively prime to a and for which $1 \leq n \leq a$; but this is somewhat more laborious and is a good exercise for the reader. (The solution of this exercise is, however, not essential for the remainder of this book.)

THEOREM 44: *If $a>0$, $b>0$, and $(a, b)=1$, then*

$$\varphi(ab)=\varphi(a)\varphi(b).$$

Proof: Without loss of generality let (canonically) $a = \prod_{n=1}^{r} p_n^{l_n} > 1$ and $b = \prod_{m=1}^{s} q_m^{k_m} > 1$. From Theorem 42 it follows that

$$\varphi(a) = \prod_{n=1}^{r} p_n^{l_n - 1}(p_n-1), \quad \varphi(b) = \prod_{m=1}^{s} q_m^{k_m - 1}(q_m-1).$$

Since $(a, b)=1$,

$$ab = \prod_{n=1}^{r} p_n^{l_n} \prod_{m=1}^{s} q_m^{k_m}$$

is the canonical decomposition of ab; hence, by Theorem 42,

$$\varphi(ab) = \prod_{n=1}^{r} p_n^{l_n - 1}(p_n-1) \cdot \prod_{m=1}^{s} q_m^{k_m - 1}(q_m-1)=\varphi(a)\varphi(b).$$

The reader will find another proof of Theorem 44, one based directly on the definition of φ, in Theorem 74.

CHAPTER V

CONGRUENCES

In this chapter m will always be >0.

DEFINITION 13: *a is said to be congruent to b modulo m, written*

$$a \equiv b \ (\text{mod } m),$$

if

$$m|(a-b).$$

a is called incongruent to b modulo m, written

$$a \not\equiv b \ (\text{mod } m),$$

if

$$m \nmid (a-b).$$

Examples:
$$31 \equiv -9 \ (\text{mod } 10),$$
$$627 \equiv 587 \ (\text{mod } 10),$$
$$5 \not\equiv 4 \quad (\text{mod } 2),$$
$$a \equiv b \ (\text{mod } 1) \text{ for arbitrary } a \text{ and } b.$$

Any concept such as "congruent," "equivalent," "equal," or "similar," in mathematics must satisfy three properties (the so-called reflexivity, symmetry, and transitivity properties), which are expressed here by means of the following three theorems.

THEOREM 45 (Reflexivity): *We always have*

$$a \equiv a \ (\text{mod } m).$$

Proof: $m|0, m|(a-a)$.

THEOREM 46 (Symmetry): *If*

$$a \equiv b \ (\text{mod } m)$$

then

$$b \equiv a \ (\text{mod } m).$$

37

Proof: $m|(a-b)$, and hence, by Theorem 1, $m|(b-a)$.

Theorem 47 (Transitivity) : *If*

$$a\equiv b \pmod m, \ b\equiv c \pmod m$$

then

$$a\equiv c \pmod m.$$

Proof: $m|a-b, \ m|b-c, \ m|(a-b)+(b-c), \ m|a-c.$

Thus, just like equations, congruences (with the same modulus) can be written in sequence as a congruence with more than two terms; for example,

$$a\equiv b\equiv c \pmod m.$$

The following theorem (which, incidentally, makes Theorems 45-47 self-evident) provides a useful necessary and sufficient condition for the validity of a congruence.

Theorem 48: *According to Theorem 7, given the numbers c and m, there is a uniquely determined number r such that*

$$c=qm+r, 0\leq r<m ;$$

let this number r be called the residue of c modulo m. Then

$$a\equiv b \pmod m$$

holds if and only if a and b have the same residue modulo m.

Proof: 1) If

$$a=q_1 m+r, \ b=q_2 m+r$$

then

$$a-b=(q_1-q_2)m,$$
$$m|a-b.$$

2) If

$$a=q_1 m+r, \ 0\leq r<m, \ a\equiv b \pmod m$$

then

$$b=a+qm=(q_1+q)m+r=q_2 m+r.$$

Theorem 48 shows that, given a number m, all the numbers fall into m classes ("residue classes") in such a way that any two numbers in the same class are congruent, and any two numbers in different classes are incongruent. One of the classes consists of the multiples of m.

Theorems 49-56 which follow are analogous to the corresponding theorems on equalities; they make clear the usefulness of the congruence sign; looking at it intrinsically, one might have objected that no new symbol is needed for $m/(a—b)$. Since the modulus m in Theorems 49-56 remains the same throughout, we shall not bother to write it for the time being.

THEOREM 49: *If*

$$a \equiv b, \quad c \equiv d$$

then

$$a+c \equiv b+d, \quad a-c \equiv b-d.$$

Proof: $m/a—b$, $m/c—d$, $m/(a—b) \pm (c—d)$, $m/(a \pm c)—(b \pm d)$.

THEOREM 50: *If*

$$a_n \equiv b_n \quad for \quad n = 1, \ldots, v,$$

then

$$\sum_{n=1}^{v} a_n \equiv \sum_{n=1}^{v} b_n$$

Proof: Follows by induction from Theorem 49.

THEOREM 51: *If*

$$a \equiv b,$$

then, for every c,

$$ac \equiv bc.$$

Proof: $m/(a—b)$, $m/(a—b)c$, $m/(ac—bc)$.

THEOREM 52: *If*

$$a \equiv b \text{ and } c \equiv d,$$

then

$$ac \equiv bd.$$

Proof: By Theorem 51 it follows from the first part of the hypothesis that $ac \equiv bc$ and from the second that $bc \equiv bd$; hence, by Theorem 47, the conclusion follows.

THEOREM 53: *If*

$$a_n \equiv b_n \quad for \quad n = 1, \ldots, v,$$

then

$$\prod_{n=1}^{v} a_n \equiv \prod_{n=1}^{v} b_n.$$

Proof: By induction, using Theorem 52.

THEOREM 54: *If*

$$a \equiv b, v > 0,$$

then

$$a^v \equiv b^v.$$

Proof: Follows from Theorem 53.

THEOREM 55: *Let*

$$f(x) = c_0 + c_1 x + \cdots + c_n x^n = \sum_{v=0}^{n} c_v x^v \quad (n \geq 0)$$

be any rational integral function with integer coefficients. If

$$a \equiv b,$$

then

$$f(a) \equiv f(b).$$

The solutions (if any exist) of the congruence

$$f(x) \equiv 0$$

thus fall into complete residue classes mod m.

Proof: By Theorem 54 it follows from the hypothesis that

$$a^v \equiv b^v \text{ for } 0 < v \leq n,$$

so that, by Theorem 51,

$$c_v a^v \equiv c_v b^v \text{ for } 0 < v \leq n;$$

since

$$c_0 \equiv c_0$$

our result

$$\sum_{v=0}^{n} c_v a^v \equiv \sum_{v=0}^{n} c_v b^v.$$

follows by Theorem 50.

Theorem 55 justifies:

DEFINITION 14: *By the number of solutions, or roots, of a congruence*

$$f(x) \equiv 0 \pmod{m}$$

we shall mean the number of those numbers of the set $x = 0, \ldots, m-1$ that satisfy the congruence, that is, the number of residue classes all of whose members satisfy the congruence.

Thus the number of solutions is always either 0 or some other finite number.

Example: $x^2 \equiv 1 \pmod 8$ has four solutions, since $x = 1, 3, 5, 7$ (but not $x = 0, 2, 4, 6$) satisfy the congruence. This fact, that $8 \mid (x^2 - 1)$ for every odd number x, should be kept in mind.

THEOREM 56: *If*

$$ac \equiv bc, \quad (c, m) = 1$$

then

$$a \equiv b.$$

Proof: $m \mid (ac - bc)$, $m \mid (a - b)c$; since $(m, c) = 1$, it follows from Theorem 15 that

$$m \mid (a - b).$$

THEOREM 57: *If*

$$ac \equiv bc \pmod m,$$

then

$$a \equiv b \left(\bmod \frac{m}{(c, m)} \right).$$

(If $(c, m) = 1$, this reduces to Theorem 56.)

Proof: $\quad\quad\quad m \mid (a - b) c,$

hence, by Theorem 3,

$$\frac{m}{(c, m)} \mid (a - b) \frac{c}{(c, m)}.$$

By Theorem 13 it follows that

$$\left(\frac{m}{(c, m)}, \frac{c}{(c, m)} \right) = 1,$$

so that by Theorem 15,

$$\frac{m}{(c, m)} \mid (a - b).$$

THEOREM 58: *Let $c > 0$. If*

$$a \equiv b \pmod m,$$

then

$$ac \equiv bc \pmod{cm},$$

and conversely.

Proof: Since $c > 0$, it follows from Theorem 3 that the relations $m \mid (a - b)$ and $cm \mid c(a - b)$ *are equivalent.*

THEOREM 59: *If*

$$a \equiv b \pmod m, \quad n > 0, \quad n \mid m,$$

then

$$a \equiv b \pmod n.$$

Proof: $m \mid (a - b)$ and $n \mid m$; hence $n \mid (a - b)$.

THEOREM 60: *If*

$$a \equiv b \pmod{m_n} \text{ for } n = 1, 2, \ldots, v \ (v \geq 2)$$

then, if m is the smallest common positive multiple of $m_1, \ldots, m_v$, *we have*

$$a \equiv b \pmod{m}.$$

Proof: $a - b$ is divisible by $m_1, \ldots, m_v$, and hence, according to Theorem 30, by m.

THEOREM 61: *If*

$$a \equiv b \pmod{m},$$

then

$$(a, m) = (b, m).$$

In particular: If $(a, m) = 1$, then $(b, m) = 1$. Consequently the numbers in a residue class are either all relatively prime to m, or none of them is.

Proof: From $b = a + mq$ it follows that $(a, m) | b$, so that $(a, m) | (b, m)$; similarly, $(b, m) | (a, m)$.

DEFINITION 15: *By a complete set of residues* mod m *is meant a set of* m *numbers each of which is congruent to a different one of the* m *numbers* $0, 1, \ldots, m - 1 \pmod{m}$, *that is, a set which contains a representative for each of the* m *classes into which all the integers* mod m *fall.*

It would suffice, of course, to require that at least one of the m numbers belong to each class. "If m objects are put into m pigeon-holes and each pigeon-hole contains at least one object, then each pigeon-hole contains *exactly* one object."

Alternatively: It would suffice to require that each pair of m numbers be incongruent. "If m objects are put into m pigeon-holes and each pigeon-hole contains at most one object, then each pigeon-hole contains *exactly* one object."

Examples: Any m consecutive numbers, for example $1, \ldots, m$, or the integers of the interval $-\frac{m}{2}$ (exclusive) to $\frac{m}{2}$ (inclusive) constitute a complete set of residues, since they are incongruent to each other.

Our old Definition 14 can now be expressed as follows: The number of solutions of

$$f(x) \equiv 0 \pmod{m}$$

is the number of its solutions taken from any complete set of residues.

DEFINITION 16: *By a reduced set of residues* mod m *is meant a set of* $\varphi(m)$ *numbers exactly one of which belongs to each of the classes all of whose numbers are relatively prime to* m.

Once again it suffices, given $\varphi(m)$ numbers, to require *either* that at least one belong to each of the above-mentioned $\varphi(m)$ classes *or* that each of the $\varphi(m)$ numbers be relatively prime to m and that each pair of them be incongruent.

Theorem 62: *If $(k, m)=1$, then the numbers*

$$0 \cdot k, 1 \cdot k, 2 \cdot k, \ldots, (m-1) \cdot k$$

constitute a complete set of residues mod m.

More generally: *If $(k, m)=1$ and $a_1, \ldots, a_m$ is any complete set of residues, then so is $a_1 k, \ldots, a_m k$.*

Proof: From

$$a_r k \equiv a_s k \pmod{m}, \quad 1 \leq r \leq m, \quad 1 \leq s \leq m$$

it follows by Theorem 56, since by assumption $(k, m)=1$, that

$$a_r \equiv a_s \pmod{m}$$

and

$$r = s;$$

the terms $a_r k$ are therefore mutually incongruent.

Theorem 63: *If $(k, m)=1$ and if $a_1, \ldots, a_{\varphi(m)}$ constitute a reduced set of residues* mod m, *then so do $a_1 k, \ldots, a_{\varphi(m)} k$.*

Proof: Each of these $\varphi(m)$ numbers is relatively prime to m (for any common factor of $a_r k$ and m would have to go into a_r and m); also any two are incongruent, by Theorem 62.

Theorem 64: *If $(a, m)=1$, then the congruence*

$$a x + a_0 \equiv 0 \pmod{m}$$

has exactly one solution.

Proof: By Theorem 62,

$$a \cdot 0, \quad a \cdot 1, \quad \ldots, \quad a(m-1)$$

constitute a complete set of residues; hence exactly one of these numbers is $\equiv -a_0 \pmod{m}$.

Theorem 65: 1) *The congruence*

(11) $$a x + a_0 \equiv 0 \pmod{m}$$

is solvable if and only if

$$(a, m) | a_0.$$

2) *In that case the number of solutions* $=(a, m)$, *and the congruence is satisfied by precisely all of the numbers* x *in a certain residue class*
mod $\left(\dfrac{m}{(a, m)}\right)$.

Remark: Theorem 64 is obviously a special case of this theorem, but is made use of to prove it.

Proof: 11) If (11) is solvable, then

$$a x + a_0 \equiv 0 \ (\text{mod } (a, m)),$$
$$a_0 \equiv 0 \ (\text{mod } (a, m)).$$

12) If

$$a_0 \equiv 0 \ (\text{mod } (a, m)),$$

then, by Theorem 64, the congruence

(12) $$\frac{a}{(a, m)} x + \frac{a_0}{(a, m)} \equiv 0 \left(\text{mod } \frac{m}{(a, m)}\right)$$

is solvable. Hence, by Theorem 58, (11) is satisfied.

2) If $(a, m) | a_0$, then (12) has exactly one solution mod $\dfrac{m}{(a, m)}$, according to Theorem 64; since (11) and (12) have the same solutions, by Theorem 58, it follows that (11) has (a, m) solutions (solutions mod m, as usual), since if $d > 0$ and $d | m$, then a residue class mod $\dfrac{m}{d}$ breaks up into d residue classes mod m.

THEOREM 66: *Let* $n > 1$ *and let at least one of the numbers* $a_1, \ldots, a_n$ *be different from* 0*; set*

$$(a_1, \ldots, a_n) = d.$$

We claim that the diophantine equation (i.e., equation with integral coefficients and unknowns)

$$a_1 x_1 + \cdots + a_n x_n = c$$

is solvable if and only if

$$d | c.$$

Hence, in particular: If $(a, b) = 1$, then

(13) $$a x + b y = 1$$

is solvable.

Proof: 1) If exactly one coefficient does not vanish, say a_1, then

$$a_1 x_1 + 0 \cdot x_2 + \cdots + 0 \cdot x_n = c$$

is obviously solvable if $a_1|c$, that is, if

$$(a_1, 0, \ldots, 0)|c.$$

2) If at least two coefficients do not vanish, then we may assume without loss of generality that no coefficient vanishes; for otherwise we simply omit those terms $a_m x_m$ for which $a_m = 0$, and this does not alter the value of the greatest common divisor of the coefficients; the number of terms that remain is then still $\geqq 2$.

Without loss of generality we may even take all the coefficients to be > 0; for we merely have to replace each negative a_m by $-a_m$ (which does not alter the greatest common divisor) and the corresponding x_m by $-x_m$.

We may therefore assume that

$$n > 1, \ a_1 > 0, \ \ldots, \ a_n > 0.$$

21) If our diophantine equation is solvable, then obviously

$$d \,|\, a_1 x_1 + \cdots + a_n x_n,$$
$$d \,|\, c.$$

22) Let

$$d|c.$$

221) If $n = 2$, then we merely have to show that

$$a_1 x_1 \equiv c \ (\mathrm{mod} \ a_2)$$

is solvable for x_1. This follows from Theorem 65, since

$$(a_1, a_2)\,|-c.$$

222) Let $n > 2$, and assume the assertion proved for $2, \ldots, n-1$; if we set

$$(a_1, \ldots, a_{n-1}) = a$$

then, by (9),

$$(a, a_n) = d.$$

From what we showed in 221), it follows that

$$a x + a_n x_n = c.$$

for suitably chosen x, x_n. By our induction hypothesis for $n-1$, it follows in addition, since

$$(a_1, \ldots, a_{n-1})\,|\,a x,$$

that

$$a_1 x_1 + \cdots + a_{n-1} x_{n-1} = a x$$

for suitably chosen $x_1, \ldots, x_{n-1}$, so that, finally,

$$a_1 x_1 + \cdots + a_{n-1} x_{n-1} + a_n x_n = c.$$

Theorem 67: *If* $(a, b) = d$ *and* $d | c$, *then*

$$ax + by = c$$

is solvable, by Theorem 66; also, given any solution x_0, y_0, *all the solutions are of the form*

$$x = x_0 + h\frac{b}{d}, \; y = y_0 - h\frac{a}{d},$$

where h is arbitrary.

Proof: 1) The fact that such a pair *x, y* satisfies the equation follows from the relation

$$a\left(x_0 + h\frac{b}{d}\right) + b\left(y_0 - h\frac{a}{d}\right) = ax_0 + by_0 = c.$$

2) The fact that no other solutions exist is seen as follows. Without loss of generality, let $b \neq 0$. (Otherwise interchange *a* and *b*, and observe that as *h* runs through all the integers, so does —*h*.) Since

$$ax + by = c = ax_0 + by_0,$$

it follows that

$$ax - c \equiv 0 \pmod{|b|},$$
$$ax_0 - c \equiv 0 \pmod{|b|},$$

and hence by Theorem 65 (with $a_0 = -c$, $m = |b|$), we have

$$x \equiv x_0 \left(\bmod \frac{|b|}{d}\right),$$

$$x = x_0 + h\frac{b}{d},$$

$$by = c - ax = c - a\left(x_0 + h\frac{b}{d}\right) = (c - ax_0) - b\frac{ha}{d} = by_0 - b\frac{ha}{d} = b\left(y_0 - h\frac{a}{d}\right),$$

$$y = y_0 - h\frac{a}{d}.$$

THEOREM 68: *If $(a, b)=1$ and if x_0, y_0 is any solution of* (13), *then all the solutions are of the form*

$$x=x_0+hb, \quad y=y_0-ha,$$

where h is arbitrary.

Proof: This follows from Theorem 67, with $d=c=1$.

THEOREM 69: 1) *The congruences*

(14) $$x\equiv a_1 \pmod{m_1},$$

(15) $$x\equiv a_2 \pmod{m_2}$$

have a common solution if and only if

(16) $$(m_1, m_2)/a_1-a_2.$$

In particular, therefore, they always do if $(m_1, m_2)=1$.

2) *If condition* (16) *is satisfied and if m represents the smallest common multiple of m_1 and m_2, then the common solutions of* (14) *and* (15) *consist of all the numbers in a certain residue class* mod m.

Proof: 11) If we set $(m_1, m_2)=d$, then it follows from (14) and (15) that

$$x\equiv a_1 \pmod{d},$$
$$x\equiv a_2 \pmod{d},$$
$$a_1\equiv a_2 \pmod{d},$$
$$d \mid a_1-a_2.$$

12) If

$$d \mid a_1-a_2,$$

then from among all solutions of (14) of the form

$$x=a_1+ym_1 \quad (y \text{ arbitrary})$$

we can certainly choose one for which (15) holds. For we need

$$a_1+ym_1\equiv a_2 \pmod{m_2};$$

this is equivalent to

(17) $$m_1y+(a_1-a_2)\equiv 0 \pmod{m_2}$$

which, by Theorem 65, 1), is solvable.

2) If (16) is satisfied, and therefore (14) and (15) along with it, then congruence (17) is satisfied for suitably chosen y_0 precisely by

$$y \equiv y_0 \left(\bmod \frac{m_2}{d} \right)$$

by virtue of Theorem 65, 2). Therefore, since $\dfrac{m_1 m_2}{d} = m$ (by Theorem 11), all the numbers x satisfying (14) and (15) are given by the formulas

$$x = a_1 + \left(y_0 + h\frac{m_2}{d} \right) m_1 = a_1 + m_1 y_0 + h\frac{m_1 m_2}{d} = a_1 + m_1 y_0 + hm, \; h \text{ arbitrary,}$$

but these constitute a certain residue class mod m.

THEOREM 70: *Let $r > 1$, and let every pair from among the numbers $m_1, \ldots, m_r$ be relatively prime. Then the congruences*

(18) $$x \equiv a_n \pmod{m_n}, \; n = 1, \ldots, r$$

are consistent, and their common solutions consist of all the numbers in a certain residue class mod $m_1 m_2 \ldots m_r$.

Proof: 1) For $r = 2$ this follows from Theorem 69, since $m = m_1 m_2$ in that case.

2) Let $r > 2$, and assume the theorem proved for $r-1$. Then the first $r-1$ congruences (18) are covered by

$$x \equiv a \pmod{m_1 \cdots m_{r-1}}.$$

for a suitably chosen a. Hence, by Theorem 69, the conclusion follows, since $m_1 \cdots m_{r-1}$ is relatively prime to m_r.

THEOREM 71: *Let $r > 1$, and let each pair of numbers from among $m_1, \ldots, m_r$ be relatively prime. Then the number of solutions of*

(19) $$f(x) \equiv 0 \pmod{m_1 m_2 \cdots m_r}$$

equals the product of the numbers of solutions of

(20) $$f(x) \equiv 0 \pmod{m_1}, \ldots, f(x) \equiv 0 \pmod{m_r}.$$

In particular: If $m > 1$ and $m = \overset{r}{\underset{n=1}{\varPi}} p_n^{l_n}$ is its canonical decomposition then, if $r > 1$, the number of solutions of

$$f(x) \equiv 0 \pmod{m}$$

equals the product of the numbers of solutions of

$$f(x) \equiv 0 \pmod{p_n^{l_n}}.$$

Proof: First of all, it is clear that (19) is satisfied if and only if the r congruences in (20) are simultaneously satisfied. Hence if one of these has no solution, then neither does (19). If the congruences in (20) are all solvable, then by Theorem 70, to each choice of a system of residue classes mod m_1, ..., mod m_r satisfying the respective congruences in (20) there corresponds one-to-one a residue class mod $m_1 \ldots m_r$ that satisfies (19).

THEOREM 72: *If*

$$f(x) = c_0 + c_1 x + \cdots + c_n x^n, \quad p \nmid c_n,$$

then the congruence

(21) $$f(x) \equiv 0 \pmod{p}$$

has at most n solutions.

Proof: 1) For $n = 0$ this is obvious, since for every x,

$$c_0 \not\equiv 0 \pmod{p},$$

so that (21) has no root.

2) Let $n > 0$, and assume the theorem true for $n-1$. If (21) had at least the $n+1$ (incongruent) roots $x_0, x_1, \ldots, x_n$, then if we note that

$$f(x) - f(x_0) = \sum_{r=1}^{n} c_r(x^r - x_0{}^r) = (x - x_0) \sum_{r=1}^{n} c_r(x^{r-1} + x_0 x^{r-2} + \cdots + x_0{}^{r-1})$$

$$= (x - x_0) g(x)$$

and

$$g(x) = b_0 + b_1 x + \cdots + b_{n-1} x^{n-1}, \quad b_{n-1} = c_n, \quad p \nmid b_{n-1},$$

it would follow that

$$(x_k - x_0) g(x_k) \equiv f(x_k) - f(x_0) \equiv 0 - 0 \equiv 0 \pmod{p},$$

for $k = 1, \ldots, n$, so that

$$g(x_k) \equiv 0 \pmod{p},$$

contrary to the induction hypothesis for $n-1$.

THEOREM 73: *Let $a > 0$, $b > 0$, and $(a, b) = 1$. Let x range over a complete set of residues mod b and y over a complete set of residues mod a. Then $ax + by$ ranges over a complete set of residues mod ab.*

Proof: Of the ab numbers $ax + by$, any two are incongruent mod ab. For if

$$a x_1 + b y_1 \equiv a x_2 + b y_2 \pmod{ab},$$

then

$$a x_1 + b y_1 \equiv a x_2 + b y_2 \pmod{b},$$

$$a x_1 \equiv a x_2 \pmod{b},$$

$$x_1 \equiv x_2 \pmod{b},$$

and similarly, by symmetry,

$$y_1 \equiv y_2 \pmod{a}.$$

Theorem 74: *Let $a>0$, $b>0$, and $(a, b)=1$. Let x and y range over reduced sets of residues* mod b *and* mod a, *respectively. Then $ax+by$ ranges over a reduced set of residues* mod ab.

Remark: This is the direct proof of Theorem 44 which we announced earlier. Since Theorem 43 was also proved directly, there thus results a new, direct proof of Theorem 42, and consequently of Theorems 41 and 40; up to this point, everything had been obtained from the Möbius Inversion formula.

Proof: If $(x, b)>1$, then certainly $(ax+by, ab)>1$; for (x, b) divides $ax+by$ and ab, and hence divides $(ax+by, ab)$. If $(y, a)>1$, then, by symmetry, $(ax+by, ab)>1$ as well.

What remains to be shown, by Theorem 73, is that if

$$(x, b)=1 \text{ and } (y, a)=1,$$

then

$$(ax+by, ab)=1.$$

In fact, let $p|(ax+by, ab)$. Then we would have $p|ab$, so that, without loss of generality, $p|a$; moreover, $p|(ax+by)$, so that $p|by$, and consequently (since $(a, b)=1$) $p|y$, contrary to the assumption that $(y, a)=1$.

Theorem 75 (The so-called Little Fermat Theorem): *If $(a, m)=1$, then*

$$a^{\varphi(m)} \equiv 1 \pmod{m}.$$

Remark: It is not known whether the so-called Last Theorem of Fermat, which is discussed in Parts 12 and 13 of my *Vorlesungen über Zahlentheorie*, is true or not. I would therefore rather refer to it as the Fermat Conjecture, and to Theorem 75 simply as Fermat's Theorem.

Proof: Let $a_1, \ldots, a_{\varphi(m)}$ be a reduced set of residues mod m. Then, by Theorem 63, $aa_1, \ldots, aa_{\varphi(m)}$ is also such a set. Hence the numbers a_n are congruent to the numbers aa_n $(n=1, \ldots, \varphi(m))$, apart from their order. Hence the product of the a_n is congruent to the product of the aa_n, or

$$1 \cdot \prod_{n=1}^{\varphi(m)} a_n \equiv \prod_{n=1}^{\varphi(m)} a_n \equiv \prod_{n=1}^{\varphi(m)} (aa_n) \equiv a^{\varphi(m)} \prod_{n=1}^{\varphi(m)} a_n \pmod{m},$$

so that, by Theorem 56,

$$1 \equiv a^{\varphi(m)} \pmod{m}.$$

THEOREM 76: *If $p \nmid a$, then*

$$a^{p-1} \equiv 1 \pmod{p};$$

for any a at all we have

$$a^p \equiv a \pmod{p}.$$

Proof: The first statement follows from Theorem 75, since $\varphi(p) = p-1$; the second follows from the first by Theorem 51 if $p \nmid a$; and if $p|a$, it is trivial, since

$$a^p \equiv 0 \equiv a \pmod{p}.$$

THEOREM 77 (The so-called Theorem of Wilson): $(p-1)! \equiv -1 \pmod{p}$.

Two Proofs: 1) For $p=2$ and $p=3$, the statement is obvious. For $p > 3$, I consider the $p-3$ numbers

(22) $2, 3, \ldots, p-3, p-2.$

For each r in this sequence, $p \nmid r$, and hence, by Theorem 64, there is exactly one s in the sequence $0, 1, \ldots, p-1$ for which

(23) $rs \equiv 1 \pmod{p}.$

$s=0$ does not obtain here; nor do $s=1$ and $s=p-1$, since otherwise r would be $\equiv \pm 1$. The s therefore occurs in the sequence (22) as well. Moreover,

$$s \neq r;$$

for

$$r^2 \equiv 1 \pmod{p}$$

would give

$$p|(r-1)(r+1),$$
$$r \equiv \pm 1 \pmod{p}.$$

Hence to each r in (22) there corresponds exactly one $s \neq r$ in (22) for which (23) holds. Since $rs = sr$, it follows, conversely, that r is uniquely determined by s. The $p-3$ numbers in (22) thus break up into $\dfrac{p-3}{2}$ pairs in such a way that the product of the numbers in each pair is $\equiv 1$. Hence

$$(p-2)! \equiv 2 \cdot 3 \cdots (p-2) \equiv 1^{\frac{p-3}{2}} \equiv 1 \pmod{p},$$
$$(p-1)! \equiv (p-1)(p-2)! \equiv -(p-2)! \equiv -1 \pmod{p}.$$

2) If we set

$$f(x) = x^{p-1} - 1 - \prod_{m=1}^{p-1}(x - m),$$

then clearly

$$f(x) = c_0 + c_1 x + \cdots + c_{p-2} x^{p-2}.$$

By Theorem 76, the congruence

$$f(x) \equiv 0 \ (\text{mod } p)$$

has at least the $p-1$ roots $x \equiv 1, 2, \ldots, p-1$. Hence, by Theorem 72,

$$c_0 \equiv c_1 \equiv \cdots \equiv c_{p-2} \equiv 0 \ (\text{mod } p).$$

Our result then follows from the fact that

$$c_0 = -1 - (-1)^{p-1}(p-1)!$$

CHAPTER VI

QUADRATIC RESIDUES

DEFINITION 17: *If the congruence*

$$x^2 \equiv n \pmod{m}$$

has a solution, then n is called a quadratic residue modulo m; otherwise, n is called a quadratic non-residue modulo m.

Example: 0, 1, and all other perfect squares are quadratic residues modulo any number.

DEFINITION 18 (Legendre's Symbol): *If $p>2$ and $p \nmid n$, let*

$$\left(\frac{n}{p}\right) = \begin{cases} 1 & \text{if } n \text{ is a quadratic residue } \pmod{p}, \\ -1 & \text{if } n \text{ is a quadratic non-residue } \pmod{p}. \end{cases}$$

Example: $\left(\dfrac{m^2}{p}\right) = 1$ if $p>2$ and $p \nmid m$; in particular, $\left(\dfrac{1}{p}\right) = 1$ if $p>2$.

THEOREM 78: *Let $p>2$. If $n \equiv n' \pmod{p}$ and $p \nmid n$, then*

$$\left(\frac{n}{p}\right) = \left(\frac{n'}{p}\right).$$

Proof: By hypothesis, we certainly have $p \nmid n'$. From $x^2 \equiv n \pmod{p}$ it follows that $x^2 \equiv n' \pmod{p}$, and conversely.

THEOREM 79: *Let $p>2$. In every reduced set of residues mod p there are exactly $\dfrac{p-1}{2}$ numbers n for which $\left(\dfrac{n}{p}\right) = 1$ and hence exactly $\dfrac{p-1}{2}$ numbers n for which $\left(\dfrac{n}{p}\right) = -1$. The first set of $\dfrac{p-1}{2}$ numbers are represented by the residue classes to which the numbers $1^2, 2^2, \ldots, \left(\dfrac{p-1}{2}\right)^2$ belong.*

In particular, therefore: Given $p>2$, there exists an n such that

$$\left(\frac{n}{p}\right) = -1.$$

53

Proof: The congruence

$$x^2 \equiv n \pmod{p},$$

if it is at all solvable, has at least one solution in the interval $0 \leq x \leq p-1$; but, by Theorem 72, it has at most two solutions in that interval, and in case $p \nmid n$ the number 0 is not one of them. Since

$$(p-x)^2 \equiv (-x)^2 \equiv x^2 \pmod{p},$$

there is consequently exactly one solution in the interval $1 \leq x \leq \dfrac{p-1}{2}$.

Hence any two of the numbers

$$1^2, \ 2^2, \ \ldots, \ \left(\frac{p-1}{2}\right)^2$$

are incongruent.

The theorem has thus been proved.

THEOREM 80 (Euler's Criterion): *If $p > 2$ and $p \nmid n$, then*

$$n^{\frac{p-1}{2}} \equiv \left(\frac{n}{p}\right) \pmod{p}.$$

Remark: The fact that

$$n^{\frac{p-1}{2}} \equiv \pm 1 \pmod{p}$$

is a consequence of Fermat's Theorem to begin with; for from

$$n^{p-1} \equiv 1 \pmod{p}$$

it follows that

(24) $$p \,\vert\, (n^{\frac{p-1}{2}} - 1)(n^{\frac{p-1}{2}} + 1).$$

Proof: The modulus in the proof will be p throughout.
1) Let

$$\left(\frac{n}{p}\right) = 1.$$

Then there is an x such that

$$x^2 \equiv n.$$

Hence, by Fermat's Theorem,

$$n^{\frac{p-1}{2}} \equiv (x^2)^{\frac{p-1}{2}} \equiv x^{p-1} \equiv 1.$$

2) Let

$$\left(\frac{n}{p}\right) = -1.$$

The congruence

$$x^{\frac{p-1}{2}} - 1 \equiv 0$$

has at most $\frac{p-1}{2}$ solutions, by Theorem 72. By 1) and Theorem 79, it has

at least $\frac{p-1}{2}$ solutions, namely the quadratic residues in any reduced set of

residues; hence there are no further solutions. Thus, by (24), our number n, being a quadratic non-residue, satisfies the congruence

$$n^{\frac{p-1}{2}} + 1 \equiv 0.$$

THEOREM 81: *If $p > 2$, $p \nmid n$, and $p \nmid n'$, then*

$$\left(\frac{n n'}{p}\right) = \left(\frac{n}{p}\right)\left(\frac{n'}{p}\right).$$

In words: The congruence $x^2 \equiv n n'$ is solvable if and only if the congruences $x^2 \equiv n$ and $x^2 \equiv n'$ are both solvable or both unsolvable. Expressed in yet another way: If n and n' are both quadratic residues or are both quadratic non-residues, then $n n'$ is a quadratic residue; if one of them is a quadratic residue and the other is a quadratic non-residue, then the product is a quadratic non-residue. All of this under the assumption that $p > 2$, $p \nmid n$, and $p \nmid n'$.

Proof: By Theorem 80, we have

$$\left(\frac{n n'}{p}\right) \equiv (n n')^{\frac{p-1}{2}} \equiv n^{\frac{p-1}{2}} n'^{\frac{p-1}{2}} \equiv \left(\frac{n}{p}\right)\left(\frac{n'}{p}\right) \pmod{p}.$$

Since

$$\left(\frac{n n'}{p}\right) - \left(\frac{n}{p}\right)\left(\frac{n'}{p}\right) = 0, \ 2 \text{ or } -2$$

and $p > 2$, we have

$$\left(\frac{n n'}{p}\right) - \left(\frac{n}{p}\right)\left(\frac{n'}{p}\right) = 0.$$

THEOREM 82: *If $p > 2$, $r \geq 2$, and $p \nmid n_1, \ldots, p \nmid n_r$, then*

$$\left(\frac{n_1 \cdots n_r}{p}\right) = \left(\frac{n_1}{p}\right) \cdots \left(\frac{n_r}{p}\right).$$

Proof: Theorem 81.

If $p>2$ and $p \nmid n$, then the symbol $\left(\dfrac{n}{p}\right)$ breaks up, by means of Theorem 82, into simpler symbols of the form $\left(\dfrac{-1}{p}\right)$, $\left(\dfrac{2}{p}\right)$, and $\left(\dfrac{q}{p}\right)$, where q is an odd prime different from p. The following three main theorems of the theory of quadratic residues (Theorems 83, 85, and 86) are concerned with these three types.

Theorem 83 (The so-called First Supplement to the Quadratic Reciprocity Law):

$$\left(\frac{-1}{p}\right)=(-1)^{\frac{p-1}{2}} \text{ for } p>2,$$

or, more explicitly,

$$\left(\frac{-1}{p}\right)=\begin{cases} 1 & \text{for } p\equiv \ \ 1 \ (\text{mod } 4), \\ -1 & \text{for } p\equiv-1 \ (\text{mod } 4). \end{cases}$$

In words: Every odd prime divisor of x^2+1 is $\equiv 1$ (mod 4), and every $p\equiv 1$ (mod 4) divides x^2+1 for suitable numbers x.

Proof: By Euler's Criterion (Theorem 80), we have

$$\left(\frac{-1}{p}\right)\equiv(-1)^{\frac{p-1}{2}} \ (\text{mod } p);$$

since $p>2$, we have equality.

Theorem 84 (The so-called Gaussian Lemma): *Let $p>2$ and $p \nmid n$. Let us consider the $\dfrac{p-1}{2}$ numbers*

$$n, \ 2n, \ \ldots, \ \frac{p-1}{2}n$$

and determine their residues mod p. *We obtain* (by Theorem 62)

$$\frac{p-1}{2}$$

distinct numbers, which are >0 and $<p$. Let m be the number of these residues which are $>\dfrac{p}{2}$ (i.e., $\geqq\dfrac{p+1}{2}$). (*m* can also $=0$; for example, it always does if $n=1$.)

We assert that

$$\left(\frac{n}{p}\right)=(-1)^m.$$

Example: $p=7$, $n=10$. The numbers 10, 20, and 30 leave residues of 3, 6, and 2, respectively. In this case $m=1$, and hence $\left(\dfrac{3}{7}\right)=-1$ by Theorem 84. And in fact, the congruence $x^2 \equiv 3 \pmod 7$ is unsolvable.

Proof: Let the modulus be p throughout. $l=\dfrac{p-1}{2}-m$ is the number of residues which are $<\dfrac{p}{2}$ (i.e., $\leq \dfrac{p-1}{2}$). In case $l>0$, denote these numbers by $a_1,\ldots,a_l$; let the residues $>\dfrac{p}{2}$ occurring in the theorem be $b_1,\ldots,b_m$, in case $m>0$. If we multiply all of the $\dfrac{p-1}{2}$ residues (that is, all of the a_s, b_t), we obtain the congruence

$$\prod_{s=1}^{l} a_s \prod_{t=1}^{m} b_t \equiv \prod_{h=1}^{\frac{p-1}{2}} hn \equiv \left(\frac{p-1}{2}\right)! \, n^{\frac{p-1}{2}}.$$

The "complements" of the numbers b_t (I mean the numbers $p-b_t$) belong to the interval from 1 to $\dfrac{p-1}{2}$. Any two of them are distinct, since this is true of the numbers b_t. Furthermore, each a_s is distinct from each $p-b_t$; for

$$a_s = p-b_t$$

would give

$$xn \equiv p-yn,\ 1 \leq x \leq \frac{p-1}{2},\ 1 \leq y \leq \frac{p-1}{2},$$
$$xn \equiv -yn,\quad x \equiv -y,\quad x+y \equiv 0,$$

in contradiction to

$$0 < x+y < p.$$

Consequently (since there are $\dfrac{p-1}{2}$ numbers) the numbers a_s and the numbers $p-b_t$, taken together, are the same as the numbers $1,\ldots,\dfrac{p-1}{2}$ in some order (the pigeon-hole principle), so that

$$\left(\frac{p-1}{2}\right)! \equiv \prod_{s=1}^{l} a_s \prod_{t=1}^{m} (p-b_t) \equiv (-1)^m \prod_{s=1}^{l} a_s \prod_{t=1}^{m} b_t \equiv (-1)^m \left(\frac{p-1}{2}\right)! \, n^{\frac{p-1}{2}},$$

$$1 \equiv (-1)^m n^{\frac{p-1}{2}},$$

and consequently, by Theorem 80,

$$\left(\frac{n}{p}\right) \equiv n^{\frac{p-1}{2}} \equiv (-1)^m,$$

$$\left(\frac{n}{p}\right) = (-1)^m.$$

THEOREM 85 (The so-called Second Supplement to the Quadratic Reciprocity Law):

$$\left(\frac{2}{p}\right)=(-1)^{\frac{p^2-1}{8}} \quad for \ p>2;$$

or (noting that $\dfrac{(8a\pm 1)^2-1}{8}=8a^2\pm 2a$ and $\dfrac{(8a\pm 3)^2-1}{8}=8a^2\pm 6a+1$) more explicitly:

$$\left(\frac{2}{p}\right)=\begin{cases} 1 & for \ p\equiv\pm 1 \ (\mathrm{mod}\ 8), \\ -1 & for \ p\equiv\pm 3 \ (\mathrm{mod}\ 8). \end{cases}$$

Proof: For $p>2$ and $n=2$, Theorem 84 gives

$$m\equiv\frac{p^2-1}{8} \ (\mathrm{mod}\ 2).$$

For, the numbers

$$2, \ 2\cdot 2, \ \ldots, \ \frac{p-1}{2}\cdot 2$$

are themselves already >0 and $<p$, and thus they are their own residues; and

$$\frac{p}{2}<2h<p$$

is true whenever

$$\frac{p}{4}<h<\frac{p}{2},$$

that is, $\left[\dfrac{p}{2}\right]-\left[\dfrac{p}{4}\right]$ times; if $p=8a+r$, where $r=1,\ 3,\ 5$, or 7, then this is $4a-2a\equiv 0,\ 4a+1-2a\equiv 1,\ 4a+2-2a-1\equiv 1,\ 4a+3-2a-1\equiv 0 \ (\mathrm{mod}\ 2)$, respectively.

A more elegant proof of Theorem 85 is presented during the proof of the next theorem.

THEOREM 86 (The Quadratic Reciprocity Law, first conjectured by Euler, first proved by Gauss): *Let $p>2$ and $q>2$ be primes, with $p\neq q$. Then*

$$\left(\frac{p}{q}\right)\left(\frac{q}{p}\right)=(-1)^{\frac{p-1}{2}\frac{q-1}{2}}$$

In words (since $\dfrac{p-1}{2}\dfrac{q-1}{2}$ is odd for $p\equiv q\equiv 3$ (mod 4), and is otherwise even): The congruences

$$x^2\equiv p \ (\mathrm{mod}\ q), \ \ y^2\equiv q \ (\mathrm{mod}\ p)$$

are both solvable or both unsolvable, unless $p\equiv q\equiv 3$ (mod 4); if $p\equiv q\equiv 3$ (mod 4), then one is solvable and the other unsolvable.

Proof: For the time being, let the value $q=2$ be admitted; but let q still be a prime number $\neq p$. If $1 \leq k \leq \dfrac{p-1}{2}$, then

(25) $$kq = q_k p + r_k, \quad 1 \leq r_k \leq p-1,$$

where the numbers r_k are the numbers a_s and b_t of the proof of Theorem 84 (with $n=q$).

In this formula,

$$q_k = \left[\frac{kq}{p}\right].$$

We already know that the numbers a_s and $p-b_t$, apart from their order, are $1, 2, \ldots, \dfrac{p-1}{2}$. If, for the sake of brevity, we set

$$\sum_{s=1}^{l} a_s = a, \quad \sum_{t=1}^{m} b_t = b,$$

then

$$\sum_{k=1}^{\frac{p-1}{2}} r_k = a + b,$$

$$\frac{p^2-1}{8} = \frac{\frac{p-1}{2} \cdot \frac{p+1}{2}}{2} = \sum_{k=1}^{\frac{p-1}{2}} k = a + mp - b.$$

By addition of the equations (25), it follows that

$$\frac{p^2-1}{8} q = p \sum_{k=1}^{\frac{p-1}{2}} q_k + \sum_{k=1}^{\frac{p-1}{2}} r_k = p \sum_{k=1}^{\frac{p-1}{2}} q_k + a + b.$$

Hence

$$\frac{p^2-1}{8} (q-1) = p \sum_{k=1}^{\frac{p-1}{2}} q_k - mp + 2b,$$

(26) $$\frac{p^2-1}{8} (q-1) \equiv \sum_{k=1}^{\frac{p-1}{2}} q_k + m \pmod{2}.$$

1) (Alternate proof of Theorem 85.) Let $q=2$. Then every $q_k=0$, so that, by (26),

$$\frac{p^2-1}{8}\equiv m \pmod 2,$$

and thus, by Theorem 84,

$$\left(\frac{2}{p}\right)=(-1)^m=(-1)^{\frac{p^2-1}{8}}.$$

2) Let $q>2$. Then, by (26),

$$m\equiv\sum_{k=1}^{\frac{p-1}{2}} q_k \pmod 2,$$

so that, by Theorem 84,

$$\left(\frac{q}{p}\right)=(-1)^m=(-1)^{\sum_{k=1}^{\frac{p-1}{2}}\left[\frac{kq}{p}\right]}.$$

By symmetry, we have

$$\left(\frac{p}{q}\right)=(-1)^{\sum_{l=1}^{\frac{q-1}{2}}\left[\frac{lp}{q}\right]},$$

$$\left(\frac{p}{q}\right)\left(\frac{q}{p}\right)=(-1)^{\sum_{k=1}^{\frac{p-1}{2}}\left[\frac{kq}{p}\right]+\sum_{l=1}^{\frac{q-1}{2}}\left[\frac{lp}{q}\right]}.$$

It therefore suffices to show that

$$\sum_{k=1}^{\frac{p-1}{2}}\left[\frac{kq}{p}\right]+\sum_{l=1}^{\frac{q-1}{2}}\left[\frac{lp}{q}\right]\equiv\frac{p-1}{2}\frac{q-1}{2}\pmod 2.$$

It will even turn out that

(27)
$$\sum_{k=1}^{\frac{p-1}{2}}\left[\frac{kq}{p}\right]+\sum_{l=1}^{\frac{q-1}{2}}\left[\frac{lp}{q}\right]=\frac{p-1}{2}\frac{q-1}{2},$$

and we shall not make use of the fact that p and q are distinct odd primes but only of the fact that they are relatively prime odd numbers >1.

Indeed, let us consider the $\frac{p-1}{2}\frac{q-1}{2}$ numbers

$$lp-kq, \text{ where } k=1, \ldots, \frac{p-1}{2}; \ l=1, \ldots, \frac{q-1}{2}.$$

(Whether they are distinct does not interest us: Exercise for the reader.)
None of these numbers is 0; for otherwise we would have

$$lp=kq, \ q|lp, \ q|l.$$

The number of positive numbers among these $\frac{p-1}{2} \frac{q-1}{2}$ numbers is

clearly $\sum\limits_{l=1}^{\frac{q-1}{2}} \left[\frac{lp}{q}\right]$; for let

$$k<\frac{lp}{q}, \ 1\leq k \leq \frac{p-1}{2}$$

for every $l=1, \ldots, \frac{q-1}{2}$; since $\frac{lp}{q}$ is not an integer, it follows that $1\leq k < \frac{lp}{q}$

has exactly $\left[\frac{lp}{q}\right]$ solutions, and moreover $k < \frac{\frac{q}{2}p}{q}=\frac{p}{2}, \ k\leq\frac{p-1}{2}$ is auto-
matically true.

The number of negative numbers among those is $\sum\limits_{k=1}^{\frac{p-1}{2}} \left[\frac{kq}{p}\right]$, by symmetry.
Thus (27) is established.

Example of the application of the Reciprocity Law: By means of this
law, we can tell at a glance which are the primes that have the number 3 as a
quadratic residue. Indeed, it follows from the Reciprocity Law for $p>3$ that

$$\left(\frac{3}{p}\right)=\left(\frac{p}{3}\right)(-1)^{\frac{p-1}{2}}.$$

By Theorems 78 and 83 we have, in this formula,

$$\left(\frac{p}{3}\right)=\begin{cases} \left(\frac{1}{3}\right)=1 & \text{for } p\equiv 1 \ (\text{mod } 3), \\ \left(\frac{-1}{3}\right)=-1 & \text{for } p\equiv 2 \ (\text{mod } 3), \ p>2; \end{cases}$$

furthermore,

$$(-1)^{\frac{p-1}{2}}=\begin{cases} 1 & \text{for } p\equiv \ \ 1 \ (\text{mod } 4), \\ -1 & \text{for } p\equiv -1 \ (\text{mod } 4). \end{cases}$$

Hence

$$\left(\frac{3}{p}\right)=\begin{cases} 1 & \text{for } p\equiv\pm 1 \pmod{12}, \\ -1 & \text{for } p\equiv\pm 5 \pmod{12}. \end{cases}$$

More generally one sees that for a fixed odd prime q the symbol $\left(\frac{q}{p}\right)$ has the same value for all p (provided there are any) that belong to the same reduced residue class mod $4q$. Indeed, $\left(\frac{p}{q}\right)$ has, by Theorem 78, the same value for all odd p belonging to a reduced residue class mod q, and $(-1)^{\frac{p-1}{2}}$ has the same value for all p belonging to a reduced residue class mod 4.

THEOREM 87: *Let $l>0$ and $p\nmid n$. Then the number of solutions of*
(28)
$$x^2\equiv n \pmod{p^l}$$
has the following value:

$$\begin{array}{ll} 1 & \textit{for } p=2,\ l=1, \\ 0 & \textit{for } p=2,\ l=2,\ n\equiv 3 \pmod 4, \\ 2 & \textit{for } p=2,\ l=2,\ n\equiv 1 \pmod 4, \\ 0 & \textit{for } p=2,\ l>2,\ n\not\equiv 1 \pmod 8, \\ 4 & \textit{for } p=2,\ l>2,\ n\equiv 1 \pmod 8, \\ 1+\left(\dfrac{n}{p}\right) & \textit{for } p>2. \end{array}$$

Proof: 1) $x^2\equiv n \pmod 2$ has a root $x\equiv 1 \pmod 2$ if $2\nmid n$.
2) $x^2\equiv 3 \pmod 4$ has no root.
3) $x^2\equiv 1 \pmod 4$ has two roots, $x\equiv\pm 1 \pmod 4$.
4) Let $p=2,\ l>2,\ 2\nmid n$, and $n\not\equiv 1 \pmod 8$. If
(29)
$$x^2\equiv n \pmod{2^l}$$
were solvable, then x would be odd and we would have

$$x^2\equiv n \pmod 8,$$
so that
$$x^2\not\equiv 1 \pmod 8.$$

However, the square of any odd number is $\equiv 1 \pmod 8$.

5) Let $p=2,\ l>2$, and $n\equiv 1 \pmod 8$. Without loss of generality, let $0<n<2^l$. The solutions of (29) need be sought merely among the 2^{l-1} odd numbers x satisfying $0<x<2^l$.

For every such x we certainly have

$$x^2\equiv m \pmod{2^l}$$

for suitably chosen $m\equiv1$ (mod 8) in the interval $0<m<2^l$. Each of these 2^{l-3} numbers m occurs at most four times. For from

$$x^2\equiv x_0{}^2 \ (\text{mod } 2^l), \ 2\nmid x_0$$

it follows that

$$2^l/(x-x_0)(x+x_0);$$

since x and x_0 are odd, so that $x-x_0$ and $x+x_0$ are even, we have

$$2^{l-2}\left|\frac{x+x_0}{2}\cdot\frac{x-x_0}{2}.\right.$$

2 does not divide both of the factors $\dfrac{x+x_0}{2}$ and $\dfrac{x-x_0}{2}$, since their sum x is odd; hence

$$2^{l-2}\left|\frac{x+x_0}{2}\right. \quad \text{or} \quad 2^{l-2}\left|\frac{x-x_0}{2}\right.,$$

that is,

$$x\equiv\mp x_0 \ (\text{mod } 2^{l-1}),$$

which yields at most four values for x.

Since the $2^{l-1}=4\cdot2^{l-3}$ numbers x are distributed among 2^{l-3} pigeon-holes in such a way that there are at most four in each, it follows that there are exactly four in each, and therefore the given n-hole contains exactly four.

6) Let $p>2$.

61) Let $\left(\dfrac{n}{p}\right)=-1$. Then we already have that

$$x^2\equiv n \ (\text{mod } p)$$

is unsolvable, so that

(28) $$x^2\equiv n \ (\text{mod } p^l)$$

is certainly unsolvable, and the number of solutions of (28) is

$$0=1+\left(\frac{n}{p}\right).$$

62) Let $\left(\dfrac{n}{p}\right)=1$. Without loss of generality, let $0<n<p^l$. The solutions of (28) need be sought merely among those $\varphi(p^l)$ numbers x in the interval $0<x<p^l$ that are not divisible by p.

For every such x we certainly have

$$x^2\equiv m \ (\text{mod } p^l)$$

for suitable m with $\left(\dfrac{m}{p}\right)=1$, $0<m<p^l$. Each of these $\dfrac{p-1}{2}\cdot p^{l-1}=\dfrac{1}{2}\varphi(p^l)$ numbers occurs at most twice. For from

$$x^2\equiv x_0{}^2 \ (\text{mod } p^l), \ p\nmid x_0$$

it follows that

$$p^l/(x+x_0)\ (x-x_0).$$

p does not divide both of the factors $x-x_0$ and $x+x_0$, since their sum $2x$ is not divisible by p ; hence

$$x \equiv \mp x_0 \ (\mathrm{mod}\ p^l),$$

which yields at most two values for x.

Since the $\varphi(p^l)$ numbers x are distributed among $\frac{1}{2}\,\varphi(p^l)$ pigeon-holes in such a way that at most two are in each, it follows that there are exactly two in each, and therefore the given n-hole contains *exactly* two. Therefore the number of solutions of (28) is

$$2 = 1 + \left(\frac{n}{p}\right).$$

THEOREM 88: *Let $m > 0$ and $(n, m) = 1$. Then the number of solutions of*

$$x^2 \equiv n \ (\mathrm{mod}\ m)$$

has the following value:

> 0, *if* $4|m$, $8 \nmid m$, *and* $n \not\equiv 1\,(\mathrm{mod}\ 4)$;
> 0, *if* $8|m$ *and* $n \not\equiv 1\,(\mathrm{mod}\ 8)$;
> 0, *if a prime* $p > 2$ *for which* $\left(\dfrac{n}{p}\right) = -1$ *goes into* m.

Otherwise, if s is the number of distinct odd $p|m$, then the number of solutions is:

> 2^s *for* $4 \nmid m$,
> 2^{s+1} *for* $4|m$, $8 \nmid m$,
> 2^{s+2} *for* $8|m$.

Proof: For $m = 1$ the statement is true (the number of solutions is 1) ; for $m > 1$ the number of solutions of (28) for the various primes $p|m$ and their accompanying multiplicities l appearing in the canonical decomposition of m is multiplicative, by Theorem 71. Our statements therefore follow. For if $p = 2$, then 0 is the number of solutions of (28) when $4|m$, unless either $l = 2$ and $n \equiv 1 \ (\mathrm{mod}\ 4)$ or $l > 2$ and $n \equiv 1 \ (\mathrm{mod}\ 8)$; if $p > 2$ it is 0 when $\left(\dfrac{n}{p}\right) = -1$. Otherwise, the power of 2, if there is any, supplies a factor of 1 to the last formula if $l = 1$; 2 if $l = 2$; and 4 if $l \geq 3$; and every odd $p|m$ that occurs supplies a factor of 2.

The introduction, which is to follow, of the so-called Jacobi symbol, a generalization of that of Legendre, will, among other things, make the decomposition of $|n|$ into prime factors unnecessary for the complete analysis of $\left(\dfrac{n}{p}\right)$, where $p>2$ and $p\nmid n$. In particular, the five main properties (Theorems 78, 81, 83, 85, and 86) of Legendre's symbol will turn out to be true for Jacobi's symbol as well.

DEFINITION 19 (Jacobi's symbol): *Let* $m>0$, *let* m *be odd, and let* $m=\overset{v}{\underset{r=1}{\Pi}}p_r$ *be the decomposition of* m *into prime factors* (with repeated factors written an appropriate number of times); *furthermore, let* $(n,m)=1$. *Then*

$$\left(\frac{n}{m}\right)=\overset{v}{\underset{r=1}{\Pi}}\left(\frac{n}{p_r}\right).$$

(This represents 1 if $m=1$.)

This definition is meaningful, since the factors on the right are defined as Legendre symbols, because $p_r\nmid n$ and $p_r>2$. And for $m=p>2$ it agrees with Definition 18.

Examples: $\left(\dfrac{1}{m}\right)=1$ for odd $m>0$; $\left(\dfrac{a^2}{m}\right)=1$ for odd $m>0$, if $(a,m)=1$.

One should not be tempted to think that for odd $m>0$ and $(n,m)=1$, we have $\left(\dfrac{n}{m}\right)=-1$ precisely whenever n is a quadratic non-residue; but rather: whenever n is a quadratic non-residue of an odd number of p_r. Thus if n is a quadratic residue of m (and consequently a quadratic residue of all the p_r) then (but not: *then only*) $\left(\dfrac{n}{m}\right)=1$.

THEOREM 89 (Generalization of Theorem 78): *Let* $m>0$ *be odd,* $n\equiv n'$ (mod m), *and* $(n,m)=1$. *Then*

$$\left(\frac{n}{m}\right)=\left(\frac{n'}{m}\right).$$

Proof: By hypothesis, we certainly have $(n',m)=1$. By Theorem 78, since $n\equiv n'$ (mod p_r) and $p_r\nmid n$, we have

$$\left(\frac{n}{p_r}\right)=\left(\frac{n'}{p_r}\right)$$

for every $p_r|m$, from which our result follows by multiplication with respect to all the r.

THEOREM 90: *For $m>0$ odd, $m'>0$ odd, $(n, m)=1$, and $(n, m')=1$* (in short, if the left-hand side of the following equation is meaningful), *we have*

$$\left(\frac{n}{m}\right)\left(\frac{n}{m'}\right)=\left(\frac{n}{m\,m'}\right).$$

Proof: mm' is >0, odd, and relatively prime to n. Consequently, if $m=\prod_{r=1}^{v} p_r$ and $m'=\prod_{r=1}^{v'} p'_r$, then

$$\left(\frac{n}{m}\right)\left(\frac{n}{m'}\right)=\prod_{r=1}^{v}\left(\frac{n}{p_r}\right)\prod_{r=1}^{v'}\left(\frac{n}{p'_r}\right)=\prod_{p}\left(\frac{n}{p}\right),$$

where the product is taken over the prime factors of mm' (with the proper multiplicities), and therefore

$$=\left(\frac{n}{m\,m'}\right).$$

THEOREM 91 (Generalization of Theorem 81): *Let $m>0$ be odd, $(n, m)=1$, and $(n', m)=1$. Then*

$$\left(\frac{nn'}{m}\right)=\left(\frac{n}{m}\right)\left(\frac{n'}{m}\right).$$

Proof: We have $(nn', m)=1$. For $p_r|m$ we have, by Theorem 81,

$$\left(\frac{nn'}{p_r}\right)=\left(\frac{n}{p_r}\right)\left(\frac{n'}{p_r}\right),$$

from which our result follows by multiplication with respect to all the r.

THEOREM 92 (Generalization of Theorem 83; the so-called First Supplement to Jacobi's Reciprocity Law): *Let $m>0$ be odd. Then*

$$\left(\frac{-1}{m}\right)=(-1)^{\frac{m-1}{2}}.$$

Proof: For $m=1$ this is obvious; consequently, let $m>1$. For odd u and u', we have

$$(u-1)(u'-1)\equiv 0 \pmod 4,$$

so that

$$uu'-1\equiv(u-1)+(u'-1) \pmod 4.$$

For odd $u_1, \ldots, u_v$, we therefore have

$$\prod_{r=1}^{v} u_r - 1 \equiv \sum_{r=1}^{v} (u_r - 1) \pmod{4},$$

(30)
$$\frac{\prod_{r=1}^{v} u_r - 1}{2} \equiv \sum_{r=1}^{v} \frac{u_r - 1}{2} \pmod{2},$$

$$(-1)^{\frac{\prod_{r=1}^{v} u_r - 1}{2}} = \prod_{r=1}^{v} (-1)^{\frac{u_r - 1}{2}}.$$

From $m = \prod_{r=1}^{v} p_r$, since (by Theorem 83)

$$\left(\frac{-1}{p_r}\right) = (-1)^{\frac{p_r - 1}{2}},$$

it therefore follows that

$$\left(\frac{-1}{m}\right) = \prod_{r=1}^{v}\left(\frac{-1}{p_r}\right) = \prod_{r=1}^{v} (-1)^{\frac{p_r - 1}{2}} = (-1)^{\frac{\prod_{r=1}^{v} p_r - 1}{2}} = (-1)^{\frac{m-1}{2}}.$$

THEOREM 93 (Generalization of Theorem 85; the so-called Second Supplement to Jacobi's Reciprocity Law): *Let $m > 0$ be odd. Then*

$$\left(\frac{2}{m}\right) = (-1)^{\frac{m^2 - 1}{8}}.$$

Proof: For $m = 1$ this is obvious; let $m > 1$.
For odd u and u' we have

$$(u^2 - 1)(u'^2 - 1) \equiv 0 \pmod{16} \text{ (and in fact even } \pmod{64});$$

hence

$$u^2 u'^2 - 1 \equiv (u^2 - 1) + (u'^2 - 1) \pmod{16}.$$

For odd $u_1, \ldots, u_v$, we therefore have

$$\prod_{r=1}^{v} u_r^2 - 1 \equiv \sum_{r=1}^{v} (u_r^2 - 1) \pmod{16},$$

$$\frac{\prod_{r=1}^{v} u_r^2 - 1}{8} \equiv \sum_{r=1}^{v} \frac{u_r^2 - 1}{8} \pmod{2},$$

$$(-1)^{\frac{\left(\prod_{r=1}^{v} u_r\right)^2 - 1}{8}} = \prod_{r=1}^{v} (-1)^{\frac{u_r^2 - 1}{8}}.$$

From $m = \overset{v}{\underset{r=1}{\Pi}} p_r$ and the fact that, by Theorem 85,

$$\left(\frac{2}{p_r}\right) = (-1)^{\frac{p_r^2 - 1}{8}},$$

it therefore follows that

$$\left(\frac{2}{m}\right) = \overset{v}{\underset{r=1}{\Pi}}\left(\frac{2}{p_r}\right) = \overset{v}{\underset{r=1}{\Pi}}(-1)^{\frac{p_r^2-1}{8}} = (-1)^{\frac{\left(\overset{v}{\underset{r=1}{\Pi}} p_r\right)^2 - 1}{8}} = (-1)^{\frac{m^2-1}{8}}.$$

Theorem 94 (Generalization of Theorem 86; Jacobi's Reciprocity Law):
Let n and m be > 0, odd, and relatively prime. Then

$$\left(\frac{n}{m}\right)\left(\frac{m}{n}\right) = (-1)^{\frac{n-1}{2}\frac{m-1}{2}}.$$

Proof: Without loss of generality, let $n > 1$ and $m > 1$; their decompositions into prime factors can be denoted by $n = \Pi p$ and $m = \Pi q$. Then, by Theorems 90 and 91, we have

$$\left(\frac{n}{m}\right) = \left(\frac{\Pi p}{\Pi q}\right) = \underset{p}{\Pi}\left(\frac{p}{\Pi q}\right) = \underset{p}{\Pi}\underset{q}{\Pi}\left(\frac{p}{q}\right),$$

$$\left(\frac{m}{n}\right) = \underset{q}{\Pi}\underset{p}{\Pi}\left(\frac{q}{p}\right),$$

so that, by Theorem 86 and (30), we have

$$\left(\frac{n}{m}\right)\left(\frac{m}{n}\right) = \underset{p,q}{\Pi}\left(\frac{p}{q}\right)\left(\frac{q}{p}\right) = \underset{p,q}{\Pi}(-1)^{\frac{p-1}{2}\frac{q-1}{2}} = (-1)^{\underset{p,q}{\Sigma}\frac{p-1}{2}\frac{q-1}{2}}$$

$$= (-1)^{\underset{p}{\Sigma}\frac{p-1}{2}\cdot\underset{q}{\Sigma}\frac{q-1}{2}} = (-1)^{\frac{\Pi p-1}{2}\frac{\Pi q-1}{2}} = (-1)^{\frac{n-1}{2}\frac{m-1}{2}}.$$

Examples of the application of Jacobi's symbol:

1) Legendre's symbol $\left(\frac{383}{443}\right)$ (443 is prime) can be computed rapidly by the application of the theorems on the Jacobi symbol, as follows:

$$\left(\frac{383}{443}\right) = -\left(\frac{443}{383}\right) = -\left(\frac{60}{383}\right) = -\left(\frac{2^2}{383}\right)\left(\frac{15}{383}\right) = -\left(\frac{15}{383}\right) = \left(\frac{383}{15}\right) = \left(\frac{8}{15}\right)$$

$$= \left(\frac{2^2}{15}\right)\left(\frac{2}{15}\right) = \left(\frac{2}{15}\right) = 1.$$

2) The Jacobi symbol $\left(\dfrac{35}{87}\right)$ (87 is not prime, but is relatively prime to 35) can be similarly computed thus:

$$\left(\frac{35}{87}\right)=-\left(\frac{87}{35}\right)=-\left(\frac{17}{35}\right)=-\left(\frac{35}{17}\right)=-\left(\frac{1}{17}\right)=-1.$$

The computation is often simplified by the use of:

THEOREM 95: *Let n and m be odd and relatively prime. Then*

$$\left(\frac{n}{|m|}\right)\left(\frac{m}{|n|}\right)=\begin{cases}-(-1)^{\frac{n-1}{2}\frac{m-1}{2}} & \text{if } n<0 \text{ and } m<0,\\[2mm](-1)^{\frac{n-1}{2}\frac{m-1}{2}} & \text{otherwise.}\end{cases}$$

Proof: 1) If n and m are >0, then this is Theorem 94.

2) If n and m are <0, then by Theorems 92 and 94,

$$\left(\frac{n}{|m|}\right)\left(\frac{m}{|n|}\right)=\left(\frac{-|n|}{|m|}\right)\left(\frac{-|m|}{|n|}\right)=\left(\frac{-1}{|m|}\right)\left(\frac{|n|}{|m|}\right)\left(\frac{|m|}{|n|}\right)\left(\frac{-1}{|n|}\right)$$

$$=(-1)^{\frac{|m|-1}{2}+\frac{|n|-1}{2}\frac{|m|-1}{2}+\frac{|n|-1}{2}}=-(-1)^{\frac{|m|-1}{2}+\frac{|n|-1}{2}\frac{|m|-1}{2}+\frac{|n|-1}{2}+1}$$

$$=-(-1)^{\left(\frac{|n|-1}{2}+1\right)\left(\frac{|m|-1}{2}+1\right)}=-(-1)^{\frac{|n|+1}{2}\frac{|m|+1}{2}}=-(-1)^{\frac{-n+1}{2}\frac{-m+1}{2}}$$

$$=-(-1)^{\frac{n-1}{2}\frac{m-1}{2}}.$$

3) If one of the numbers n and m is positive and the other negative, then without loss of generality let $n>0$ and $m<0$. Then, by Theorems 92 and 94, we have

$$\left(\frac{n}{|m|}\right)\left(\frac{m}{|n|}\right)=\left(\frac{n}{|m|}\right)\left(\frac{-|m|}{n}\right)=\left(\frac{n}{|m|}\right)\left(\frac{|m|}{n}\right)\left(\frac{-1}{n}\right)=(-1)^{\frac{n-1}{2}\frac{|m|-1}{2}+\frac{n-1}{2}}$$

$$=(-1)^{\frac{n-1}{2}\frac{|m|+1}{2}}=(-1)^{\frac{n-1}{2}\frac{-m+1}{2}}=(-1)^{\frac{n-1}{2}\frac{m-1}{2}}.$$

Example: $\left(\dfrac{-3}{p}\right)=\left(\dfrac{p}{3}\right)$ for $p>3$, since $p>0$ and $-3\equiv1$ (mod 4).

The rest of this chapter is not important in itself, but is used in Part Four (which is itself applied only later on, in Volume 3 of my *Vorlesungen über Zahlentheorie*). Thus the reader, if he is curious about how number theory continues, may skip the rest of this chapter for the time being. But I urge him to be sure to read Part Four (and therefore the rest of this chapter), especially since it deals with one of the mainstreams of classical number theory and of Dirichlet's classical work, and since I am not happy about the fact that nowadays, aside from the ABC of number theory, we study only modern concepts.

Definition 20 (Kronecker's symbol): (Throughout the rest of this chapter) *let $d \equiv 0$ or 1 (mod 4), and let d not be a perfect square* (thus $d = 5$, 8, 12, 13, 17, 20, 21, ... or $-3, -4, -7, -8, ...$). *Let $m > 0$. Then $\left(\dfrac{d}{m}\right)$ is always given a meaning by means of the following:*

$$\left(\frac{d}{p}\right) = 0 \quad \text{if} \quad p | d,$$

$$\left(\frac{d}{2}\right) = \begin{cases} 1 & \text{if } d \equiv 1 \ (\text{mod } 8), \\ -1 & \text{if } d \equiv 5 \ (\text{mod } 8) \end{cases}$$

(hence $\left(\dfrac{d}{2}\right) = $ Jacobi's symbol $\left(\dfrac{2}{|d|}\right)$ for $2 \nmid d$),

$$\left(\frac{d}{p}\right) = \textit{Legendre's symbol, if } p > 2 \textit{ and } p \nmid d,$$

$$\left(\frac{d}{m}\right) = \prod_{r=1}^{v} \left(\frac{d}{p_r}\right) \textit{ for } m = \prod_{r=1}^{v} p_r \textit{ (i.e., 1 for } m = 1\textit{)}.$$

For those d and m for which the Kronecker and Jacobi symbols are defined (namely for the above d and for odd $m > 0$ relatively prime to d) both definitions obviously agree (as they should).

We notice at once that for $(d, m) > 1$ we always have

$$\left(\frac{d}{m}\right) = 0,$$

and for $(d, m) = 1$ we always have

$$\left(\frac{d}{m}\right) = \pm 1.$$

Theorem 96: *If $m_1 > 0$ and $m_2 > 0$, then*

$$\left(\frac{d}{m_1 m_2}\right) = \left(\frac{d}{m_1}\right)\left(\frac{d}{m_2}\right).$$

Proof: This follows immediately from Definition 20,

THEOREM 97: *Let $k>0$ and let $(d, k)=1$. The number of solutions of*

(31) $$x^2 \equiv d \pmod{4k}$$

is

$$2 \sum_{f|k} \left(\frac{d}{f}\right),$$

where f runs through the square-free positive divisors of k.

Remark: Since whenever x_0 satisfies the congruence so does $x_0 + 2k$ (because $(x_0 + 2k)^2 \equiv x_0^2 + 4kx_0 + 4k^2 \equiv x_0^2 \pmod{4k}$), it follows that $\sum_{f|k} \left(\frac{d}{f}\right)$ is the number of x in the interval $0 \leq x < 2k$ which satisfy congruence (31). It is in this form that we shall later apply Theorem 97.

Proof: 1) Let d be odd, and therefore $\equiv 1 \pmod 4$; then $(d, 4k)=1$. For every p^l in the canonical decomposition of $4k$, the number of solutions of

$$x^2 \equiv d \pmod{p^l}$$

is, by Theorem 87,

$$2 \text{ for } p=2, \; l=2,$$

$$2\left(1 + \left(\frac{d}{p}\right)\right) \text{ for } p=2, \; l>2$$

($l=1$ does not occur when $p=2$, since $4|4k$), and

$$1 + \left(\frac{d}{p}\right) \text{ for } p>2.$$

From Theorem 71 it follows that the number of solutions of (31) is

$$2 \prod_{p|k} \left(1 + \left(\frac{d}{p}\right)\right) = 2 \sum_{f|k} \left(\frac{d}{f}\right)$$

(since for $p=2$ we have $l=2$ if $2 \nmid k$ and $l>2$ if $2|k$).

2) Let d be even, and therefore $\equiv 0 \pmod 4$. Then k is odd. The congruence

$$x^2 \equiv d \equiv 0 \pmod 4$$

has two solutions;

$$x^2 \equiv d \pmod{p^l}$$

has $1 + \left(\frac{d}{p}\right)$ solutions for $p^l|k$, $l>0$, so that in this case as well the number of solutions of (31) is

$$2 \prod_{p|k} \left(1 + \left(\frac{d}{p}\right)\right) = 2 \sum_{f|k} \left(\frac{d}{f}\right).$$

Let us set $|d| = a$ throughout the rest of this chapter.

Theorem 98: *If $m>0$ and $(d, m)=1$, then*

1) *for d odd, we have*

$$\left(\frac{d}{m}\right)=\left(\frac{m}{a}\right)$$

(the symbol on the right is a Jacobi symbol);

2) *for d even, if 2 goes into d exactly b times, so that $d=2^b u$ and u is odd, and if we set $|u|=v$, then*

$$\left(\frac{d}{m}\right)=\left(\frac{2}{m}\right)^b (-1)^{\frac{u-1}{2}\frac{m-1}{2}}\left(\frac{m}{v}\right)$$

(both symbols on the right are Jacobi symbols).

Proof: 1) Let d be odd, so that $d\equiv1$ (mod 4). We have $m=2^l w$, where w is odd and >0, and $l\geqq0$. By Theorem 96 and Definition 20, we have

$$\left(\frac{d}{m}\right)=\left(\frac{d}{2^l w}\right)=\left(\frac{d}{2}\right)^l\left(\frac{d}{w}\right)=\left(\frac{2}{a}\right)^l\left(\frac{d}{w}\right),$$

so that by Theorems 95 and 91 we have

$$\left(\frac{d}{m}\right)=\left(\frac{2}{a}\right)^l\left(\frac{w}{a}\right)=\left(\frac{2^l w}{a}\right)=\left(\frac{m}{a}\right).$$

2) Let d be even. Then

$$\left(\frac{d}{m}\right)=\left(\frac{2^b u}{m}\right)=\left(\frac{2}{m}\right)^b\left(\frac{u}{m}\right),$$

so that by Theorem 95, since m is odd and >0, we have

$$\left(\frac{d}{m}\right)=\left(\frac{2}{m}\right)^b (-1)^{\frac{u-1}{2}\frac{m-1}{2}}\left(\frac{m}{v}\right).$$

Theorem 99: *The number-theoretic function $\left(\dfrac{d}{m}\right)$ of m has the following properties:*

1) $\left(\dfrac{d}{m}\right)=0$ *for* $(d, m)>1$.

2) $\left(\dfrac{d}{1}\right)\neq0$.

3) $\left(\dfrac{d}{m_1}\right)\left(\dfrac{d}{m_2}\right)=\left(\dfrac{d}{m_1 m_2}\right)$.

4) $\left(\dfrac{d}{m_1}\right)=\left(\dfrac{d}{m_2}\right)$ *for* $m_1\equiv m_2$ (mod a).

5) $\left(\dfrac{d}{m}\right)=-1$ *for suitable m.*

Proof: 1) follows from the definition.

2) $\left(\dfrac{d}{1}\right)=1.$

3) we know by Theorem 96.

41) Let $(a, m_1)>1$. Then we have $(a, m_2)>1$, so that

$$\left(\frac{d}{m_1}\right)=0=\left(\frac{d}{m_2}\right).$$

42) Let $(a, m_1)=1$, so that $(a, m_2)=1$.

421) Let d be odd. By Theorems 98 and 89, we have

$$\left(\frac{d}{m_1}\right)=\left(\frac{m_1}{a}\right)=\left(\frac{m_2}{a}\right)=\left(\frac{d}{m_2}\right).$$

422) Let d be even. By Theorem 98, we have

$$\left(\frac{d}{m_1}\right)=\left(\frac{2}{m_1}\right)^b(-1)^{\frac{u-1}{2}\frac{m_1-1}{2}}\left(\frac{m_1}{v}\right),$$

$$\left(\frac{d}{m_2}\right)=\left(\frac{2}{m_2}\right)^b(-1)^{\frac{u-1}{2}\frac{m_2-1}{2}}\left(\frac{m_2}{v}\right).$$

On the right, we have

$$\left(\frac{m_1}{v}\right)=\left(\frac{m_2}{v}\right)$$

by Theorem 89 (since $v|a$ and $m_1\equiv m_2 \pmod{v}$); furthermore (since $4|a$ and $m_1\equiv m_2 \pmod 4$), we have

$$(-1)^{\frac{u-1}{2}\frac{m_1-1}{2}}=(-1)^{\frac{u-1}{2}\frac{m_2-1}{2}};$$

finally, we have

$$\left(\frac{2}{m_1}\right)^b=\left(\frac{2}{m_2}\right)^b;$$

for this is obvious when $b=2$, and when $b>2$ it is a consequence of Theorem 93 and of the fact that $8|a$ and $m_1\equiv m_2 \pmod 8$.

51) Let d be odd. Then a is not a perfect square; for if $d>0$ we have $a=d$, and if $d<0$ we have $a\equiv 3 \pmod 4$. For suitable p we therefore have $a=p^l g$, where $p>2$, l is odd, $p\nmid g$, and g is odd. Let s be a quadratic non-residue mod p (s exists, by Theorem 79); choose $m>0$, by Theorem 69, so that

$$m\equiv s \pmod p, \quad m\equiv 1 \pmod g.$$

Then $(a, m) = 1$, so that by Theorem 98 we have

$$\left(\frac{d}{m}\right) = \left(\frac{m}{a}\right) = \left(\frac{m}{p}\right)^l \left(\frac{m}{g}\right) = \left(\frac{s}{p}\right)^l \left(\frac{1}{g}\right) = (-1)^l = -1.$$

52) Let d be even.

521) Let b be odd. Then I choose $m > 0$ such that

$$m \equiv 5 \pmod 8, \quad m \equiv 1 \pmod v$$

(which is possible, since $(8, v) = 1$). Then we have $(a, m) = 1$, and by Theorem 98

$$\left(\frac{d}{m}\right) = \left(\frac{2}{m}\right)^b (-1)^{\frac{u-1}{2} \frac{m-1}{2}} \left(\frac{m}{v}\right) = \left(\frac{2}{m}\right) \cdot 1 \cdot \left(\frac{1}{v}\right) = -1.$$

522) Let b be even. Then u is not a perfect square, and by Theorem 98, if $(a, m) = 1$ and $m > 0$, we have

$$\left(\frac{d}{m}\right) = (-1)^{\frac{u-1}{2} \frac{m-1}{2}} \left(\frac{m}{v}\right).$$

5221) Let $u \equiv 3 \pmod 4$. Then I choose $m > 0$ such that

$$m \equiv -1 \pmod 4, \quad m \equiv 1 \pmod v.$$

Then we have $(a, m) = 1$ and

$$\left(\frac{d}{m}\right) = (-1)^{\frac{u-1}{2}} \left(\frac{1}{v}\right) = -1.$$

5222) Let $u \equiv 1 \pmod 4$. Then for $(a, m) = 1$ and $m > 0$, we have

$$\left(\frac{d}{m}\right) = \left(\frac{m}{v}\right).$$

v is not a perfect square, since we have either $v = u$ or $v \equiv -u \equiv -1 \pmod 4$. For suitable p we therefore have $v = p^l g$, where $p > 2$, l is odd, $p \nmid g$, and g is odd. Let s be a quadratic non-residue mod p; choose $m > 0$, by Theorem 70, such that

$$m \equiv s \pmod p, \quad m \equiv 1 \pmod g, \quad m \equiv 1 \pmod 2.$$

Then $(a, m) = 1$, and

$$\left(\frac{d}{m}\right) = \left(\frac{m}{p^l g}\right) = \left(\frac{m}{p}\right)^l \left(\frac{m}{g}\right) = \left(\frac{s}{p}\right)^l \left(\frac{1}{g}\right) = (-1)^l = -1.$$

THEOREM 100: $\left(\dfrac{d}{a-1}\right) = \begin{cases} 1 & \text{for } d>0, \\ -1 & \text{for } d<0. \end{cases}$

Proof: 1) Let d be odd. Then, by Theorem 98, we have

$$\left(\frac{d}{a-1}\right) = \left(\frac{a-1}{a}\right) = \left(\frac{-1}{a}\right) = (-1)^{\frac{a-1}{2}} = (-1)^{\frac{|d|-1}{2}} = \begin{cases} 1 & \text{for } d>0, \\ -1 & \text{for } d<0. \end{cases}$$

2) Let d be even, so that $d=2^b u$, $b\geq 2$, with u odd. Then, by Theorem 98,

$$\left(\frac{d}{a-1}\right) = \left(\frac{2}{a-1}\right)^b (-1)^{\frac{u-1}{2}} \left(\frac{a-1}{|u|}\right).$$

Here, on the one hand, we have

$$\left(\frac{2}{a-1}\right)^b = 1;$$

for if $b=2$ this is obvious, and if $b\geq 3$ we have $a-1 \equiv 7 \pmod 8$; on the other hand, we have

$$(-1)^{\frac{u-1}{2}}\left(\frac{a-1}{|u|}\right) = (-1)^{\frac{u-1}{2}}\left(\frac{-1}{|u|}\right) = (-1)^{\frac{u-1}{2}+\frac{|u|-1}{2}} = \begin{cases} 1 & \text{for } d>0, \\ -1 & \text{for } d<0. \end{cases}$$

THEOREM 101: *For $n>0$, $m>0$, and $n \equiv -m \pmod a$, we have*

$$\left(\frac{d}{n}\right) = \begin{cases} \left(\dfrac{d}{m}\right) & \text{if } d>0, \\ -\left(\dfrac{d}{m}\right) & \text{if } d<0. \end{cases}$$

Proof: $\left(\dfrac{d}{n}\right) = \left(\dfrac{d}{am-m}\right) = \left(\dfrac{d}{m(a-1)}\right) = \left(\dfrac{d}{m}\right)\left(\dfrac{d}{a-1}\right)$

and Theorem 100.

CHAPTER VII

PELL'S EQUATION

In this chapter we discuss the so-called Pell equation, that is, the diophantine equation

$$(32) \qquad x^2 - dy^2 = 1,$$

where d is given (as an arbitrary integer).

In the cases in which $d < 0$ (ellipse) and in which $d =$ a perfect square > 0 (hyperbola the ratio of whose major and minor axes is rational), (32) will easily prove to have only a finite number of solutions, and for $d = 0$ (double line) an infinite number. On the other hand, the fact that (32) has an infinite number of solutions for any positive, non-square d (hyperbola the ratio of whose major and minor axes is irrational), will turn out to be a fairly deep theorem (and a gateway to classical number theory).

If this were not a textbook in number theory, I would not elaborate on the term "non-square," and I would take for granted the equivalence of the two notions

1) $\sqrt{d}$ is not an integer, and

2) $\sqrt{d}$ is not a rational number.

Since, however, I have proved even simpler things in this book, I offer the following calculation: If

$$d = \left(\frac{a}{b}\right)^2, \ a > 0, \ b > 0, \ (a, b) = 1,$$

then

$$b^2 d = a^2, \ b^2/a^2, \ (b^2, a^2) = 1, \ b^2 = 1, \ b = 1, \ d = a^2.$$

I will first take care of the trivial cases.

For $d < -1$, since $1 \geqq |d| y^2$, we must have

$$y = 0, \ x = \pm 1.$$

For $d = -1$,

$$x^2 + y^2 = 1$$

obviously has the four solutions

$$x = \pm 1, \ y = 0; \ x = 0, \ y = \pm 1.$$

For $d=a^2>0$,

$$x^2-d\,y^2=x^2-a^2y^2=(x+a\,y)\,(x-a\,y)=1$$

is clearly possible only if

$$x+a\,y=x-a\,y=\pm1.$$

In that case,

$$x=\frac{(x+a\,y)+(x-a\,y)}{2}=\pm1,\ y=0.$$

For $d=0$,

$$x^2=1$$

is clearly satisfied for $x=\pm1$ and y arbitrary.

If $d>0$ is non-square (which I will assume from now on), then (32) certainly has the two solutions

$$x=\pm1,\ y=0.$$

Our main goal is to show that there are infinitely many more. At the moment, it is clear only that any further solutions will occur in quadruples $\pm x$, $\pm y$, so that all of them will be taken care of once we know those that lie in the positive quadrant $x>0$, $y>0$. Moreover, in this quadrant, the larger y is, the larger x will be.

THEOREM 102: *Let a be any real number, and let $m>0$. Then we can find x and y such that*

$$|x-\alpha y|<\frac{1}{m},\ 0<y\leqq m.$$

Proof: In the expression $u-av$, let $v=0, 1, \ldots, m$, and let $u=[av]+1$ for each v, so that

$$0<u-\alpha v\leqq1.$$

(If a is irrational, then the $m+1$ numbers $u-av$ which occur will all be distinct.) At least one of the m intervals

$$\frac{h}{m}<\xi\leqq\frac{h+1}{m};\ h=0, 1, \ldots, m-1$$

must contain two of the $m+1$ numbers (pigeon-hole principle). Hence there are two numbers, v_1 and v_2, such that $0\leqq v_1<v_2\leqq m$, and two numbers, u_1 and u_2, such that

$$|(u_2-u_1)-\alpha(v_2-v_1)|=|(u_2-\alpha v_2)-(u_1-\alpha v_1)|<\frac{1}{m}.$$

If we set $v_2-v_1=y$ and $u_2-u_1=x$ then, since $0<y\leqq m$, everything has been proved.

Theorem 103 : *The inequality*

(33)
$$|x-y\sqrt{d}|<\frac{1}{y}$$

has an infinite number of solutions. (Here we must necessarily have $y>0$; hence also $x>y\sqrt{d}-\dfrac{1}{y}\geqq\sqrt{d}-1>0$.)

Proof: We obtain a solution by Theorem 102, with $a=\sqrt{d}$, $m=1$. It suffices to show that for each solution x', y' of (33), we can find a solution x, y for which

$$|x-y\sqrt{d}|<|x'-y'\sqrt{d}|.$$

For we will then have a sequence of solutions x_n, y_n ($n=1, 2, \ldots$) of (33) for which

$$|x_1-y_1\sqrt{d}|>|x_2-y_2\sqrt{d}|>\cdots>|x_n-y_n\sqrt{d}|>\cdots$$

such that we never have both $x_{n_1}=x_{n_2}$ and $y_{n_1}=y_{n_2}$ for $n_1\gtrless n_2$.

In order to accomplish this, given x' and y', let us choose m so large that

$$\frac{1}{m}<|x'-y'\sqrt{d}|$$

(This can be done, since $\sqrt{d}$ is irrational and $y'>0$, so that $x'-y'\sqrt{d}\neq0$.) Now x and y may be chosen in accordance with Theorem 102. Then we have

$$|x-y\sqrt{d}|<\frac{1}{m}\begin{cases}<|x'-y'\sqrt{d}|,\\[4pt]\leqq\dfrac{1}{y}.\end{cases}$$

Theorem 104: *There exists a non-zero number k (dependent on d) for which the equation*

(34)
$$x^2-dy^2=k$$

has an infinite number of positive solutions x, y.

Proof: For every solution of (33), we have

$$|x+y\sqrt{d}|=|(x-y\sqrt{d})+2y\sqrt{d}|<\frac{1}{y}+2y\sqrt{d}\leqq y+2y\sqrt{d}=(1+2\sqrt{d})y,$$

$$0<|x^2-dy^2|=|(x+y\sqrt{d})(x-y\sqrt{d})|<(1+2\sqrt{d})y\frac{1}{y}=1+2\sqrt{d},$$

$$x^2-dy^2=k,\ 0<|k|<1+2\sqrt{d}.$$

Consequently at least one of these numbers k corresponds to an infinite number of distinct positive number-pairs x, y. (Pigeon-hole principle: If we place an infinite number of objects in a finite number of pigeon-holes, then at least one pigeon-hole will contain an infinite number of the objects.)

Theorem 105: *Pell's equation* (32) *has at least one solution with non-zero y* (and hence at least one solution with $x > 0$ and $y > 0$).

The proof of this result is the most difficult part of our job; later on we will easily be able to deduce from it the existence of an infinite number of solutions, as well as obtain a knowledge of all of them.

Proof: In accordance with Theorem 104, let us choose a number k for which (34) has an infinite number of positive solutions. These fall into k^2 classes according as

$$x \equiv 0, 1, \ldots, |k| - 1; \quad y \equiv 0, 1, \ldots, |k| - 1 \pmod{|k|};$$

some of these classes may, of course, be empty. Consequently at least one of the k^2 classes must contain an infinite number of positive solutions x, y of (34) (pigeon-hole principle), and therefore at least two. We thus have five numbers, namely k, x_1, y_1, x_2, and y_2, having the following properties:

$$x_1{}^2 - d\,y_1{}^2 = k,\, x_2{}^2 - d\,y_2{}^2 = k,\, x_1 > 0,\, y_1 > 0,\, x_2 > 0,\, y_2 > 0,\, k \gtrless 0,$$

$x_1 \equiv x_2 \pmod{|k|}$, $y_1 \equiv y_2 \pmod{|k|}$; and not both $x_1 = x_2$, $y_1 = y_2$.

I now set

$$x = \frac{x_1 x_2 - d\,y_1 y_2}{k}, \, y = \frac{x_1 y_2 - x_2 y_1}{k},$$

and I will be through as soon as I have shown that

1) x and y are integers.
2) $x^2 - dy^2 = 1$.
3) $y \neq 0$.

Proof of 1). It follows, from the above congruences, that

$$x_1 x_2 - d\,y_1 y_2 \equiv x_1{}^2 - d\,y_1{}^2 \equiv k \equiv 0 \pmod{|k|},$$
$$x_1 y_2 - x_2 y_1 \equiv x_1 y_1 - x_1 y_1 \equiv 0 \pmod{|k|}.$$

Proof of 2). $k^2(x^2 - d\,y^2) = (x_1 x_2 - d\,y_1 y_2)^2 - d\,(x_1 y_2 - x_2 y_1)^2$
$$= x_1{}^2 x_2{}^2 + d^2 y_1{}^2 y_2{}^2 - d\,x_1{}^2 y_2{}^2 - d\,x_2{}^2 y_1{}^2 = (x_1{}^2 - d\,y_1{}^2)(x_2{}^2 - d\,y_2{}^2) = k^2,$$
$$x^2 - d\,y^2 = 1.$$

Proof of 3). If y were 0, then it would follow that

$$x = \pm 1,$$

$$\pm y_2 = y_2\, x - x_2\, y = \frac{y_2(x_1 x_2 - d\,y_1 y_2) - x_2(x_1 y_2 - x_2 y_1)}{k} = \frac{y_1(x_2{}^2 - d\,y_2{}^2)}{k} = y_1;$$

and consequently, since $y_1 > 0$ and $y_2 > 0$, that

$$y_1 = y_2,$$

so that, since $x_1 > 0$, $x_2 > 0$, $x_1^2 = k + d\,y_1^2$, $x_2^2 = k + d\,y_2^2$, that

$$x_1 = x_2,$$

contrary to the above.

THEOREM 106: *If x_1, y_1 and x_2, y_2 each satisfy Pell's equation* (32), *and if x_3, y_3 are determined by*

(35) $$\pm (x_1 + y_1 \sqrt{d})(x_2 + y_2 \sqrt{d}) = x_3 + y_3 \sqrt{d}$$

(*that is, we set $x_3 = \pm(x_1 x_2 + d\,y_1 y_2)$, $y_3 = \pm(x_1 y_2 + x_2 y_1)$), then x_3, y_3 is also a solution of* (32).

Proof: From (35) it follows that

$$\pm (x_1 - y_1 \sqrt{d})(x_2 - y_2 \sqrt{d}) = x_3 - y_3 \sqrt{d},$$

so that by multiplication we obtain

$$(x_1^2 - d\,y_1^2)(x_2^2 - d\,y_2^2) = x_3^2 - d\,y_3^2$$

(of course, we can obtain this identity directly from the formulas for x_3 and y_3), and consequently

$$x_3^2 - d\,y_3^2 = 1 \cdot 1 = 1.$$

THEOREM 107: *If x, y is a solution of* (32), *if $y \neq 0$, and if we set $x + y\sqrt{d} = \eta$, then*

$$\begin{aligned} \eta > 1 \quad &\text{for} \quad x > 0, \ y > 0, \\ 0 < \eta < 1 \quad &\text{for} \quad x > 0, \ y < 0, \\ -1 < \eta < 0 \quad &\text{for} \quad x < 0, \ y > 0, \\ \eta < -1 \quad &\text{for} \quad x < 0, \ y < 0. \end{aligned}$$

Proof: 1) For $x > 0$ and $y > 0$, we have

$$\eta > y \geqq 1;$$

consequently, for $x < 0$ and $y < 0$, we have

$$\eta < -1.$$

2) For $x>0$ and $y<0$, we have

$$1=(x+y\sqrt{d})\,(x-y\sqrt{d}),\ \ x-y\sqrt{d}>1,$$

and therefore

$$0<\eta<1;$$

consequently, for $x<0$ and $y>0$, we have

$$-1<\eta<0.$$

THEOREM 108: *If x_0, y_0 is that solution of* (32) *for which y_0 has the smallest positive value and x_0 is positive, then the general solution is given by the formulas*

(36) $$\pm(x_0+y_0\sqrt{d})^n=x+y\sqrt{d},\ n\gtreqless 0.$$

(In any case, $\pm(x_0+y_0\sqrt{d})^n$ is of the form $x+y\sqrt{d}$, where x and y are integers. This is obvious for $n\geq 0$, and for $n<0$ it is also obvious, since $(x_0+y_0\sqrt{d})^{-1}=x_0-y_0\sqrt{d}$.)

Proof: 1) The fact that (36) always yields a solution follows, for $n>0$, from Theorem 106 and, for $n<0$, from the fact that

$$\pm(x_0+y_0\sqrt{d})^n=\pm(x_0-y_0\sqrt{d})^{|n|}$$

together with Theorem 106; for $n=0$ it is obvious ($x=\pm 1$, $y=0$).

2) Let us set $x_0+y_0\sqrt{d}=\varepsilon$. We must show that

$$\pm\varepsilon^n=x+y\sqrt{d}$$

yields all the solutions, that is, that $\pm\varepsilon^n$, $n\gtreqless 0$ yields all of the solutions in which $y\neq 0$. All of the solutions in which $y\neq 0$ arise from those in which $x>0$ and $y>0$, when we consider all expressions of the form $\pm(x+y\sqrt{d})$ and $\pm(x-y\sqrt{d})=\pm(x+y\sqrt{d})^{-1}$. Since $\varepsilon>1$, we therefore have to show, by Theorem 107, that all of the solutions in which $x+y\sqrt{d}>1$ are given by the formulas

$$\varepsilon^n=x+y\sqrt{d},\ n>0.$$

In any case, it follows from the fact that $x+y\sqrt{d}>1$ and the minimality in the definition of ε, that there exists a number $n>0$ for which

$$\varepsilon^n\leq x+y\sqrt{d}<\varepsilon^{n+1}.$$

Then we have

$$1\leq(x+y\sqrt{d})(\varepsilon^{-1})^n=(x+y\sqrt{d})(x_0-y_0\sqrt{d})^n<\varepsilon.$$

From Theorem 106 it follows that in the equation

$$(x+y\sqrt{d})(x_0-y_0\sqrt{d})^n = x'+y'\sqrt{d},$$

x', y' is a solution. By the definition of ε, we cannot have

$$1 < x'+y'\sqrt{d} < \varepsilon.$$

Consequently

$$x'+y'\sqrt{d}=1,$$
$$x+y\sqrt{d}=\varepsilon^n.$$

It is also necessary, for a later purpose, for me to treat the equation

(37) $$x^2-dy^2=4,$$

which is analogous to (32), where $d \equiv 0$ or 1 (mod 4) and is not a perfect square; to be sure, this is easily reducible to the earlier equation, the main difficulty having already been disposed of in Theorem 105.

(What the state of affairs is as regards those remaining values of d that I do not consider is left as an *Exercise* for the reader.)

The "trivial" solutions $x=\pm 2$, $y=0$ always occur. If $d < -4$, there are obviously no further solutions; if $d=-4$, there are the additional solutions $x=0$, $y=\pm 1$; if $d=-3$, there are, in addition to the two trivial solutions, the four solutions $x=\pm 1$, $y=\pm 1$. Thus, from here on, I can again assume that $d > 0$.

THEOREM 109: *If x_1, y_1 and x_2, y_2 are solutions of (37), and if we set*

$$\frac{x_1+y_1\sqrt{d}}{2}\frac{x_2+y_2\sqrt{d}}{2}=\frac{x+y\sqrt{d}}{2} \quad (x,\ y\ \text{rational}),$$

then x and y are integral and constitute a solution of (37).

Proof: 1) $$x=\frac{x_1x_2+dy_1y_2}{2},\ y=\frac{x_1y_2+x_2y_1}{2},$$

$$x_1 \equiv x_1^2 \equiv dy_1^2+4 \equiv dy_1,\ x_2 \equiv dy_2 \pmod{2},$$
$$x_1x_2+dy_1y_2 \equiv dy_1dy_2+dy_1y_2 \equiv dy_1y_2+dy_1y_2 \equiv 2dy_1y_2 \equiv 0 \pmod{2},$$
$$x_1y_2+x_2y_1 \equiv dy_1y_2+dy_2y_1 \equiv 2dy_1y_2 \equiv 0 \pmod{2}.$$

2) $$\frac{x_1-y_1\sqrt{d}}{2}\frac{x_2-y_2\sqrt{d}}{2}=\frac{x-y\sqrt{d}}{2},$$

$$1=1\cdot 1=\frac{x_1^2-dy_1^2}{4}\frac{x_2^2-dy_2^2}{4}=\frac{x^2-dy^2}{4}.$$

THEOREM 110: *If x, y is a solution of* (37) *for which $y \neq 0$* (such a solution exists, by Theorem 105; for from $x'^2 - dy'^2 = 1$ it follows that $(2x')^2 - d(2y')^2 = 4$), *and if we set*

$$\frac{x + y\sqrt{d}}{2} = \eta,$$

then the four statements whose wording coincides with that of Theorem 107 *also hold.*

Proof: 1) If $x > 0$ and $y > 0$, then

$$\eta > \frac{1+1}{2} = 1,$$

so that if $x < 0$ and $y < 0$,

$$\eta < -1.$$

2) If $x > 0$ and $y < 0$, then

$$1 = \frac{x + y\sqrt{d}}{2} \frac{x - y\sqrt{d}}{2}, \quad \frac{x - y\sqrt{d}}{2} > 1,$$

$$0 < \eta < 1;$$

so that if $x < 0$ and $y > 0$,

$$-1 < \eta < 0.$$

THEOREM 111: *Let x_0, y_0 be that solution of* (37) *for which y_0 has the smallest possible positive value and for which $x_0 > 0$. Let me set*

$$\varepsilon = \frac{x_0 + y_0\sqrt{d}}{2}.$$

Then the general solution is given by the following formulas:

(38) $$\pm \varepsilon^n = \frac{x + y\sqrt{d}}{2}, \quad n \gtrless 0, \quad x \text{ and } y \text{ rational,}$$

$\Big(x$ and y are integral by Theorem 109 and in light of

$$\varepsilon^{-1} = \frac{x_0 - y_0\sqrt{d}}{2} \Big)$$

Proof: 1) The fact that (38) always yields a solution follows from Theorem 109; for $n = 0$ we obtain the two trivial solutions.

2) Because of Theorem 110, we need only show (see the proof of Theorem 108) that for $n>0$, ε^n yields all the solutions for which $\dfrac{x+y\sqrt{d}}{2}>1$. In any case, since $\dfrac{x+y\sqrt{d}}{2}\geq\varepsilon$, there is an $n>0$ such that

$$\varepsilon^n\leq\frac{x+y\sqrt{d}}{2}<\varepsilon^{n+1}.$$

Then we have

$$1\leq\frac{x+y\sqrt{d}}{2}(\varepsilon^{-1})^n=\frac{x+y\sqrt{d}}{2}\left(\frac{x_0-y_0\sqrt{d}}{2}\right)^n<\varepsilon,$$

so that, by the definition of ε, we have

$$\frac{x+y\sqrt{d}}{2}\varepsilon^{-n}=1,$$

$$\frac{x+y\sqrt{d}}{2}=\varepsilon^n.$$

———

After the foregoing theory of Pell's equation, the reader will be as surprised at the following fact as I was when, in 1909, I first learned it from a work of Thue: Every diophantine equation

$$a_n x^n+a_{n-1}x^{n-1}y+\cdots+a_0 y^n=a,$$

where $n\geq3$, has only a finite number of solutions, provided the form on the left cannot be decomposed into homogeneous factors of lower degree with integral coefficients. Thus the situation is quite different from what it is in the case of the hyperbola, even when the curve goes to infinity (otherwise it is trivial). I will wait until Part Nine (of my *Vorlesungen über Zahlentheorie*) before carrying out the proof, since some properties of the so-called algebraic numbers are required for it.

PART TWO

BRUN'S THEOREM AND DIRICHLET'S THEOREM

INTRODUCTION

In Part Two, my aim is to prepare the reader for the forthcoming applications of analysis to several important examples. Here, methods of real analysis will still suffice; even when, in Chapter III, complex numbers are employed (roots of unity), the variables still remain real; and the theorems used—on infinite series with complex terms (convergence, absolute convergence, and uniform convergence)—follow immediately from the corresponding theorems on real series. However, in Parts Five, Six, and Seven of *Vorlesungen über Zahlentheorie* (which is a continuation of the present work) I repeatedly make use of the elements of the theory of functions of a complex variable.

Although the methods of this second part are elementary, I nevertheless discuss two theorems whose proofs, in spite of many simplifications obtained since their original discovery, are by no means short. Thus neither of these theorems, Brun's (1919) in Chapter II or Dirichlet's (1837) in Chapter III, is analytically deep, even though they both require extensive number-theoretic machinery. This is the reason why I introduce them at this stage. In order to orient the reader regarding the significance of Brun's Theorem, I first present, in Chapter I, the proofs of several simple asymptotic properties of prime number distribution, which also appear later (in Part Seven of my *Vorlesungen über Zahlentheorie*) in considerably refined form, following the introduction of some complex function theory. Not everything presented in Chapter I is later applied in Chapter II (Chapter III is completely independent of Chapters I and II) ; but it is no extra trouble to prove the theorems stated there all at the same time.

CHAPTER I

SOME ELEMENTARY INEQUALITIES
OF PRIME-NUMBER THEORY

Throughout this chapter and the next, the symbols $\alpha_1, \ldots, \alpha_{39}$ will be used to represent strictly positive constants the determination of whose values, or an estimate of whose values, will not matter (they will only appear in inequalities).

THEOREM 112: *If $\xi \geq 2$, then*

$$\alpha_1 \frac{\xi}{\log \xi} < \pi(\xi) < \alpha_2 \frac{\xi}{\log \xi}.$$

This means: The number $\pi(\xi)$ of primes up to ξ has the order of magnitude $\dfrac{\xi}{\log \xi}$ as $\xi \to \infty$ This modest step toward proving the Hadamard-de la Vallée Poussin Prime-Number Theorem (1896),

$$\lim_{\xi = \infty} \frac{\pi(\xi)}{\dfrac{\xi}{\log \xi}} = 1,$$

was first made by Chebyshev (in 1852).

Proof: For every $\eta \gtreqless 0$, we have

(39)
$$[\eta] - 2\left[\frac{\eta}{2}\right] \leq 1;$$

for

$$[\eta] - 2\left[\frac{\eta}{2}\right] < \eta - 2\left(\frac{\eta}{2} - 1\right) = 2,$$

and the left-hand side is an integer.

Let $n \geq 2$. For every $p \leq 2n$, let r denote the largest natural number for which $p^r \leq 2n$ $\left(\text{in other words, } r = \left[\dfrac{\log 2n}{\log p}\right]\right)$. First I will show that

(40)
$$\prod_{n < p \leq 2n} p \, \Big| \, \frac{(2n)!}{n! \, n!} \, \Big| \, \prod_{p \leq 2n} p^r.$$

88

(The expression in the middle is an integer, being the binomial coefficient $\binom{2n}{n}$. The right-hand side obviously represents the smallest common multiple of all the natural numbers $\leq 2n$.)

The first half of (40) follows from the fact that every p for which $n < p \leq 2n$ divides $(2n)!$, but not $n! \, n!$. The second half of (40) is proved as follows. $\dfrac{(2n)!}{n! \, n!}$ contains only prime factors which are $\leq 2n$, and contains each $p \leq 2n$ exactly

$$\sum_{m=1}^{r} \left(\left[\frac{2n}{p^m} \right] - 2 \left[\frac{n}{p^m} \right] \right)$$

times, by Theorem 27; therefore, by (39), it contains each such p at most

$$\sum_{m=1}^{r} 1 = r$$

times.

From (40) (where the left-hand side has $\pi(2n) - \pi(n)$ factors which are all $> n$, and the right-hand side $\pi(2n)$ factors which are all $\leq 2n$), it follows further that

$$n^{\pi(2n) - \pi(n)} \leq \prod_{n < p \leq 2n} p \leq \frac{(2n)!}{n! \, n!} \leq \prod_{p \leq 2n} p^r \leq (2n)^{\pi(2n)},$$

$$(\pi(2n) - \pi(n)) \log n \leq \log \frac{(2n)!}{n! \, n!} \leq \pi(2n) \log(2n).$$

Now, on the one hand, we have

$$\frac{(2n)!}{n! \, n!} = \binom{2n}{n} \leq \sum_{a=0}^{2n} \binom{2n}{a} = (1+1)^{2n} = 2^{2n},$$

and, on the other hand,

$$\frac{(2n)!}{n! \, n!} = \frac{(n+1) \cdots 2n}{1 \cdots n} = \prod_{a=1}^{n} \frac{n+a}{a} \geq \prod_{a=1}^{n} 2 = 2^n;$$

consequently, on the one hand, we have

$$(\pi(2n) - \pi(n)) \log n \leq \log(2^{2n}) = 2n \log 2,$$

(41) $$\pi(2n) - \pi(n) < \alpha_3 \frac{n}{\log n},$$

and, on the other hand,

$$\pi(2n) \log(2n) \geq \log(2^n) = n \log 2,$$

(42) $$\pi(2n) > \alpha_4 \frac{n}{\log n}.$$

If $\xi \geq 4$, then by (42) we have

$$\pi(\xi) \geq \pi\left(2\left[\frac{\xi}{2}\right]\right) > \alpha_4 \frac{\left[\frac{\xi}{2}\right]}{\log\left[\frac{\xi}{2}\right]} > \alpha_5 \frac{\xi}{\log \xi};$$

and for $\xi \geq 2$ (since $\pi(\xi) \geq 1$ whenever $2 \leq \xi < 4$) we therefore have

$$\pi(\xi) > \alpha_1 \frac{\xi}{\log \xi},$$

which proves the first part of our theorem.

On the other hand, since $\eta = 2 + 2\left(\frac{\eta}{2} - 1\right) < 2 + 2\left[\frac{\eta}{2}\right]$, it follows from (41) that

$$\pi(\eta) - \pi\left(\frac{\eta}{2}\right) = \pi(\eta) - \pi\left(\left[\frac{\eta}{2}\right]\right) \leq 2 + \pi\left(2\left[\frac{\eta}{2}\right]\right) - \pi\left(\left[\frac{\eta}{2}\right]\right)$$

$$< 2 + \alpha_3 \frac{\left[\frac{\eta}{2}\right]}{\log\left[\frac{\eta}{2}\right]} < \alpha_6 \frac{\eta}{\log \eta}$$

for $\eta \geq 4$; consequently, for $\eta \geq 2$, we have

$$\pi(\eta) - \pi\left(\frac{\eta}{2}\right) < \alpha_7 \frac{\eta}{\log \eta}.$$

If we use the trivial inequality $\pi\left(\frac{\eta}{2}\right) \leq \frac{\eta}{2}$ (up to $\frac{\eta}{2}$ there are no more prime numbers than there are natural numbers), we see that, for $\eta \geq 2$,

$$\log \eta \, \pi(\eta) - \log \frac{\eta}{2} \pi\left(\frac{\eta}{2}\right) = \log \eta\left(\pi(\eta) - \pi\left(\frac{\eta}{2}\right)\right) + \log 2 \cdot \pi\left(\frac{\eta}{2}\right)$$

$$< \log \eta \cdot \alpha_7 \frac{\eta}{\log \eta} + \frac{\eta}{2} < \alpha_8 \, \eta.$$

Consequently, if $m \geq 0$ and $2^m \leq \frac{\xi}{2}$, then

$$\log \frac{\xi}{2^m} \pi\left(\frac{\xi}{2^m}\right) - \log \frac{\xi}{2^{m+1}} \pi\left(\frac{\xi}{2^{m+1}}\right) < \alpha_8 \frac{\xi}{2^m}$$

for $\xi \geq 2$. This is then summed over all the m under consideration; since, for the largest of these m (call it v), we have

$$2^{v+1} > \frac{\xi}{2}, \quad \frac{\xi}{2^{v+1}} < 2, \quad \pi\left(\frac{\xi}{2^{v+1}}\right) = 0,$$

it follows that

$$\log\xi\,\pi(\xi)=\sum_{m=0}^{v}\left(\log\frac{\xi}{2^m}\pi\left(\frac{\xi}{2^m}\right)-\log\frac{\xi}{2^{m+1}}\pi\left(\frac{\xi}{2^{m+1}}\right)\right)<\alpha_8\,\xi\sum_{m=0}^{v}\frac{1}{2^m}<\alpha_8\,\xi\sum_{m=0}^{\infty}\frac{1}{2^m}=\alpha_2\xi,$$

$$\pi(\xi)<\alpha_2\frac{\xi}{\log\xi},$$

which proves the second part of our theorem.

THEOREM 113: *If p_r represents the r-th prime, then for $r>1$ we have*

$$\alpha_9\,r\log r<p_r<\alpha_{10}\,r\log r.$$

Proof: 1) By the second half of Theorem 112, upon replacing ξ by p_r, we have

$$r=\pi(p_r)<\alpha_2\frac{p_r}{\log p_r},$$

$$p_r>\alpha_9\,r\log p_r.$$

Now certainly $p_r>r$ (for successive primes differ by at least 1 and $p_1=2>1$); consequently, for $r>0$, we have

$$p_r>\alpha_9\,r\log r.$$

2) By the first half of Theorem 112 we have

(43) $$\alpha_1\frac{p_r}{\log p_r}<\pi(p_r)=r.$$

Hence, for $r>\alpha_{11}$, we have

$$\frac{\log p_r}{\sqrt{p_r}}<\alpha_1<\frac{r\log p_r}{p_r},$$

$$p_r<r^2,$$

$$\log p_r<2\log r;$$

and hence, for $r>\alpha_{11}$, it follows from (43) that

(44) $$\alpha_1\,p_r<r\log p_r<2r\log r.$$

It follows from (44), for $r>1$, that

$$p_r<\alpha_{10}\,r\log r.$$

THEOREM 114: *The series*

$$\sum_p \frac{1}{p},$$

summed over all the primes in ascending order, diverges.

Two Proofs: 1) (Based on Theorem 113.)   From the second half of Theorem 113 it follows, for $r > 1$, that

$$\frac{1}{p_r} > a_{12} \frac{1}{r \log r}.$$

Since the series

$$\sum_{r=2}^{\infty} \frac{1}{r \log r}$$

diverges, it follows that $\sum_p \dfrac{1}{p}$ also diverges.

2) (Direct.)   From Theorem 22 it follows, for $\xi \geq 2$, that

$$\prod_{p \leq \xi} \frac{1}{1 - \dfrac{1}{p}} = \prod_{p \leq \xi} \left(1 + \frac{1}{p} + \frac{1}{p^2} + \cdots \text{ ad inf.}\right) = \sum_{a=1}^{\infty}{}' \frac{1}{a},$$

where the symbol Σ' signifies that the sum is taken over all those numbers a that are not divisible by any $p > \xi$.   These a include all of the natural numbers $\leq \xi$.   Consequently we have

(45)
$$\prod_{p \leq \xi} \frac{1}{1 - \dfrac{1}{p}} \geq \sum_{a=1}^{[\xi]} \frac{1}{a}.$$

Because of the divergence of of the harmonic series $\sum_{a=1}^{\infty} \dfrac{1}{a}$, it follows that as $\xi \to \infty$,

$$\prod_{p \leq \xi} \frac{1}{1 - \dfrac{1}{p}} \to \infty,$$

$$-\sum_{p \leq \xi} \log \left(1 - \frac{1}{p}\right) \to \infty.$$

For $0 < \eta < \frac{1}{2}$ we now have

$$-\log (1-\eta) = \eta + \frac{\eta^2}{2} + \frac{\eta^3}{3} + \cdots < \eta + \eta^2 + \eta^3 + \cdots = \frac{\eta}{1-\eta} < 2\eta;$$

and hence

$$2 \sum_{p \leq \xi} \frac{1}{p} \to \infty.$$

THEOREM 115: *For $\xi \geqq 3$ we have*

$$(46) \qquad \sum_{2 < p \leqq \xi} \frac{1}{p} < \alpha_{13} \log \log \xi,$$

$$(47) \qquad \prod_{2 < p \leqq \xi} \left(1 - \frac{2}{p}\right) < \frac{\alpha_{14}}{\log^2 \xi}.$$

To clarify: (46) implies that there are few, and (47) that there are many, primes. Accordingly, (46) can be shown to result from the first half of Theorem 113. On the other hand, (47) can be proved at once directly; the second half of Theorem 113 would not give a close enough estimate.

One should note that $\log \log \xi \geqq \log \log 3 > 0$.

Proof: 1) For $r > 1$ it follows, by Theorem 113, that

$$\frac{1}{p_r} < \frac{\alpha_{15}}{r \log r},$$

so that, for $\xi \geqq 3$,

$$\sum_{2 < p \leqq \xi} \frac{1}{p} < \alpha_{15} \sum_{r=2}^{\pi(\xi)} \frac{1}{r \log r} \leqq \alpha_{15} \sum_{r=2}^{[\xi]} \frac{1}{r \log r} < \alpha_{15} \left(\frac{1}{2 \log 2} + \int_{2}^{[\xi]} \frac{d\eta}{\eta \log \eta} \right)$$

$$< \alpha_{15} \left(\log \log \xi + \alpha_{16} \right) < \alpha_{13} \log \log \xi.$$

2) For $\xi \geqq 3$, it follows from (45) that

$$\frac{1}{4} \prod_{2 < p \leqq \xi} \left(1 - \frac{2}{p}\right) < \frac{1}{4} \prod_{2 < p \leqq \xi} \left(1 - \frac{2}{p} + \frac{1}{p^2}\right) = \prod_{p \leqq \xi} \left(1 - \frac{1}{p}\right)^2 = \left(\prod_{p \leqq \xi} \left(1 - \frac{1}{p}\right) \right)^2$$

$$\leqq \left(\sum_{a=1}^{[\xi]} \frac{1}{a} \right)^{-2} < \left(\int_{1}^{[\xi]+1} \frac{d\eta}{\eta} \right)^{-2} < \left(\int_{1}^{\xi} \frac{d\eta}{\eta} \right)^{-2} = \frac{1}{\log^2 \xi}.$$

CHAPTER II

BRUN'S THEOREM ON PRIME PAIRS

This chapter is somewhat difficult; the reader may skip it entirely. Brun's Theorem will be applied neither in the remainder of this book nor in my *Vorlesungen über Zahlentheorie*.

There is only one pair of prime numbers that differ by 1—namely, the primes 2 and 3—since all of the succeeding primes are odd.

No matter how far out we go in a table of primes, we find pairs of primes that differ by 2, for example,

$$3,5; \ 5,7; \ 11,13; \ 17,19; \ 29,31; \ \ldots; \ 101,103; \ \ldots \ .$$

(Incidentally, each of these pairs, aside from the second, begins with a number greater than the second number of the preceding pair; this is because one of the numbers n, $n+2$, and $n+4$ is always divisible by 3, so that if these are all to be primes, we must have $n=3$.)

The question now arises whether there are infinitely many "prime pairs," that is, whether there are infinitely many numbers n for which n and $n+2$ are prime. The methods of number theory and of analysis have, to this day, not proven powerful enough to answer this question. (One would certainly place one's bet on a yes answer.)

All the more remarkable is the following theorem of Brun (Theorem 120) which is proved by elementary methods (the so-called method of the Sieve of Eratosthenes): *If there are infinitely many prime pairs, then the series*

$$\frac{1}{3}+\frac{1}{5}+\frac{1}{5}+\frac{1}{7}+\frac{1}{11}+\frac{1}{13}+\frac{1}{17}+\frac{1}{19}+\frac{1}{29}+\frac{1}{31}+\cdots,$$

which is summed over all of these primes, converges. (In order to understand the significance of this theorem, compare it with Theorem 114.)

In any case, it follows that there are not "too many" prime pairs.

I begin with three simple lemmas (Theorems 116-118). The entire difficulty, then, lies in Theorem 119; Theorem 120 follows easily from it.

THEOREM 116: *If $b>0$ and if $m>0$ is odd, then*

$$\sum_{l=0}^{m-1} (-1)^l \binom{b}{l} \geqq 0.$$

Two Proofs: 1) It is easily seen by induction, for $b>0$ and $n\geq0$, that

(48)
$$\sum_{l=0}^{n}(-1)^l\binom{b}{l}=(-1)^n\binom{b-1}{n}.$$

For if $n=0$, it is true $(1=1)$; and in the induction from n to $n+1$ the right-hand side increases by

$$(-1)^{n+1}\binom{b-1}{n+1}-(-1)^n\binom{b-1}{n}=(-1)^{n+1}\left(\binom{b-1}{n+1}+\binom{b-1}{n}\right)$$

$$=(-1)^{n+1}\binom{b}{n+1}.$$

(At the bottom of this, of course, lie the series expansions

$$\sum_{n=0}^{\infty}(-1)^n\binom{b-1}{n}\xi^n=\sum_{n=0}^{b-1}(-1)^n\binom{b-1}{n}\xi^n=(1-\xi)^{b-1}=\frac{1}{1-\xi}(1-\xi)^b$$

$$=\sum_{a=0}^{\infty}\xi^a\cdot\sum_{l=0}^{b}(-1)^l\binom{b}{l}\xi^l=\sum_{a=0}^{\infty}\xi^a\cdot\sum_{l=0}^{\infty}(-1)^l\binom{b}{l}\xi^l,$$

which hold for $|\xi|<1$, from a comparison of whose coefficients (48) follows.)
If $n=m-1$ is even, then our assertion follows from (48).

2) The binomial coefficients $\binom{b}{l}$, $0\leq l\leq b$, increase until midway

(where, if b is odd, namely for $l=\dfrac{b-1}{2}$ and $l=\dfrac{b+1}{2}$, two equal ones occur)

and then they decrease; also, they occur with alternating signs.

For $m-1\leq\dfrac{b}{2}$ it follows that the sum in the statement of the theorem

is >0, since the last term is >0.
For $m-1\geq b$ it is $(1-1)^b=0$.
For $\dfrac{b}{2}<m-1<b$ it is

$$\sum_{l=0}^{m-1}(-1)^l\binom{b}{l}=-\sum_{l=m}^{b}(-1)^l\binom{b}{l}=\sum_{l=m}^{b}(-1)^{l+1}\binom{b}{l},$$

where the first term on the right is >0 and the terms are alternate in sign and decrease in absolute value; thus here, too, the sum is >0.

Theorem 117 : *If S_n is the n-th elementary symmetric function of s positive numbers $\xi_1, \xi_2, \ldots, \xi_s$ ($1 \leq n \leq s$), then*

$$S_n \leq \frac{S_1{}^n}{n!} .$$

Proof: In the expansion of

$$S_1{}^n = (\xi_1 + \cdots + \xi_s)^n,$$

each of the $\binom{s}{n}$ products $\xi_{h_1} \xi_{h_2} \cdots \xi_{h_n}$, where $1 \leq h_1 < h_2 < \cdots < h_n \leq s,$ has the coefficient $n!$.

Theorem 118: *Let $d > 0$ and $\xi > 0$. Then the number of positive numbers $n \leq \xi$ which belong to any given residue class mod d differs from $\frac{\xi}{d}$ by less than 1.*

Proof: Of each set of d consecutive numbers n, exactly one is to be counted; up to ξ there are $\left[\frac{\xi}{d}\right]$ complete sets of residues and, if $\frac{\xi}{d}$ is not integral, usually (but not always) a partial set. The desired number is thus $\left[\frac{\xi}{d}\right]$ or $\left[\frac{\xi}{d}\right] + 1$; the latter does not occur if $\frac{\xi}{d}$ is integral; hence the number is always $> \frac{\xi}{d} - 1$ and $< \frac{\xi}{d} + 1$.

Theorem 119: *Let $P(\xi)$ denote the number of primes $p \leq \xi$ for which $p + 2$ is prime. Then, for $\xi \geq 3$, we have*

$$P(\xi) < \alpha_{17} \frac{\xi}{\log^2 \xi} (\log \log \xi)^2.$$

Remark: A glance at the following proof of Theorem 120 shows that for any (arbitrarily small) positive $\delta < 1$, the inequality

(49) $$P(\xi) < \alpha_{18} \frac{\xi}{\log^{1+\delta} \xi}$$

(which is weaker if ξ is large) would suffice. On the other hand, a proof of

$$P(\xi) < \alpha_{18} \frac{\xi}{\log \xi}$$

($\delta = 0$ in (49)) would be of no use, for the convergence of the Brun series could not follow from this, since the same inequality holds for $\pi(\xi)$, by Theorem 112, and yet $\sum_p \frac{1}{p}$ diverges.

Proof: Let $\xi > 5$ and let η be chosen anywhere in the interval $5 \leq \eta < \xi$. Later on, I shall choose η as a particular function of ξ; the proof will be clearer, however, if this is not done immediately.

The number of positive numbers $n \leq \xi$ having a particular property is at most η plus the number of n in the interval $\eta < n \leq \xi$ having that property (since I have counted all of the numbers $1, 2, \ldots, [\eta]$ and thus have not lost any there). It follows that for our $P(\xi)$ the relation

(50) $$P(\xi) \leq \eta + Q(\xi)$$

holds, where $Q(\xi)$ is the number of n in the interval $\eta < n \leq \xi$ for which n and $n+2$ are prime.

Let p_h be the h-th prime and let $\pi(\eta) = r$; then $p_2, p_3, \ldots, p_r$ are the odd primes $\leq \eta$, and we have $r(\xi) \geq 3$, since $\eta \geq 5$. (I write $r(\xi)$ without further ado, since I think of η as a function of ξ.) By $A(\xi)$, I shall mean the number of numbers n for which

$$0 < n \leq \xi, \ n \not\equiv 0, \text{and } n \not\equiv -2 \pmod{p_h} \text{ for } h = 2, \ldots, r$$

holds. We obviously have

(51) $$Q(\xi) \leq A(\xi);$$

for every n counted in $Q(\xi)$ is $> \eta$, and hence $> p_h$, for $h = 2, \ldots, r$, so that neither the prime n nor the prime $n+2$ is divisible by p_h.

From (50) and (51) it follows that

(52) $$P(\xi) \leq \eta + A(\xi).$$

Let $\Omega(d)$ be the number of distinct prime factors of $d > 0$. For every odd, square-free number $d > 0$, I shall denote by $B(d, \xi)$ the number of positive numbers $n \leq \xi$ which for every $p | d$ (if any) satisfy one of the conditions

(53) $$n \equiv 0 \quad \text{or} \quad n \equiv -2 \pmod{p}.$$

(Then, in particular, we have

$$B(1, \xi) = [\xi],$$

since no n in the interval $0 < n \leq \xi$ is excluded.) By Theorem 118, we have

(54) $$\left| B(d, \xi) - 2^{\Omega(d)} \frac{\xi}{d} \right| < 2^{\Omega(d)};$$

for n ranges over the interval $0 < n \leq \xi$ and, by Theorem 70, belongs to $2^{\Omega(d)}$ residue classes mod d (namely, two residue classes modulo each of the $\Omega(d)$ prime factors of $d = \prod_{p|d} p$; $p = 2$ does not occur, since d is odd, so that (53) does actually represent two distinct residue classes).

As regards the requisite determination of an upper bound for $A(\xi)$, I shall first show how it can not be done; after this, however, by taking a somewhat different path, we shall finally reach our goal. Meanwhile, this blind alley will be instructive to the reader who wishes not only to learn what is already known, but also how to undertake exploration on his own.

Using the abbreviation

$$p_2 \cdots p_r = k,$$

I shall first prove the identity

$$(55) \left\{ \begin{array}{l} A(\xi) = \sum_{d|k} \mu(d) B(d,\xi) = B(1,\xi) - B(p_2,\xi) - \cdots - B(p_r,\xi) \\ \quad + B(p_2 p_3, \xi) + \cdots + (-1)^{r-1} B(p_2 \cdots p_r, \xi); \end{array} \right.$$

then I shall show that it does not suffice, and I shall finally replace it by a useful inequality.

(55) is proved as follows: Every n in the interval $0 < n \leq \xi$ which is counted in $A(\xi)$ is also counted in $B(1,\xi)$ on the right, but not in any $B(d,\xi)$ for which $d > 1$, since for no p_h ($h=2,\ldots,r$) do we have $n \equiv 0$ or $-2 \pmod{p_h}$. Every n in the interval $0 < n \leq \xi$ which is not counted in $A(\xi)$ is $\equiv 0$ or -2 for b distinct primes p_h ($h=2,\ldots,r$), where $1 \leq b \leq r-1$; say for $p_{h_1}, \ldots, p_{h_b}$ ($2 \leq h_1 < h_2 < \ldots < h_b \leq r$). Then this n is counted on the right-hand side of (55) in all of the terms $B(d,\xi)$ for which $d | p_{h_1} p_{h_2} \cdots p_{h_b}$; altogether, therefore,

$$\sum_{d | p_{h_1} \cdots p_{h_b}} \mu(d) = 0$$

times, by Theorem 35.

Thus (55) is proved; it does not, however, lead us to our goal. We may, of course, conclude from (55) and (54) that

$$(56) \quad A(\xi) < \sum_{d|k} \mu(d) 2^{\Omega(d)} \frac{\xi}{d} + \sum_{d|k} 2^{\Omega(d)} = \xi \prod_{2 < p \leq \eta} \left(1 - \frac{2}{p}\right) + \sum_{h=0}^{r-1} 2^h \binom{r-1}{h}$$

(since for every h for which $0 \leq h \leq r-1$ there are exactly $\binom{r-1}{h}$ divisors of $k = p_2 \ldots p_r$ for which $\Omega(d) = h$). However, because of the fact that

$$\sum_{h=0}^{r-1} 2^h \binom{r-1}{h} \geq 2^{r-1},$$

we obtain not even an estimate of the form

$$A(\xi) < \alpha_{19} \frac{\xi}{\log \xi}$$

for the right-hand side of (56), no matter what our choice of $\eta(\xi)$

(and even such an estimate would be useless; see the Remark above). For η must be so large that

(57)
$$\prod_{2<p\leq p_r}\left(1-\frac{2}{p}\right)=\prod_{2<p\leq\eta}\left(1-\frac{2}{p}\right)<\alpha_{19}\frac{1}{\log\xi}$$

holds and, at the same time, so small that

$$2^r<2\alpha_{19}\frac{\xi}{\log\xi}<\alpha_{20}\xi$$

holds. This can never happen, however, for the following reasons. By Theorem 113 we would have

(58)
$$p_r<\alpha_{10}\,r\log r<\alpha_{21}r^2<\alpha_{21}\left(\frac{\log\,(\alpha_{20}\,\xi)}{\log 2}\right)^2<\alpha_{22}\log^2\xi;$$

by (57) we would have (*sit venia verbo e*; other than this, my lower case italic letters actually do represent integers)

$$\frac{1}{\log\xi}>\alpha_{23}\prod_{2<p\leq p_r}\left(1-\frac{2}{p}\right)=\alpha_{24}\prod_{5\leq p\leq p_r}\left(1-\frac{2}{p}\right)=\alpha_{24}\,e^{\sum\limits_{5\leq p\leq p_r}\log\left(1-\frac{2}{p}\right)}$$

$$>\alpha_{24}e^{-4\sum\limits_{5\leq p\leq p_r}\frac{1}{p}}=\alpha_{25}e^{-4\sum\limits_{2<p\leq p_r}\frac{1}{p}},$$

$$\sum_{2<p\leq p_r}\frac{1}{p}>\frac{1}{4}\log(\alpha_{25}\log\xi)>\alpha_{26}\log\log\xi,$$

and therefore, by (46) and (58),

$$\alpha_{26}\log\log\xi<\alpha_{18}\log\log p_r<\alpha_{18}\log\log\,(\alpha_{22}\log^2\xi)<\alpha_{18}\log\log\log\xi+\alpha_{27};$$

for $\xi>\alpha_{28}$ we would therefore have

$$\log\log\xi<\alpha_{29}\log\log\log\xi,$$

which is certainly false for large ξ.

And now let us leave this blind alley!

Brun's essential idea lies in replacing equation (55) by the inequality

(59)
$$A(\xi)\leq\sum_{\substack{d|k\\\Omega(d)<m}}\mu(d)B(d,\xi),$$

where m is an arbitrary odd positive integer (which will ultimately be taken as a function of ξ). (59) is seen as follows: Every n in the interval $0<n\leq\xi$

which is counted in $A(\xi)$ is counted on the right-hand side exactly once (namely for $d=1$), as was already remarked above; every n in the interval $0<n\leqq\xi$ which is not counted in $A(\xi)$ is counted on the right-hand side precisely in those terms $B(d,\xi)$ (where $d|k$) for which (in our old notation) $d/p_{h_1}\cdots p_{h_b}$ and for which, moreover, $\Omega(d)<m$. The complete count on the right for these n is therefore, by Theorem 116,

$$\sum_{\substack{d/p_{h_1}\cdots p_{h_b}\\ \Omega(d)<m}} \mu(d) = \sum_{l=0}^{m-1}(-1)^l\binom{b}{l}\geqq 0.$$

Thus (59) is proved.

Now it follows further, from (59) and (54), that

$$(60)\qquad A(\xi) < \xi \sum_{\substack{d|k\\ \Omega(d)<m}} \frac{\mu(d)2^{\Omega(d)}}{d} + \sum_{h=0}^{m-1}2^h\binom{r-1}{h}.$$

In this formula, on the one hand, we have

$$\sum_{h=0}^{m-1}2^h\binom{r-1}{h}\leqq 2^m\sum_{h=0}^{m-1}\binom{r-1}{h}=2^m\sum_{h=0}^{m-1}\frac{(r-1)\cdots(r-h)}{h!}$$

$$(61)\qquad \leqq 2^m\sum_{h=0}^{m-1}r^h=2^m\frac{r^m-1}{r-1}<2^m r^m\leqq(2\eta)^m$$

(since $r-1\geqq 2$ and $r=\pi(\eta)\leqq\eta$), and on the other hand, we have

$$\sum_{\substack{d|k\\ \Omega(d)<m}} \frac{\mu(d)2^{\Omega(d)}}{d} = \sum_{d|k}\frac{\mu(d)2^{\Omega(d)}}{d} - \sum_{n=m}^{r-1}\sum_{\substack{d|k\\ \Omega(d)=n}} \frac{\mu(d)2^{\Omega(d)}}{d}$$

(for $m\geqq r$ the last sum is empty and denotes 0), and

$$(62) = \prod_{2<p\leqq p_r}\left(1-\frac{2}{p}\right) - \sum_{n=m}^{r-1}(-1)^n 2^n\sum_{\substack{d|k\\ \Omega(d)=n}}\frac{1}{d} = \prod_{2<p\leqq\eta}\left(1-\frac{2}{p}\right) - \sum_{n=m}^{r-1}(-1)^n 2^n S_n,$$

where S_n is the n-th elementary symmetric function of $\dfrac{1}{p_2},\ldots,\dfrac{1}{p_r}$.

By Theorem 117 and (46), we have $\left(\text{since } e^n = \sum\limits_{h=0}^{\infty}\frac{n^h}{h!}>\frac{n^n}{n!}\right)$

$$S_n\leqq\frac{S_1^n}{n!}<\frac{(eS_1)^n}{n^n}<\left(\frac{3\alpha_{13}\log\log\eta}{n}\right)^n,$$

$$\left|\sum_{n=m}^{r-1}(-1)^n 2^n S_n\right|\leqq\sum_{n=m}^{r-1}\left(\frac{6\alpha_{13}\log\log\eta}{m}\right)^n\leqq\sum_{n=m}^{r-1}\left(\frac{\alpha_{30}\log\log\eta}{m}\right)^n,$$

where, for a later purpose, I shall take $a_{30} > 2$. Consequently, if

$$m > 2a_{30} \log \log \eta$$

then

(63) $$\left| \sum_{n=m}^{r-1} (-1)^n 2^n S_n \right| < \sum_{n=m}^{\infty} \frac{1}{2^n} = \frac{2}{2^m}.$$

From (62), (47), and (63), it follows that

(64) $$\left| \sum_{\substack{d|k \\ \Omega(d) < m}} \frac{\mu(d) 2^{\Omega(d)}}{d} \right| < \frac{a_{14}}{\log^2 \eta} + \frac{2}{2^m},$$

and from (52), (60), (64), and (61), it follows that

(65) $$P(\xi) < \eta + \frac{a_{14} \xi}{\log^2 \eta} + \frac{2\xi}{2^m} + (2\eta)^m.$$

In these formulas, we let $\eta(\xi)$ and $m(\xi)$ be subject to the conditions

(66) $$5 \leqq \eta < \xi, \quad m > 2a_{30} \log \log \eta, \quad m \text{ odd}.$$

For $\xi > a_{31}$, these conditions are satisfied, provided I choose

$$\eta = \xi^{\frac{1}{3a_{30} \log \log \xi}}, \quad m = 2[a_{30} \log \log \xi] - 1.$$

This is non-trivial only for the condition $m > 2a_{30} \log \log \eta$, but this condition is a consequence of the fact that, for $\xi > a_{32}$, we have

$$2a_{30} \log \log \eta = 2a_{30} \log \frac{\log \xi}{3a_{30} \log \log \xi} < 2a_{30} \log \log \xi - 3 < m.$$

For this choice of η and m, I obtain, using (65),

$$P(\xi) < a_{33} \left(\eta + \frac{\xi}{\log^2 \eta} + \frac{\xi}{2^{2a_{30} \log \log \xi}} + (2\eta)^{2a_{30} \log \log \xi} \right)$$

for $\xi > a_{31}$. Each of the four terms in the parentheses is

$$< \alpha_{34} \frac{\xi}{\log^2 \xi} (\log \log \xi)^2;$$

for we have

$$\eta < \alpha_{35} \xi^{\frac{1}{2}},$$

$$\frac{\xi}{\log^2 \eta} = \frac{\xi}{\log^2 \xi} (3\alpha_{30} \log \log \xi)^2 \quad \text{(that is the worst term)},$$

$$\frac{\xi}{2^{2\alpha_{30} \log \log \xi}} = \frac{\xi}{\log^{2\alpha_{30} \log 2} \xi} < \frac{\xi}{\log^2 \xi} \quad (\text{ since } \alpha_{30} > 2, \ 2\log 2 > 1),$$

$$(2\eta)^{2\alpha_{30} \log \log \xi} = e^{2\alpha_{30} \log \log \xi \left(\frac{\log \xi}{3 \alpha_{30} \log \log \xi} + \log 2 \right)} < e^{\frac{2}{3} \log \xi + \alpha_{36} \log \log \xi} < \alpha_{37} e^{\frac{3}{4} \log \xi}$$

$$= \alpha_{37} \xi^{\frac{3}{4}}.$$

Hence, for $\xi > \alpha_{31}$, we have

$$P(\xi) < \alpha_{38} \frac{\xi}{\log^2 \xi} (\log \log \xi)^2;$$

therefore, for $\xi \geq 3$, we have

$$P(\xi) < \alpha_{17} \frac{\xi}{\log^2 \xi} (\log \log \xi)^2.$$

Theorem 120: *If there are infinitely many primes p for which $p+2$ is prime, then the series*

$$\sum_p \frac{1}{p},$$

summed over all of those p, converges.

Remark: This agrees, of course, with the wording used in the beginning of this chapter, even though only the first prime of each pair is used in the sum; for we have $\dfrac{2}{p} > \dfrac{1}{p} + \dfrac{1}{p+2} > \dfrac{1}{p}$.

Proof: I shall use Theorem 119 only in the weaker form

$$P(n) < \alpha_{39} \frac{n}{\log^{\frac{3}{2}} n} \quad \text{for } n \geq 3.$$

From this it follows that if p'_r is the r-th prime for which p'_r+2 is also prime (if there are infinitely many such primes p'_r at all), then for all $r \geq 1$ we have

$$r = P(p'_r) < \alpha_{39} \frac{p'_r}{\log^{\frac{3}{2}} p'_r} < \alpha_{39} \frac{p'_r}{\log^{\frac{3}{2}}(r+1)},$$

$$\frac{1}{p'_r} < \frac{\alpha_{39}}{r \log^{\frac{3}{2}}(r+1)};$$

and from the convergence of

$$\sum_{r=1}^{\infty} \frac{1}{r \log^{\frac{3}{2}}(r+1)}$$

it follows that

$$\sum_{r=1}^{\infty} \frac{1}{p'_r}$$

converges.

CHAPTER III

DIRICHLET'S THEOREM ON THE PRIME NUMBERS IN AN ARITHMETIC PROGRESSION

§ 1

Further Theorems on Congruences

DEFINITION 21: *Let $m>0$ and $(a, m)=1$. We say that a "belongs to the exponent f mod m" if a^f is the first of all the powers a^1, a^2, ... of a with positive integral exponents for which*

$$a^f \equiv 1 \pmod{m}.$$

(f exists, since by Fermat's Theorem we have $a^{\varphi(m)} \equiv 1$.)

THEOREM 121: *If a belongs to the exponent f, then, if $b_1 \geq 0$ and $b_2 \geq 0$, we have*

$$a^{b_1} \equiv a^{b_2} \pmod{m}$$

if and only if

$$b_1 \equiv b_2 \pmod{f}.$$

(Here a^0 denotes 1 even for $a=0$, which occurs only in the trivial case $m=1$.)

In particular, therefore: 1) $a^0, a^1, \ldots, a^{f-1}$ *are incongruent* (mod m).

2) *If $b \geq 0$, then*

$$a^b \equiv 1 \pmod{m}$$

if and only if

$$f/b.$$

3) *By Fermat's Theorem it follows that we always have*

$$f/\varphi(m).$$

Proof: Without loss of generality, let $b_2 \geq b_1 \geq 0$.

1) From

$$a^{b_2} \equiv a^{b_1} \pmod{m}$$

it follows that

$$a^{b_2-b_1} \equiv 1 \pmod{m}.$$

Division of b_2-b_1 by f yields

$$b_2-b_1 = qf+r, \quad q \geq 0, \quad 0 \leq r < f.$$

Then we have

$$1\equiv a^{b_2-b_1}\equiv a^{qf+r}\equiv(a^f)^q a^r\equiv a^r \pmod{m},$$

so that, by the definition of f, we have

$$r=0,$$
$$f\,|\,b_2-b_1.$$

2) From

$$b_2-b_1=qf$$

it follows (since $q\geqq0$) that

$$a^{b_2}\equiv a^{b_1+qf}\equiv a^{b_1}(a^f)^q\equiv a^{b_1} \pmod{m}.$$

THEOREM 122. *Let q be a prime, let $l>0$, and let $q^l|p-1$. Then there exists a number a which belongs to q^l (mod p).*

Proof: By Theorem 72, the congruence

$$x^{\frac{p-1}{q}}\equiv1 \pmod{p}$$

has at most $\dfrac{p-1}{q}\leqq\dfrac{p-1}{2}\leqq p-2$ solutions (since $p\geqq3$). Hence there is at least one number c for which $1\leqq c\leqq p-1$ such that

$$c^{\frac{p-1}{q}}\not\equiv1 \pmod{p}.$$

If we set

$$a=c^{\frac{p-1}{q^l}},$$

then we have

$$a^{q^l}\equiv c^{p-1}\equiv1 \pmod{p}.$$

Let a belong to f. Then $f|q^l$, by Theorem 121. If we did not have $f=q^l$, then it would follow that $f|q^{l-1}$, so that

$$a^{q^{l-1}}\equiv c^{\frac{p-1}{q}}\equiv1 \pmod{p}.$$

THEOREM 123: *There exists a number g which belongs to $p-1$ (mod p).*

Proof: 1) If $p=2$, then $g=1$ satisfies the condition of the theorem.
2) If $p>2$, let the canonical decomposition of $p-1$ be

$$p-1=\prod_{n=1}^{r}p_n^{l_n}.$$

If $r=1$, then Theorem 122 gives us what we want. If $r>1$, then by Theorem

122 we may choose a number a_n belonging to $p_n{'}^{l_n}$ for each $n=1, \ldots, r$. If we then set

$$g = \prod_{n=1}^{r} a_n,$$

then g belongs to f. By Theorem 121, we have $f|p-1$. If we did not have $f=p-1$ then, without loss of generality, we would have $f\left/\dfrac{p-1}{p_1}\right.$, so that (since $p_n{'}^{l_n}\left/\dfrac{p-1}{p_1}\right.$ for $n=2, \ldots, r$)

$$1 \equiv g^{\frac{p-1}{p_1}} \equiv a_1^{\frac{p-1}{p_1}} \prod_{n=2}^{r} a_n^{\frac{p-1}{p_1}} \equiv a_1^{\frac{p-1}{p_1}},$$

and consequently, by Theorem 121,

$$p_1{}^{l_1}\left/\dfrac{p-1}{p_1}\right.,$$

which is not the case.

Definition 22: *Every g belonging to $p-1$ (mod p) is called a primitive root modulo p.*

The powers of a primitive root (with exponent ≥ 0) consequently represent all of the reduced residue classes.

Theorem 124: *If $p>2$ and $l>0$, then there exists a number g belonging to $\varphi(p^l)$ (mod p^l).*

From Theorem 121 it therefore follows that for $p \nmid a$

$$a \equiv g^b \ (\text{mod } p^l), \quad b \geq 0$$

is always solvable for b and, indeed, is satisfied by all of the numbers $b \geq 0$ in a particular residue class mod $\varphi(p^l)$.

Proof: For $l=1$ this is proved by Theorem 123. Therefore, let $l>1$. Let g be a primitive root mod p. I may certainly think of g as being so chosen that

(67) $$g^{p-1} \not\equiv 1 \ (\text{mod } p^2).$$

For whenever g is a primitive root mod p, so also is $g+p$, and if

$$g^{p-1} \equiv 1 \ (\text{mod } p^2),$$

then

$$(g+p)^{p-1} \equiv g^{p-1} + (p-1) g^{p-2} p \equiv 1 + (p-1) g^{p-2} p \ (\text{mod } p^2),$$

so that certainly

$$(g+p)^{p-1} \not\equiv 1 \ (\text{mod } p^2).$$

I shall now prove that the g determined by (67) (which is, incidentally, a primitive root mod p) satisfies the condition of the theorem.

To this end, I shall first prove, by mathematical induction, that for all $l>1$ we have

(68) $$g^{p^{l-2}(p-1)}=1+h_l\,p^{l-1}, \quad p \nmid h_l.$$

For $l=2$ this is assured by the Fermat Theorem, together with (67). If (68) holds for l, then it follows for $l+1$ thus:

$$g^{p^{l-1}(p-1)}=(1+h_l\,p^{l-1})^p=1+h_l\,p^l+h_l{}^2\,p\,\frac{p-1}{2}\,p^{2\,(l-1)}+n\,p^{3\,(l-1)}.$$

In this formula, both the third term and the fourth term on the right-hand side are divisible by p^{l+1}, since $2l-1\geq l+1$ and $3l-3\geq l+1$, respectively. The right-hand side therefore $=1+h_{l+1}p^l$, where $p\nmid h_{l+1}$.

Let g belong to f $(\bmod\ p^l)$. By Theorem 121, we have $f\,|\,p^{l-1}\,(p-1)$; since g belongs to $p-1$ modulo p, it follows that $p-1\,|\,f$ by Theorem 121, so that $f=p^m(p-1)$, $0\leq m\leq l-1$. If it were not true (as asserted) that $f=p^{l-1}\,(p-1)$, then we would have $f\,|\,p^{l-2}\,(p-1)$, so that

$$g^{p^{l-2}(p-1)}\equiv 1 \pmod{p^l},$$

contrary to (68).

THEOREM 125: *If $l>2$, then 5 belongs to 2^{l-2} $(\bmod\ 2^l)$.*

(The reader may consider it an *Exercise* to prove that there is no number belonging to $\varphi(2^l)=2^{l-1}$. Theorems 125 and 126 compensate for this.)

Proof: I shall first prove by induction that for $l>2$

(69) $$5^{2^{l-3}}=1+h_l\,2^{l-1}, \quad 2\nmid h_l.$$

For $l=3$ this is true $(5^1=1+1\cdot 4)$. From the truth of (69) for an $l\geq 3$, follows its truth for $l+1$, because

(70) $\quad 5^{2^{l-2}}=(1+h_l\,2^{l-1})^2=1+h_l\,2^l+h_l{}^2\,2^{2l-2}=1+h_{l+1}\,2^l, \quad 2\nmid h_{l+1}.$

From (69) and (70) it follows that

$$5^{2^{l-3}}\not\equiv 1 \pmod{2^l}, \quad 5^{2^{l-2}}\equiv 1 \pmod{2^l}.$$

Let 5 belong to f; then we have $f\nmid 2^{l-3}$ and $f\,|\,2^{l-2}$, so that $f=2^{l-2}$.

Theorem 126:   *For $l>2$, every odd number a satisfies the relation*

$$a\equiv(-1)^{\frac{a-1}{2}}\, 5^b \pmod{2^l},\ b\geq 0$$

for precisely those numbers $b\geq 0$ belonging to a particular residue class mod 2^{l-2}.

Proof: 1) Let $a\equiv 1 \pmod 4$. For $0\leq b<2^{l-2}$, 5^b represents exactly 2^{l-2} numbers incongruent mod 2^l, by Theorem 125. All of these are $\equiv 1$ (mod 4); however, every reduced set of residues mod 2^l contains exactly 2^{l-2} numbers that are $\equiv 1$ (mod 4); hence it follows that

$$a\equiv 5^b \pmod{2^l},\ b\geq 0$$

is solvable for b (pigeon-hole principle!). Since, if $b\geq 0$, 5^b is periodic with period 2^{l-2} mod 2^l, it follows that the assertions of our theorem are proved.

2) Let $a\equiv 3 \pmod 4$. Then we apply 1) to the number $-a$.

§ 2

Characters

i will now represent the familiar complex number, but all other lower case italic letters except e will still, as before, represent integers.

Let $k>0$ be fixed. Let us set $\varphi(k)=h$.

DEFINITION 23: *A number-theoretic function* $\chi(a)$ *is called a character* mod k, *provided that*

  I) $\chi(a)=0$ *for* $(a, k)>1$,
  II) $\chi(1)\neq0$,
  III) $\chi(a_1a_2)=\chi(a_1)\chi(a_2)$ *for* $(a_1, k)=1$ *and* $(a_2, k)=1$ (*and therefore, by* I), *always*),
  IV) $\chi(a_1)=\chi(a_2)$ *for* $a_1\equiv a_2$ (mod k) *and* $(a_1, k)=1$ (*and therefore, by* I), *whenever* $a_1\equiv a_2$ (mod k)).

Examples: 1) $k=4$, $\chi(a)=0$, 1, 0, and —1 for $a\equiv0$, 1, 2, and 3 (mod 4), respectively.

2) (For the reader who has read the end of Part One, Chapter VI.) From Theorem 99, 1) to 4), it follows that the Kronecker symbol $\left(\dfrac{\pm k}{a}\right)$ is a character mod k; here we must have $\pm k\equiv0$ or 1 (mod 4), and $\pm k$ must be non-square.

THEOREM 127: *For every character we have*

$$\chi(1)=1.$$

Proof: By III), we have

$$\chi(1)=\chi(1\cdot 1)=\chi(1)\cdot\chi(1),$$

so that by II) we have

$$\chi(1)=1.$$

THEOREM 128: *If* $(a, k)=1$, *then* $(\chi(a))^h=1$; *thus* $\chi(a)$ *is an h-th root of unity and* $|\chi(a)|=1$.

Proof: From Fermat's Theorem it follows that

$$a^h\equiv 1 \pmod{k};$$

by III), IV), and Theorem 127, we therefore have

$$(\chi(a))^h=\chi(a^h)=\chi(1)=1$$

Theorem 129: *For every k there is a finite number of characters and, moreover, at least one.*

(I shall of course call two number-theoretic functions distinct if they do not coincide for all *a*.)

Proof: 1) For any *a* in the interval $1 \leq a \leq k$, it follows from I) and Theorem 128 that $\chi(a)$ must be chosen from a finite collection of possible values (0 or an *h*-th root of unity); from IV) it follows further that the value of $\chi(a)$ for $1 \leq a \leq k$ determines its value for all *a*. Hence there cannot be an infinite number of characters mod *k*.

2) The function

$$\chi(a) = \begin{cases} 0 & \text{for } (a, k) > 1, \\ 1 & \text{for } (a, k) = 1 \end{cases}$$

is clearly a character, since I) to IV) are satisfied.

Definition 24: *The character defined in part 2) of the preceding proof is called the principal character and is denoted by $\chi_0(a)$.*

Theorem 130: *If $\chi(a)$ is a character, then so is its complex conjugate function $\bar{\chi}(a)$.*

(If $\chi(a)$ is everywhere real, then of course it does not differ from $\bar{\chi}(a)$.)

Proof: Conditions I) to IV) are obviously satisfied.

Theorem 131: *If a runs over a positive complete set of residues* mod *k*, *then*

$$\sum_a \chi(a) = \begin{cases} h & \text{for } \chi_0, \\ 0 & \text{otherwise.} \end{cases}$$

Proof: From IV it follows that the value of the sum is, at any rate, independent of the choice of the set of residues.

1) For the character $\chi = \chi_0$, the sum has *h* terms $=1$ and *k—h* terms $=0$.

2) Otherwise, let us choose (as we may) a number $b > 0$ for which

$$(b, k) = 1, \quad \chi(b) \neq 1.$$

Since, by Theorem 62, *ba* runs over a complete set of residues mod *k* as *a* does, it follows that

$$\xi = \sum_a \chi(a) = \sum_a \chi(ba) = \sum_a \chi(b)\,\chi(a) = \chi(b) \sum_a \chi(a) = \chi(b)\xi,$$

$$(\chi(b) - 1)\,\xi = 0,$$

$$\xi = 0.$$

THEOREM 132: *If $\chi_1(a)$ and $\chi_2(a)$ are characters, then $\chi_1(a)\chi_2(a)$ is also a character.*

In particular: If $\chi(a)$ is a character, then $\chi^2(a)$ is also a character.

Proof: I) to IV) are obviously satisfied.

THEOREM 133: *If $\chi_1(a)$ is a character, then as $\chi(a)$ runs over all c characters, so does $\chi(a)\chi_1(a)$.*

Proof: If

$$\chi_2(a)\,\chi_1(a) = \chi_3(a)\,\chi_1(a),$$

then it follows for $(a, k)=1$, since $\chi_1(a)\neq 0$, that

$$\chi_2(a) = \chi_3(a),$$

and, by I), this is satisfied for $(a, k)>1$ as well. The c functions $\chi(a)\chi_1(a)$ are therefore c distinct characters, and consequently (pigeon-hole principle!) they are the c characters.

THEOREM 134: *If $d>0$, $(d, k)=1$, and $d\not\equiv 1$ (mod k), then there exists a character for which $\chi(d)\neq 1$.*

Proof: Since $\chi(a)=0$ must always hold for $(a, k)>1$, it follows that we need define the character $\chi(a)$ suitably and verify II), III), and IV) only for $(a, k)=1$.

Since $d\not\equiv 1$ (mod k), it follows that there either is a number $p^l|k$, where $p>2$ and $l>0$, for which

$$d\not\equiv 1 \ (\text{mod } p^l)$$

or else a number $2^l|k$, where $l>0$, for which

$$d\not\equiv 1 \ (\text{mod } 2^l).$$

1) Let $d\not\equiv 1$ (mod p^l), $p>2$, $l>0$, and $p^l|k$; therefore $p\nmid d$, since $(d, k)=1$. Let g have the property of Theorem 124. For $(a, k)=1$ we have $p\nmid a$, and therefore

$$a\equiv g^b \ (\text{mod } p^l), \ b\geqq 0.$$

Let me set

$$\varrho = e^{\frac{2\pi i}{\varphi(p^l)}}, \ \chi(a)=\varrho^b.$$

Then $\chi(a)$ is completely determined by a (once the above choice is made of a fixed number g), since ϱ^b has period $\varphi(p^l)$ and b is uniquely determined mod $\varphi(p^l)$.

$\chi(a)$ is a character. For

II) $\chi(1)=\varrho^0=1$;

III) for $(a_1, k)=1$, $(a_2, k)=1$, $a_1\equiv g^{b_1}$, $a_2\equiv g^{b_2}$ (mod p^l) we have

$$a_1\,a_2\equiv g^{b_1+b_2}\ (\text{mod}\ p^l),$$
$$\chi(a_1\,a_2)=\varrho^{b_1+b_2}=\varrho^{b_1}\,\varrho^{b_2}=\chi(a_1)\,\chi(a_2);$$

IV) is obvious; for $a_1\equiv a_2$ (mod k) yields $a_1\equiv a_2$ (mod p^l).
Finally, it follows from $d\not\equiv 1$ (mod p^l) and $p\nmid d$, that

$$d\equiv g^r\ (\text{mod}\ p^l),\ \ \varphi(p^l)\nmid r,$$
$$\chi(d)=\varrho^r\neq 1.$$

2) Let $d\not\equiv 1$ (mod 2^l), $l>0$, and $2^l|k$, and therefore $l>1$ (since k is even, so that $d\equiv 1$ (mod 2)).

21) Let $d\equiv 1$ (mod 4), so that $l>2$. Then for $(a, k)=1$, we have by Theorem 126, because $(a, 2)=1$, that

Let me set

$$a\equiv(-1)^{\frac{a-1}{2}}\,5^b\ (\text{mod}\ 2^l),\ b\geq 0.$$

$$\varrho=e^{\frac{2\pi i}{2^{l-2}}},\ \chi(a)=\varrho^b.$$

Then $\chi(a)$ is well-defined, since ϱ^b has the period 2^{l-2} and b is determined mod 2^{l-2}.

$\chi(a)$ is a character. For

II) $\chi(1)=\varrho^0=1$;

III) for $(a_1, k)=1$, $(a_2, k)=1$, $a_1\equiv(-1)^{\frac{a_1-1}{2}}\,5^{b_1}$, $a_2\equiv(-1)^{\frac{a_2-1}{2}}\,5^{b_2}$ (mod 2^l) we have, by (30),

$$a_1\,a_2\equiv(-1)^{\frac{a_1-1}{2}+\frac{a_2-1}{2}}\,5^{b_1+b_2}\equiv(-1)^{\frac{a_1\,a_2-1}{2}}\,5^{b_1+b_2}\ (\text{mod}\ 2^l),$$
$$\chi(a_1\,a_2)=\varrho^{b_1+b_2}=\varrho^{b_1}\,\varrho^{b_2}=\chi(a_1)\,\chi(a_2);$$

IV) is obvious; for $a_1\equiv a_2$ (mod k) yields $a_1\equiv a_2$ (mod 2^l).
Finally, it follows from $d\not\equiv 1$ (mod 2^l) and $d\equiv 1$ (mod 4), that

$$d\equiv 5^r\ (\text{mod}\ 2^l),\ 2^{l-2}\nmid r,$$
$$\chi(d)=\varrho^r\neq 1.$$

22) Let $d\equiv -1$ (mod 4). Then, for $(a, k)=1$ (where, therefore, a is odd), I set

$$\chi(a)=(-1)^{\frac{a-1}{2}}.$$

$\chi(a)$ is a character. For

II) $\chi(1)=1$;

III) For $(a_1, k)=1$ and $(a_2, k)=1$, we have

$$\chi(a_1\,a_2)=(-1)^{\frac{a_1 a_2-1}{2}}=(-1)^{\frac{a_1-1}{2}}(-1)^{\frac{a_2-1}{2}}=\chi(a_1)\,\chi(a_2);$$

IV) is obvious, since $4|k$.

Finally, we have

$$\chi(d)=-1\neq 1.$$

THEOREM 135: *For fixed $a>0$,*

$$\sum_\chi \chi(a)=\begin{cases} c & for\ a\equiv 1\ (\mathrm{mod}\ k), \\ 0 & for\ a\not\equiv 1\ (\mathrm{mod}\ k), \end{cases}$$

where the sum is taken over all of the c characters.

Proof: 1) For $a\equiv 1$ (mod k), the sum (as follows from Theorem 127) has c terms each of which $=1$.

2) For $(a, k)>1$ all of the terms vanish.

3) For $(a, k)=1$ and $a\neq 1$, we may choose a character χ_1 for which $\chi_1(a)\neq 1$, by Theorem 134. By Theorem 133, we have

$$\eta=\sum_\chi \chi(a)=\sum_\chi \chi(a)\,\chi_1(a)=\chi_1(a)\sum_\chi \chi(a)=\chi_1(a)\,\eta,$$
$$(\chi_1(a)-1)\,\eta=0,$$
$$\eta=0.$$

THEOREM 136: $c=h$.

(That is, there are exactly $\varphi(k)$ characters mod k.)

Proof: If a runs over a positive complete set of residues mod k, and χ runs through all the characters then, by Theorems 135 and 131, we have

$$\sum_{a,\chi} \chi(a)=\begin{cases} \sum_a\sum_\chi \chi(a)=c+0+\cdots+0=c, \\ \sum_\chi\sum_a \chi(a)=h+0+\cdots+0=h. \end{cases}$$

THEOREM 137: *Let $(l, k)=1$, $l>0$, and $a>0$. Then*

$$\sum_\chi \frac{1}{\chi(l)}\,\chi(a)=\begin{cases} h & for\ a\equiv l\ (\mathrm{mod}\ k), \\ 0 & for\ a\not\equiv l\ (\mathrm{mod}\ k). \end{cases}$$

Remark: On the left-hand side, we can write $\bar\chi(l)$ instead of $\dfrac{1}{\chi(l)}$.

Proof: Let us choose $j>0$ in such a way that

$$jl\equiv 1 \pmod{k}.$$

Since

$$\chi(j)\,\chi(l)=\chi(jl)=1,$$

it follows that

$$\sum_{\chi}\frac{1}{\chi(l)}\chi(a)=\sum_{\chi}\chi(j)\,\chi(a)=\sum_{\chi}\chi(ja),$$

so that, by Theorems 135 and 136,

$$\sum_{\chi}\frac{1}{\chi(l)}\chi(a)=\begin{cases}h & \text{for } ja\equiv 1, \text{ i.e. } a\equiv l \pmod{k},\\ 0 & \text{otherwise.}\end{cases}$$

DEFINITION 25: $\chi(a)$ *is called a character of the first kind if it is the principal character; of the second kind, if it is real but is not the principal character* (so that its value is always 0, 1, or —1, and —1 actually occurs); *and of the third kind, if it is not everywhere real.*

Examples: 1) The character given as the first example following Definition 23 is a character of the second kind.

2) For $k=5$, $\chi(a)=0, 1, i, -i, -1$ for $a\equiv 0, 1, 2, 3, 4 \pmod 5$ is a character of the third kind.

3) By Theorem 99, 1) to 5), the Kronecker symbol $\left(\dfrac{\pm k}{a}\right)$ is a character of the second kind mod k. The fact that it is not the principal character, which follows from 5), is the most important thing as far as its later applications in Part Four are concerned.

§ 3

L-Series

From now on, the letter s need no longer stand for an integer.

THEOREM 138: *For each of the h characters* mod k, *the series*

(71)
$$\sum_{a=1}^{\infty} \frac{\chi(a)}{a^s} = L(s, \chi)$$

is absolutely convergent for $s > 1$.

(The easily answered question as to whether these h functions of s are, moreover, distinct, is unimportant; as an *Exercise*, the reader may think it over.)

Proof: By Definition 23, I), and Theorem 128, we have

$$|\chi(a)| \leq 1,$$
$$\left| \frac{\chi(a)}{a^s} \right| \leq \frac{1}{a^s},$$

from which the theorem follows because of the convergence of $\sum_{a=1}^{\infty} \frac{1}{a^s}$.

THEOREM 139: *If χ is not the principal character, then we have*

$$\left| \sum_{a=u}^{v} \chi(a) \right| \leq \frac{h}{2}$$

for $v \geq u \geq 1$.

Proof: By Theorem 131, $\Sigma \chi(a)$ vanishes taken over a positive complete set of residues. Hence we may assume the number of terms of our sum, namely $v - u + 1$, to be $\leq k - 1$. In a complete set of residues, exactly h values of $|\chi(a)|$ are 1, and the rest $= 0$. If, in our "partial" set of residues, there occur at most $\frac{h}{2}$ terms for which $|\chi(a)| = 1$, then

$$\left| \sum_{a=u}^{v} \chi(a) \right| \leq \sum_{a=u}^{v} |\chi(a)| \leq \frac{h}{2};$$

if there occur more than $\frac{h}{2}$ such terms, then

$$\left| \sum_{a=u}^{v} \chi(a) \right| = \left| \sum_{a=u}^{u+k-1} \chi(a) - \sum_{a=v+1}^{u+k-1} \chi(a) \right| = \left| \sum_{a=v+1}^{u+k-1} \chi(a) \right| \leq \sum_{a=v+1}^{u+k-1} |\chi(a)| < \frac{h}{2}.$$

115

Theorem 140: *Let $v \geq u$, let γ_a be an arbitrary complex number for each a satisfying $u \leq a \leq v$, and let*

$$\sum_{a=u}^{w} \gamma_a = R(w) \quad \text{for} \quad u \leq w \leq v,$$

$$\operatorname*{Max}_{u \leq w \leq v} |R(w)| = \nu,$$

$$\varepsilon_u \geq \varepsilon_{u+1} \geq \cdots \geq \varepsilon_v \geq 0.$$

Then we have

$$\left| \sum_{a=u}^{v} \varepsilon_a \gamma_a \right| \leq \varepsilon_u \nu.$$

Proof: Let $R(u-1)$ denote 0. Then we have

$$\sum_{a=u}^{v} \varepsilon_a \gamma_a = \sum_{a=u}^{v} \varepsilon_a (R(a) - R(a-1)) = \sum_{a=u}^{v-1} R(a)(\varepsilon_a - \varepsilon_{a+1}) + R(v)\varepsilon_v,$$

$$\left| \sum_{a=u}^{v} \varepsilon_a \gamma_a \right| \leq \nu \left(\sum_{a=u}^{v-1} (\varepsilon_a - \varepsilon_{a+1}) + \varepsilon_v \right) = \nu \varepsilon_u.$$

Theorem 141: *If χ is not the principal character, then the series* (71) *converges uniformly for $s \geq 1$.*

Proof: For $v \geq u \geq 1$, it follows from Theorem 139 and Theorem 140 $\left(\text{with } \varepsilon_a = \dfrac{1}{a^s} \right)$ that

(72)
$$\left| \sum_{a=u}^{v} \frac{\chi(a)}{a^s} \right| \leq \frac{h}{2} \frac{1}{u^s} \leq \frac{h}{2u},$$

so that, given $\delta > 0$,

$$\left| \sum_{a=u}^{v} \frac{\chi(a)}{a^s} \right| < \delta \quad \text{for} \quad v \geq u \geq u_0(\delta),$$

where u_0 does not depend on s.

Theorem 142: 1) *The series*

(73)
$$\sum_{a=1}^{\infty} \frac{\chi(a) \log a}{a^s}$$

converges absolutely for $s > 1$ and it converges uniformly for $s > 1 + \varepsilon$ if we fix an arbitrary $\varepsilon > 0$,

2) *If $s > 1$, then*

$$L'(s, \chi) = - \sum_{a=1}^{\infty} \frac{\chi(a) \log a}{a^s}.$$

Proof: 1) For $s > 1 + \varepsilon$, we have

$$\left| \frac{\chi(a) \log a}{a^s} \right| \leq \frac{\log a}{a^{1+\varepsilon}},$$

and

$$\sum_{a=1}^{\infty} \frac{\log a}{a^{1+\varepsilon}}$$

converges.

2) This follows from (71) and 1).

THEOREM 143: *If χ is not the principal character, then the series (73) converges uniformly for $s \geq 1$, and for these values of s its sum is $< h$ in absolute value.*

Proof: 1) Let $s \geq 1$. Since

$$\frac{d}{d\xi} \frac{\log \xi}{\xi^s} = \frac{1 - s \log \xi}{\xi^{s+1}},$$

it follows that $\dfrac{\log \xi}{\xi^s}$ is a decreasing function for $\xi > e^{\frac{1}{s}}$ and, since $3 > e \geq e^{\frac{1}{s}}$, for $\xi \geq 3$; hence, by Theorems 139 and 140, we have, for $v \geq u \geq 3$,

$$(74) \qquad \left| \sum_{a=u}^{v} \frac{\chi(a) \log a}{a^s} \right| \leq \frac{h}{2} \frac{\log u}{u^s} \leq \frac{h}{2} \frac{\log u}{u},$$

from which the uniform convergence follows.

2) For $s \geq 1$, it follows from (74), upon letting $u = 3$ and $v \to \infty$, that

$$\left| \sum_{a=1}^{\infty} \frac{\chi(a) \log a}{a^s} \right| \leq \frac{\log 2}{2} + \frac{h}{2} \frac{\log 3}{3} < \frac{1}{2} + \frac{h}{2} \leq h.$$

THEOREM 144: *The series*

$$\sum_{a=1}^{\infty} \frac{\chi(a)\mu(a)}{a^s}$$

converges absolutely for $s > 1$.

Proof:

$$\left| \frac{\chi(a)\mu(a)}{a^s} \right| \leq \frac{1}{a^s}.$$

THEOREM 145: *For $s > 1$, we have*

$$L(s, \chi) \sum_{a=1}^{\infty} \frac{\chi(a)\mu(a)}{a^s} = 1,$$

so that

$$L(s, \chi) \neq 0$$

Proof: From the absolute convergence of both series on the left-hand side of the next formula, together with Theorem 35, we have

$$\sum_{b=1}^{\infty} \frac{\chi(b)}{b^s} \sum_{a=1}^{\infty} \frac{\chi(a)\mu(a)}{a^s} = \sum_{l=1}^{\infty} \sum_{ba=l} \frac{\chi(b)\chi(a)\mu(a)}{b^s a^s} = \sum_{l=1}^{\infty} \frac{\chi(l)}{l^s} \sum_{a|l} \mu(a) = 1.$$

Theorem 146: *For s > 1, we have*

$$\prod_{p} \left(1 - \frac{\chi(p)}{p^s}\right) = \frac{1}{L(s, \chi)}.$$

(The product is indexed by increasing values of p.)

Proof: For $\xi > 1$, we have

$$\prod_{p \leq \xi} \left(1 - \frac{\chi(p)}{p^s}\right) = \sum_{a=1}^{\infty}{}' \frac{\chi(a)\mu(a)}{a^s},$$

where a runs over those natural numbers that are not divisible by any $p > \xi$. Among these, there occur all of the numbers $a \leq \xi$. Hence we have

$$\prod_{p \leq \xi} \left(1 - \frac{\chi(p)}{p^s}\right) = \sum_{1 \leq a \leq \xi} \frac{\chi(a)\mu(a)}{a^s} + \sum_{a > \xi}{}' \frac{\chi(a)\mu(a)}{a^s}.$$

As $\xi \to \infty$, the first sum on the right approaches

$$\sum_{a=1}^{\infty} \frac{\chi(a)\mu(a)}{a^s} = \frac{1}{L(s, \chi)}$$

by Theorem 145; the second approaches 0, since it is

$$\leq \sum_{a > \xi} \frac{1}{a^s}$$

in absolute value.

Theorem 147: *For s > 1, we have*

$$\sum_{a=1}^{\infty} \frac{\chi(a)\Lambda(a)}{a^s} = -\frac{L'(s, \chi)}{L(s, \chi)},$$

where $\Lambda(a)$ is defined as in (5). *The series on the left converges absolutely.*

Proof: 1) $|\chi(a)\Lambda(a)| \leq \log a$ yields the absolute convergence of the series on the left for $s > 1$.

2) By (6), we have

$$\sum_{a|l} \Lambda(a) = \log l,$$

so that for $s > 1$ we have

$$L(s, \chi) \sum_{a=1}^{\infty} \frac{\chi(a)\Lambda(a)}{a^s} = \sum_{b=1}^{\infty} \frac{\chi(b)}{b^s} \sum_{a=1}^{\infty} \frac{\chi(a)\Lambda(a)}{a^s} = \sum_{l=1}^{\infty} \frac{\chi(l)}{l^s} \sum_{a|l} \Lambda(a) = \sum_{l=1}^{\infty} \frac{\chi(l)\log l}{l^s}$$

$$= -L'(s, \chi),$$

by Theorem 142.

THEOREM 148: *As $s \to 1$ (from the right),*

$$- \frac{L'(s, \chi_0)}{L(s, \chi_0)} \to \infty.$$

Proof: By Theorem 147, we have

$$- \frac{L'(s, \chi_0)}{L(s, \chi_0)} = \sum_{\substack{a=1 \\ (a,k)=1}}^{\infty} \frac{\Lambda(a)}{a^s} = \sum_{a=1}^{\infty} \frac{\Lambda(a)}{a^s} - \sum_{p|k} \log p \sum_{m=1}^{\infty} \frac{1}{p^{ms}} = \sum_{a=1}^{\infty} \frac{\Lambda(a)}{a^s} - \sum_{p|k} \frac{\log p}{p^s - 1}.$$

As $s \to 1$, the second term approaches a finite value. Thus we merely have to show that the first term approaches infinity. I should like to give two proofs.

1) If Theorem 147 is applied to $k=1$, it follows that the first term

$$= \frac{\displaystyle\sum_{a=1}^{\infty} \frac{\log a}{a^s}}{\displaystyle\sum_{a=1}^{\infty} \frac{1}{a^s}}.$$

In this formula, the denominator approaches infinity, as $s \to 1$, since

$$\sum_{a=1}^{\infty} \frac{1}{a^s} > \int_1^{\infty} \frac{d\alpha}{\alpha^s} = \frac{1}{s-1}.$$

Let g be a given number >1. For $s>1$ we have

$$\sum_{a=1}^{\infty} \frac{\log a}{a^s} \geqq \sum_{a=g}^{\infty} \frac{\log a}{a^s} > \log g \sum_{a=g}^{\infty} \frac{1}{a^s} = \log g \left(\sum_{a=1}^{\infty} \frac{1}{a^s} - \sum_{a=1}^{g-1} \frac{1}{a^s} \right),$$

$$\frac{\displaystyle\sum_{a=1}^{\infty} \frac{\log a}{a^s}}{\displaystyle\sum_{a=1}^{\infty} \frac{1}{a^s}} > \log g \left(1 - \frac{\displaystyle\sum_{a=1}^{g-1} \frac{1}{a^s}}{\displaystyle\sum_{a=1}^{\infty} \frac{1}{a^s}} \right);$$

the right-hand side is $> \frac{1}{2} \log g$ for $1 < s < 1 + \varepsilon(g)$. This suffices.

2) We use Theorem 114. Since $\sum_p \frac{1}{p}$ diverges, it follows *a fortiori* that $\sum_p \frac{\log p}{p}$ diverges, and consequently so does $\sum_{a=1}^{\infty} \frac{\Lambda(a)}{a}$. Hence, for every $\omega > 0$ there is a corresponding $b(\omega)$ for which

$$\sum_{a=1}^{b} \frac{\Lambda(a)}{a} > \omega.$$

For $1<s<1+\varepsilon(\omega)$ we therefore have

$$\sum_{a=1}^{b} \frac{\Lambda(a)}{a^s} > \omega,$$

so that

$$\sum_{a=1}^{\infty} \frac{\Lambda(a)}{a^s} > \omega.$$

Theorem 149: *For $0<\eta<1$ and $\nu \gtreqless 0$, we have*

$$(1-\eta)^3 |1-\eta e^{\nu i}|^4 |1-\eta e^{2\nu i}|^2 < 1.$$

Proof: The geometric mean of three positive numbers is at most equal to their arithmetic mean; therefore, since

$$2 \cos \nu + \cos 2\nu = 2 \cos \nu + 2 \cos^2 \nu - 1 = -\frac{3}{2} + 2\left(\cos \nu + \frac{1}{2}\right)^2 \geqq -\frac{3}{2},$$

we have

$$|1-\eta e^{\nu i}|^4 |1-\eta e^{2\nu i}|^2 = (1-2\eta \cos \nu + \eta^2)(1-2\eta \cos \nu + \eta^2)(1-2\eta \cos 2\nu + \eta^2)$$
$$\leqq (1-\frac{2}{3}\eta(2\cos\nu + \cos 2\nu) + \eta^2)^3 \leqq (1+\eta+\eta^2)^3 < \left(\frac{1}{1-\eta}\right)^3.$$

Theorem 150: *For $s>1$ we have*

$$(L(s,\chi_0))^3 |L(s,\chi)|^4 |L(s,\chi^2)|^2 \geqq 1.$$

(By Theorem 132, χ^2 is a character.)

Proof: In Theorem 149, let me set

$$\chi(p)=e^{\nu i}, \quad \frac{1}{p^s} = \eta$$

for $p \nmid k$. This yields

$$\left(1-\frac{\chi_0(p)}{p^s}\right)^3 \left|1-\frac{\chi(p)}{p^s}\right|^4 \left|1-\frac{\chi^2(p)}{p^s}\right|^2 \leqq 1;$$

this holds also if $p|k$ $(1=1)$. Multiplication with respect to p, by Theorem 146, yields the result of the theorem.

Theorem 151: *For every character of the third kind we have*

$$L(1,\chi)\neq 0.$$

Proof: Since χ^2 is not the principal character (for otherwise χ would be real), it follows from (72) (with $u=1$ and $v\to\infty$) that

$$|L(s,\chi^2)|<h$$

for $s>1$. On the other hand, for $1<s<2$, we have

$$L(s,\chi_0) = \sum_{\substack{a=1 \\ (a,k)=1}}^{\infty} \frac{1}{a^s} \leq \sum_{a=1}^{\infty} \frac{1}{a^s} < 1 + \int_1^{\infty} \frac{d\alpha}{\alpha^s} = 1 + \frac{1}{s-1} = \frac{s}{s-1} < \frac{2}{s-1}.$$

Hence, by Theorem 150, we have

$$|L(s,\chi)| \geq \frac{1}{(L(s,\chi_0))^{\frac{3}{4}}} \frac{1}{|L(s,\chi^2)|^{\frac{1}{2}}} > \frac{(s-1)^{\frac{3}{4}}}{2^{\frac{3}{4}}} \frac{1}{\sqrt{h}} > \frac{(s-1)^{\frac{3}{4}}}{2\sqrt{h}}.$$

If we had

$$L(1,\chi)=0,$$

then it would follow by Theorem 143 (since $L'(\xi,\chi)$ is continuous for $\xi \geq 1$, by Theorem 143) that, for $s>1$,

$$|L(s,\chi)| = |L(s,\chi)-L(1,\chi)| = \left| \int_1^s L'(\xi,\chi)\,d\xi \right| < h(s-1).$$

Hence, for $1<s<2$, we would have

$$(s-1)^{\frac{1}{4}} > \frac{1}{2h^{\frac{3}{2}}}.$$

This, however, is false for $s=1+\dfrac{1}{16h^6}$.

THEOREM 152: *For every character of the second kind we have*

$$L(1,\chi)\neq 0.$$

This is the deepest of all of the lemmas that are necessary for Dirichlet's proof. Dirichlet proved it only by the considerably roundabout method of using the so-called theory of the class number of quadratic forms. Incidentally,

$$L(1,\chi)\geq 0$$

is trivial, because of Theorem 146, since $L(s,\chi)\geq 0$ for $s>1$ and since, by Theorem 141, the series is continuous for $s\geq 1$.

Proof: Let us consider the number-theoretic function

$$f(a)=\sum_{d|a}\chi(d).$$

Then, for $l\geq 0$, we have

$$f(p^l)=1+\chi(p)+\cdots+\chi(p^l)=\begin{cases}1+0+\cdots+0 & =1 \text{ for } \chi(p)=0,\\ 1+1+\cdots+1 & \geq 1 \text{ for } \chi(p)=1,\\ 1-1+\cdots+(-1)^l=\begin{cases}0 \text{ for } \chi(p)=-1, 2\nmid l,\\ 1 \text{ for } \chi(p)=-1, 2\mid l.\end{cases}\end{cases}$$

Hence we have

(75)
$$f(p^l)\geq\begin{cases}0 \text{ always}\\ 1 \text{ if } 2\mid l.\end{cases}$$

Let $a_1>0$, $a_2>0$, and $(a_1, a_2)=1$. There is a one-to-one correspondence between all positive numbers $d|a_1a_2$, and all products of positive numbers $d_1|a_1$ by positive numbers $d_2|a_2$. We therefore have

(76) $\quad f(a_1 a_2)=\underset{d|a_1 a_2}{\Sigma}\chi(d)=\underset{\substack{d_1|a_1\\d_2|a_2}}{\Sigma}\chi(d_1 d_2)=\underset{d_1|a_1}{\Sigma}\chi(d_1)\cdot\underset{d_2|a_2}{\Sigma}\chi(d_2)=f(a_1)f(a_2).$

From (75) and (76) it follows that

(77)
$$f(a)\geq\begin{cases}0 \text{ always,}\\ 1 \text{ if } a=\text{ a perfect square.}\end{cases}$$

Let us set

$$m=(4h)^6$$

and

$$z=\overset{m}{\underset{n=1}{\Sigma}}2(m-n)f(n)=\underset{\substack{ab\leq m\\a>0, b>0}}{\Sigma}2(m-ab)\chi(b)$$

for the sake of brevity. Then, by (77), we have

(78) $\quad z\geq\overset{\sqrt{m}}{\underset{b=1}{\Sigma}}2(m-b^2)\geq\overset{\frac{1}{2}\sqrt{m}}{\underset{b=1}{\Sigma}}2(m-b^2)\geq\overset{\frac{1}{2}\sqrt{m}}{\underset{b=1}{\Sigma}}2\left(m-\frac{m}{4}\right)=\frac{3}{4}m^{\frac{3}{2}}=\frac{3}{4}(4h)^9.$

On the other hand (and the reader should draw the curvilinear triangle in the ab-plane bounded by the positive branch of the hyperbola $ab=m$ and by the lines $a=1$ and $b=1$, and in addition the auxiliary line $b=m^{\frac{2}{3}}$), it follows from $ab\leq m$, $a>0$, and $b>0$ that either $a\leq\sqrt[3]{m}$, $b>m^{\frac{2}{3}}$ or $b\leq m^{\frac{2}{3}}$. Thus we have

(79)
$$z=z_1+z_2,$$

provided we set

$$z_1=\overset{\sqrt[3]{m}}{\underset{a=1}{\Sigma}}\quad\underset{m^{\frac{2}{3}}<b\leq\frac{m}{a}}{\Sigma}2(m-ab)\chi(b),\qquad z_2=\overset{m^{\frac{2}{3}}}{\underset{b=1}{\Sigma}}\quad\underset{0<a\leq\frac{m}{b}}{\Sigma}2(m-ab)\chi(b).$$

From Theorem 139 and Theorem 140 (with b in place of a, $\gamma_b = \chi(b)$, and $\varepsilon_b = 2(m-ab)$ for $m^{\frac{2}{3}} < b \leq \dfrac{m}{a}$, $v \leq \dfrac{h}{2}$, $\varepsilon_u < 2m$), it follows that

(80)
$$z_1 \leq \sum_{a=1}^{\sqrt[3]{m}} \Big| \sum_{m^{\frac{2}{3}} < b \leq \frac{m}{a}} 2(m-ab)\chi(b) \Big| \leq \sum_{a=1}^{\sqrt[3]{m}} 2m \frac{h}{2} = m^{\frac{4}{3}} h.$$

On the other hand,

$$z_2 = \sum_{b=1}^{m^{\frac{2}{3}}} \chi(b) \sum_{0 < a \leq \frac{m}{b}} (2m - 2ab).$$

In this formula, if we set

$$\frac{m}{b} - \left[\frac{m}{b}\right] = \vartheta = \vartheta(m, b)$$

(where $0 \leq \vartheta < 1$), we obtain

$$\sum_a (2m - 2ab) = 2m \sum_a 1 - b \sum_a 2a = 2m \left[\frac{m}{b}\right] - b \left[\frac{m}{b}\right]\left(\left[\frac{m}{b}\right] + 1\right)$$

$$= 2m\left(\frac{m}{b} - \vartheta\right) - b\left(\left(\frac{m}{b} - \vartheta\right)^2 + \frac{m}{b} - \vartheta\right)$$

$$= \frac{2m^2}{b} - 2m\vartheta - b\left(\frac{m^2}{b^2} - 2\vartheta\frac{m}{b} + \vartheta^2 + \frac{m}{b} - \vartheta\right) = \frac{m^2}{b} - m + b(\vartheta - \vartheta^2).$$

Hence (observing that $|\vartheta - \vartheta^2| \leq 1$) we have

$$z_2 = m^2 \sum_{b=1}^{m^{\frac{2}{3}}} \frac{\chi(b)}{b} - m \sum_{b=1}^{m^{\frac{2}{3}}} \chi(b) + \sum_{b=1}^{m^{\frac{2}{3}}} \chi(b) b (\vartheta - \vartheta^2)$$

$$\leq m^2 \left(L(1, \chi) - \sum_{b=m^{\frac{2}{3}}+1}^{\infty} \frac{\chi(b)}{b}\right) + m\frac{h}{2} + m^{\frac{2}{3}} \sum_{b=1}^{m^{\frac{2}{3}}} 1,$$

so that by (72) (letting $u = m^{\frac{2}{3}} + 1$, $v \to \infty$) we have

$$z_2 < m^2 L(1, \chi) + m^2 \frac{h}{2} \frac{1}{m^{\frac{2}{3}}} + m^{\frac{4}{3}} \frac{h}{2} + m^{\frac{4}{3}} h = m^2 L(1, \chi) + m^{\frac{4}{3}} h\left(\frac{1}{2} + \frac{1}{2} + 1\right)$$

(81)
$$= m^2 L(1, \chi) + 2m^{\frac{4}{3}} h.$$

From (78) to (81), it follows that

$$\frac{3}{4}(4h)^9 \leq z < m^2 L(1, \chi) + 3m^{\frac{4}{3}} h = m^2 L(1, \chi) + 3(4h)^8 h = m^2 L(1, \chi) + \frac{3}{4}(4h)^9,$$

$$0 < m^2 L(1, \chi),$$

$$0 < L(1, \chi).$$

Theorem 153: *For any character of the second or third kind,*

$$\frac{L'(s, \chi)}{L(s, \chi)}$$

is bounded for s>1.

(The bound may of course depend on k and χ. However, χ need not be mentioned here, since for every k there are only $\varphi(k)$ possible values of χ.)

Proof: By Theorem 141, $L(s, \chi)$ is continuous for $s \geqq 1$; by Theorem 145, it is never 0 for $1 < s \leqq 2$; and by Theorem 151 and 152, it is never 0 for $s=1$. Hence $\dfrac{1}{L(s, \chi)}$ is bounded for $1 \leqq s \leqq 2$; and for $s>2$ the same is true, by Theorems 144 and 145. Finally, by Theorem 143, $L'(s, \chi)$ is bounded for $s \geqq 1$.

§ 4

Dirichlet's Proof

THEOREM 154: *Let $(l, k) = 1$ and $l > 0$. Then for $s > 1$ we have*

(82)
$$-\frac{1}{h} \sum_{\chi} \frac{1}{\chi(l)} \frac{L'(s, \chi)}{L(s, \chi)} = \sum_{a \equiv l} \frac{\Lambda(a)}{a^s}.$$

(The term on the right is summed over all numbers $a \equiv l \pmod{k}$ in in-creasing—or, of course, arbitrary—order. The fact that not all of the terms vanish will later follow from Theorem 155 and is, for the moment, irrelevant.)

Proof: By Theorem 147 and Theorem 137, we have

$$-\sum_{\chi} \frac{1}{\chi(l)} \frac{L'(s, \chi)}{L(s, \chi)} = \sum_{\chi} \frac{1}{\chi(l)} \sum_{a=1}^{\infty} \frac{\chi(a)\Lambda(a)}{a^s} = \sum_{a=1}^{\infty} \frac{\Lambda(a)}{a^s} \sum_{\chi} \frac{1}{\chi(l)} \chi(a) = \sum_{a \equiv l} \frac{\Lambda(a)}{a^s} h.$$

THEOREM 155: *Let $(l, k) = 1$. Then there exist infinitely many primes $p \equiv l \pmod{k}$.*

Proof: Without loss of generality, let $l > 0$. As $s \to 1$, the left-hand side of (82) (which, by (82), is *eo ipso* real) approaches ∞; for the term of the sum that involves χ_0 approaches $-\infty$, by Theorem 148, and the other $h-1$ terms remain bounded, by Theorem 153. Hence we have

$$\sum_{p \equiv l} \frac{\log p}{p^s} + \sum_{\substack{p, m \\ m > 1 \\ p^m \equiv l}} \frac{\log p}{p^{ms}} = \sum_{a \equiv l} \frac{\Lambda(a)}{a^s} \to \infty.$$

The sum for which $m > 1$ remains bounded, since

$$\sum_{a=2}^{\infty} \frac{2 \log a}{a^2} > \sum_{a=2}^{\infty} \frac{\log a}{a(a-1)} \geq \sum_{p} \frac{\log p}{p(p-1)} = \sum_{\substack{p, m \\ m > 1}} \frac{\log p}{p^m} > \sum_{\substack{p, m \\ m > 1}} \frac{\log p}{p^{ms}}$$

$$\geq \sum_{\substack{p, m \\ m > 1 \\ p^m \equiv l}} \frac{\log p}{p^{ms}} \qquad (s > 1).$$

Hence we have

$$\sum_{p \equiv l} \frac{\log p}{p^s} \to \infty.$$

It follows that this sum can neither be empty nor contain only a finite number of terms.

PART THREE

DECOMPOSITION INTO TWO, THREE, AND FOUR SQUARES

INTRODUCTION

These investigations really belong to the most elementary parts of number theory. I go into them only now, because at one point I intend to apply Dirichlet's Theorem on Arithmetic Progressions. Part Three will answer the questions $(n>0)$:

1) *When can n be written as the sum of two squares?*

Answer (Theorem 164): If and only if n has no prime factor $p \equiv 3$ (mod 4) that occurs with odd multiplicity.

2) *When this is the case, how many solutions does the diophantine equation*

$$n = x^2 + y^2$$

have?

Answer (Theorem 163): The number of solutions (and this is true even in the case of unsolvability) equals four times the excess of the number of positive d/n of the form $d \equiv 1$ (mod 4) over the number of positive d/n of the form $d \equiv 3$ (mod 4).

3) *When can n be written as the sum of three squares?*

Answer (Theorems 186 and 187): If and only if n is not of the form $4^a(8b+7)$, where $a \geq 0$ and $b \geq 0$.

(I am not asking in how many ways this can be done; this difficult problem, although solved, would lead us too far afield.)

4) *When can n be written as the sum of four squares?*

Answer (Theorem 169): Always.

5) *How many solutions does the diophantine equation*

$$n = x_1^2 + x_2^2 + x_3^2 + x_4^2$$

have?

Answer (Theorem 172): If n is odd, eight times the sum of the positive divisors of n; if n is even, 24 times the sum of the positive odd divisors of n.

The question that immediately suggests itself in consequence of 4), as to whether a finite number of summands (depending only on k) always suffices also for third, fourth, ... , and, in general, k-th powers of integers ≥ 0 (the qualification '≥ 0' is unnecessary if k is even), will constitute one of the topics of Part Six of *Vorlesungen über Zahlentheorie* and is one of the most important that I have to discuss with my readers; not only will this question be answered there affirmatively (by the Hilbert Theorem), but we shall also delve a good deal further into the subject (the Hardy-Littlewood Theorem).

CHAPTER I

FAREY FRACTIONS

This subject, which is over 100 years old, has more recently shown itself to be extraordinarily useful in the development of number theory. The reader will first come across its main applications in Parts Five and Six of *Vorlesungen über Zahlentheorie*.

DEFINITION 26: *For a fixed number $n>0$, let all of the reduced fractions with positive denominators $\leq n$, that is, all of the rational numbers*

$$\frac{a}{b}, \ (a, b) = 1, \ 0<b\leq n,$$

be arranged in increasing order of magnitude; the sequence thus obtained is called the Farey sequence belonging to n.

Incidentally, there are exactly $\overset{n}{\underset{b=1}{\Sigma}}\varphi(b)$ of our fractions in each interval $g\leq\xi<g+1$ (for if b is held fixed, then the values of a resulting from $g\leq\frac{a}{b}<g+1$ constitute the reduced set of residues mod b lying in the interval $gb\leq a<gb+b$); since the Farey sequence is after all transformed into itself upon translation by 1, we will know it completely if we merely restrict ourselves to the interval $0\leq\xi\leq1$. However, this is of no interest to me at the moment.

Example: The section of the Farey sequence belonging to $n=7$ which lies in the interval $0\leq\xi\leq1$ is

$$\frac{0}{1}, \frac{1}{7}, \frac{1}{6}, \frac{1}{5}, \frac{1}{4}, \frac{2}{7}, \frac{1}{3}, \frac{2}{5}, \frac{3}{7}, \frac{1}{2}, \frac{4}{7}, \frac{3}{5}, \frac{2}{3}, \frac{5}{7}, \frac{3}{4}, \frac{4}{5}, \frac{5}{6}, \frac{6}{7}, \frac{1}{1}.$$

THEOREM 156: *Let $\frac{a}{b}$ and $\frac{a'}{b'}$ be two successive terms of the Farey sequence belonging to n. Then, first of all, we have*

$$b+b'\geq n+1,$$

and second, we have

$$ba'-ab'=\pm1 \ \text{according to whether} \ \frac{a}{b}\lessgtr\frac{a'}{b'}.$$

131

Proof: By symmetry, we may let

$$\frac{a}{b} < \frac{a'}{b'}.$$

By Theorem 68, we can determine numbers x and y corresponding to a and b for which

(83) $$b\,x - a\,y = 1, \quad n - b < y \leq n;$$

for we have $(b, -a) = 1$ and $b > 0$, so that there is a number y in the complete set of residues mod b indicated above and then a suitable x corresponding to y. Then we have

$$y > 0, \quad (x, y) = 1, \quad \frac{x}{y} = \frac{a}{b} + \frac{1}{b\,y} > \frac{a}{b}.$$

If I succeed in showing that

$$\frac{x}{y} = \frac{a'}{b'},$$

then I shall be through. For then

$$b'\,x = a'\,y, \quad y/b', \quad b'/y,$$
$$b' = y, \quad a' = x,$$

and therefore, by (83),

$$b\,a' - a\,b' = 1, \quad b + b' > n.$$

Suppose that

$$\frac{x}{y} \neq \frac{a'}{b'}.$$

Then, since $\dfrac{a'}{b'}$ is the right-hand neighbor of $\dfrac{a}{b}$ and since $\dfrac{x}{y}$ also belongs to the Farey sequence because $(x, y) = 1$ and $0 < y \leq n$, it would follow that

$$\frac{x}{y} > \frac{a'}{b'},$$

so that in the formula

$$\frac{x}{y} - \frac{a'}{b'} = \frac{x\,b' - y\,a'}{y\,b'}$$

the numerator on the right would be > 0 and therefore ≥ 1. We would consequently have

$$\frac{x}{y} - \frac{a'}{b'} \geq \frac{1}{y\,b'}.$$

Likewise $\left(\text{ since } \dfrac{a'}{b'} > \dfrac{a}{b}\right)$, we would have

$$\frac{a'}{b'} - \frac{a}{b} = \frac{ba' - ab'}{bb'} \geq \frac{1}{bb'}.$$

By addition, and by the use of (83) and the fact that $b' \leq n$, we would obtain

$$\frac{1}{by} = \frac{bx - ay}{by} = \frac{x}{y} - \frac{a}{b} \geq \frac{1}{yb'} + \frac{1}{bb'} = \frac{b+y}{ybb'} > \frac{n}{ybb'} \geq \frac{1}{by},$$

which is a contradiction.

DEFINITION 27: *If* $\dfrac{a}{b}$ *and* $\dfrac{a'}{b'}$ *are two successive terms in the Farey sequence belonging to* n, *then* $\dfrac{a+a'}{b+b'}$ *is called their mediant.*

THEOREM 157: *The mediant* $\dfrac{a+a'}{b+b'}$ *lies between* $\dfrac{a}{b}$ *and* $\dfrac{a'}{b'}$ (*and thus is certainly not a term in the Farey sequence*); *its distance from* $\dfrac{a}{b}$ *and* $\dfrac{a'}{b'}$ *is* $\dfrac{1}{b(b+b')}$ *and* $\dfrac{1}{b'(b+b')}$, *respectively.*

Proof: Without loss of generality, let $\dfrac{a}{b} < \dfrac{a'}{b'}$; then, by Theorem 156, we have

$$\frac{a'}{b'} - \frac{a+a'}{b+b'} = \frac{ba' - ab'}{b'(b+b')} = \frac{1}{b'(b+b')} > 0,$$

$$\frac{a+a'}{b+b'} - \frac{a}{b} = \frac{ba' - ab'}{b(b+b')} = \frac{1}{b(b+b')} > 0.$$

THEOREM 158: *Given any number* $n > 0$ *and any real number* ξ, *there is a fraction* $\dfrac{a}{b}$ *for which*

$$(a, b) = 1, \quad 0 < b \leq n, \quad \left|\xi - \frac{a}{b}\right| \leq \frac{1}{b(n+1)}.$$

Proof: If we consider all of the Farey fractions belonging to n and the mediants of every pair, then ξ is certainly contained in at least one interval between a Farey fraction $\dfrac{a}{b}$ (inclusive) and one of the two mediants $\dfrac{a+a'}{b+b'}$ (inclusive) belonging to it. Hence, by Theorems 156 and 157, we have

$$\left|\xi - \frac{a}{b}\right| \leq \left|\frac{a+a'}{b+b'} - \frac{a}{b}\right| = \frac{1}{b(b+b')} \leq \frac{1}{b(n+1)}.$$

THEOREM 159: *Given $\eta \geqq 1$ and $\xi \gtreqless 0$, there exists a fraction $\dfrac{a}{b}$ such that*

$$(a, b)=1, \ 0<b\leqq\eta, \ \left|\xi-\frac{a}{b}\right|<\frac{1}{b\,\eta}.$$

Proof: Theorem 158, with $n=[\eta]$.

CHAPTER II

DECOMPOSITION INTO TWO SQUARES

The letters n, n_1, n_2, d, d_1, and d_2 will in this chapter always represent positive numbers.

THEOREM 160: *If*

$$n>1, \quad l^2 \equiv -1 \; (\text{mod } n),$$

then

(84) $$n=x^2+y^2, \quad x>0, \quad y>0, \quad (x, y)=1, \quad y \equiv lx \; (\text{mod } n)$$

is always solvable, and uniquely so.

Proof: 1) (Solvability.) By Theorem 159 with $\left(\eta = \sqrt{n}, \; \xi = -\dfrac{l}{n} \right)$, corresponding to given n and l there exist two numbers a and b for which

$$(a, \; b)=1, \quad 0<b \leq \sqrt{n}, \quad \left| -\frac{l}{n}-\frac{a}{b} \right| < \frac{1}{b\sqrt{n}}.$$

If we set

$$lb+na=c,$$

then it follows that

$$c \equiv lb \; (\text{mod } n), \quad |c| < \sqrt{n},$$

so that

$$0<b^2+c^2<2n.$$

Since

$$b^2+c^2 \equiv b^2+l^2b^2 \equiv (1+l^2)b^2 \equiv 0 \; (\text{mod } n),$$

it follows that

$$b^2+c^2=n.$$

Furthermore, we have $(b, c)=1$; for from

$$n=b^2+(lb+na)^2=(1+l^2)b^2+2lnba+n^2a^2$$

it follows that

135

$$1=\frac{1+l^2}{n}\,b^2+lba+lba+na^2=ub+a(lb+na)=ub+ac.$$

$c \neq 0$; for otherwise we would have $b^2=n>1$ and $(b,c)>1$.
In the case $c>0$, the choice

$$x=b,\quad y=c$$

accomplishes what we want.
In the case $c<0$, the choice

$$x=-c,\quad y=b$$

does it. For,

$$n=(-c)^2+b^2,\quad -c>0,\quad b>0,\quad (-c,b)=1,\quad b\equiv-l^2b\equiv-lc\equiv l(-c)\ (\mathrm{mod}\ n).$$

2) (Uniqueness.)   Let x_1, y_1 and x_2, y_2 satisfy the conditions in (84).
Then we have

$$n^2=(x_1{}^2+y_1{}^2)(x_2{}^2+y_2{}^2)=(x_1x_2+y_1y_2)^2+(x_1y_2-y_1x_2)^2,$$
$$x_1x_2+y_1y_2\equiv x_1x_2+lx_1lx_2\equiv(1+l^2)x_1x_2\equiv0\ (\mathrm{mod}\ n),$$

so that, since $x_1x_2+y_1y_2>0$, we have

$$x_1x_2+y_1y_2=n,\quad x_1y_2-y_1x_2=0,$$
$$x_1n=x_1(x_1x_2+y_1y_2)-y_1(x_1y_2-y_1x_2)=x_2(x_1{}^2+y_1{}^2)=x_2n,$$
$$x_1=x_2,$$
$$y_1=y_2.$$

THEOREM 161:   *Let $V(n)$ be the number of solutions of*

(85) $$l^2\equiv-1\ (\mathrm{mod}\ n).$$

Then the number of solutions of

(86) $$n=x^2+y^2,\ (x,y)=1$$

equals $4V(n)$.

Remark: The value of $V(n)$ was determined in Theorem 88 (the n of that theorem $=-1$ here and the m of that theorem $=n$ here):

$$V(n)=\begin{cases}0 & \text{if } 4|n \text{ or if a prime } p\equiv3\ (\mathrm{mod}\ 4) \text{ divides } n,\\ 2^s & \text{if } 4\nmid n, \text{ no prime } p\equiv3\ (\mathrm{mod}\ 4) \text{ divides } n, \text{ and } s \text{ is the}\\ & \text{number of distinct odd primes } p|n.\end{cases}$$

Proof: 1) For $n=1$ the statement is trivial; we have

$$V(1)=1,$$

and the four decompositions read

$$1=(\pm 1)^2+0^2=0^2+(\pm 1)^2.$$

2) For $n>1$, we necessarily have $x\neq 0$ and $y\neq 0$ (since $(x,y)=1$), and therefore the number of solutions of (86) must be four times the number of solutions with the supplementary conditions that $x>0$ and $y>0$. It follows from Theorem 160 that for each l satisfying (85) there exists a solution of (86) for which

$$x>0, y>0, \text{ and } y\equiv lx \pmod{n}.$$

Conversely, every solution of (86) for which $x>0$ and $y>0$ yields exactly one l (mod n) satisfying (85) for which

(87) $$y\equiv lx \pmod{n}.$$

For since $(x,y)=1$, we have $(x,n)=1$, and therefore (87) is uniquely solvable for l (mod n), so that

$$0\equiv n\equiv x^2+y^2\equiv x^2+l^2x^2\equiv(1+l^2)x^2 \pmod{n},$$
$$0\equiv 1+l^2 \pmod{n}.$$

THEOREM 162: *The number $U(n)$ of solutions of*

(88) $$n=x^2+y^2$$

is given by the formula

$$U(n)=4\sum_{d^2|n} V\left(\frac{n}{d^2}\right).$$

(That is, d runs through all the positive numbers whose squares divide n.)

Proof: If the pairs x, y are classified according to the various values of $(x,y)=d$, where $d^2|n$, then our theorem clearly follows from Theorem 161, since for $(x,y)=d$, (88) is equivalent to the statement

$$\frac{n}{d^2}=x_1{}^2+y_1{}^2, \; x_1=\frac{x}{d}, \; y_1=\frac{y}{d}, (x_1,y_1)=1.$$

THEOREM 163:

(89)
$$U(n) = 4 \sum_{d|n} \chi(d),$$

where $\chi(d)$ is the non-principal character mod 4 (see Part Two, Chapter III, § 2), *that is,*

$$\chi(d) = \begin{cases} 0 & \text{for } d \equiv 0 \pmod{2}, \\ 1 & \text{for } d \equiv 1 \pmod{4}, \\ -1 & \text{for } d \equiv 3 \pmod{4}. \end{cases}$$

Written differently,

$$U(n) = 4 \sum_{\substack{u|n \\ u \text{ odd}}} (-1)^{\frac{u-1}{2}}.$$

Remark: Thus, this theorem also justifies the wording of the answer to Question 2) in the Introduction.

Proof: If $(n_1, n_2) = 1$, then by Theorem 71 we have

$$V(n_1 n_2) = V(n_1) \, V(n_2),$$

so that by Theorem 162 we have

$$\frac{U(n_1 n_2)}{4} = \sum_{d^2|n_1 n_2} V\left(\frac{n_1 n_2}{d^2}\right) = \sum_{\substack{d_1^2|n_1 \\ d_2^2|n_2}} V\left(\frac{n_1}{d_1^2} \frac{n_2}{d_2^2}\right) = \sum_{\substack{d_1^2|n_1 \\ d_2^2|n_2}} V\left(\frac{n_1}{d_1^2}\right) V\left(\frac{n_2}{d_2^2}\right)$$

(since the numbers d for which $d^2|n_1 n_2$ are in one-to-one correspondence with the products $d_1 d_2$ for which $d_2^2|n_1$ and $d_2^2|n_2$)

(90)
$$= \sum_{d_1^2|n_1} V\left(\frac{n_1}{d_1^2}\right) \sum_{d_2^2|n_2} V\left(\frac{n_2}{d_2^2}\right) = \frac{U(n_1)}{4} \frac{U(n_2)}{4}.$$

If we let

$$\sum_{d|n} \chi(d) = W(n),$$

then $W(n)$ also has the property that

$$W(n_1 n_2) = W(n_1) W(n_2) \text{ for } (n_1, n_2) = 1;$$

for

$$\sum_{d|n_1 n_2} \chi(d) = \sum_{\substack{d_1|n_1 \\ d_2|n_2}} \chi(d_1 d_2) = \sum_{d_1|n_1} \chi(d_1) \sum_{d_2|n_2} \chi(d_2).$$

It therefore suffices, since (89) is obvious for $n=1$ ($4=4\cdot1$), to prove (89) for $n=p^l$, $l>0$, where this statement now reads:

$$\frac{U(p^l)}{4}=\chi(p^l)+\cdots+\chi(p)+1.$$

We do, in fact, have $V(1)=1$, and by Theorem 87 (the value of n there being -1 here), or else by the Remark of Theorem 161, we also have

$$V(p^m)=\begin{cases}1 & \text{for } p=2,\ m=1,\\ 0 & \text{for } p=2,\ m>1,\\ 0 & \text{for } p\equiv3 \pmod 4,\ m>0,\\ 2 & \text{for } p\equiv1 \pmod 4,\ m>0.\end{cases}$$

It follows from Theorem 162 that, for even l,

$$\frac{U(p^l)}{4}=V(p^l)+V(p^{l-2})+\cdots+V(p^2)+V(1)$$

(91)
$$=\begin{cases}1 & \text{for } p=2,\\ \dfrac{l}{2}\cdot2+1=l+1 & \text{for } p\equiv1 \pmod 4,\\ 1 & \text{for } p\equiv3 \pmod 4,\end{cases}$$

and that, for odd l,

(92) $$\frac{U(p^l)}{4}=V(p^l)+V(p^{l-2})+\cdots+V(p)=\begin{cases}1 & \text{for } p=2,\\ 2\dfrac{l+1}{2}=l+1 & \text{for } p\equiv1 \pmod 4,\\ 0 & \text{for } p\equiv3 \pmod 4;\end{cases}$$

on the other hand, it follows by definition that

$$\chi(p^l)+\cdots+\chi(p)+1=\begin{cases}0+\cdots+0+1=1 & \text{for } p=2,\\ 1+\cdots+1+1=l+1 & \text{for } p\equiv1 \pmod 4,\\ 1-1+\cdots+1=1 & \text{for } p\equiv3 \pmod 4,\ 2/l,\\ -1+1-\cdots+1=0 & \text{for } p\equiv3 \pmod 4,\ 2\nmid l.\end{cases}$$

(I am well aware that I have repeated several computations that occurred at the beginning of the proof of Theorem 152.)

THEOREM 164:

$$\frac{U(n)}{4} = \begin{cases} 0, \text{ if there is a prime } p\equiv 3 \text{ (mod 4) } \text{that divides } n \text{ with (precisely) } \text{odd multiplicity,} \\ T(m) \text{ otherwise, where } m \text{ is the product of the powers of} \\ \text{the primes } p|n \text{ of the form } p\equiv 1 \text{ (mod 4) } \text{appearing in the} \\ \text{canonical decomposition of } n. \end{cases}$$

Proof: For $n=1$ the statement is obvious ($1=1$). For $(n_1, n_2)=1$ the equation

$$F(n_1 n_2) = F(n_1)F(n_2)$$

holds for $\frac{U(n)}{4}$ (by (90)) as well as (obviously) for the right-hand side of the statement to be proved. It therefore suffices to prove the statement for $n=p^l$, $l>0$. In this case, it follows from (91) and (92) that we do, in fact, have

$$\frac{U(p^l)}{4} = \begin{cases} 1=T(1) & \text{for } p=2, \\ l+1=T(p^l) & \text{for } p\equiv 1 \text{ (mod 4)}, \\ 1=T(1) & \text{for } p\equiv 3 \text{ (mod 4)}, \; 2/l, \\ 0=0 & \text{for } p\equiv 3 \text{ (mod 4)}, \; 2\nmid l. \end{cases}$$

THEOREM 165: *Every prime $p\equiv 1$ (mod 4) can be written as a sum of two squares and, moreover, this can be done in eight ways.*

Proof: From Theorem 163 or Theorem 164, $U(p)=4\cdot 2=8$. (Even Theorem 161 suffices, since $V(p)=2$ and in the equation $p=x^2+y^2$ we certainly have $(x, y)=1$.)

$p\equiv 1$ (mod 4) can be written in "essentially" only one way as a sum of two squares, since the eight representations can all be obtained from any one of them by changing the signs of x and y and by interchanging the summands. Stated precisely:

$$p=x^2+y^2, \; x>0, \; y>0, \; 2/x$$

has exactly one solution for $p\equiv 1$ (mod 4).

CHAPTER III

DECOMPOSITION INTO FOUR SQUARES

Introduction

I shall consider the diophantine equation

$$n = x_1{}^2 + x_2{}^2 + x_3{}^2 + x_4{}^2$$

before the equation

$$n = x_1{}^2 + x_2{}^2 + x_3{}^2,$$

for the proof of the solvability of the former equation, as well as the determination of the number of its roots, is easier than the answer, which follows in Chap. IV, to the question as to when the latter equation is solvable.

§1

Lagrange's Theorem

The following proof could be shortened somewhat if we were to bring in some of the above theorems on quadratic residues and on decomposition into a sum of two squares. However, the presentation of an as brief as possible direct proof seems to me to be of interest.

THEOREM 166 (Euler's identity):

$$(93) \begin{cases} (x_1^2+x_2^2+x_3^2+x_4^2)(y_1^2+y_2^2+y_3^2+y_4^2) \\ =(x_1y_1+x_2y_2+x_3y_3+x_4y_4)^2+(x_1y_2-x_2y_1+x_3y_4-x_4y_3)^2 \\ +(x_1y_3-x_3y_1+x_4y_2-x_2y_4)^2+(x_1y_4-x_4y_1+x_2y_3-x_3y_2)^2. \end{cases}$$

(We shall use (93) only when $x_1, \ldots, y_4$ are integers; this identity holds, however, for arbitrary complex numbers.)

Proof: Let us verify the assertion. On the left, after multiplying out, we have sixteen expressions of the form $x_a^2 y_b^2$ ($a=1, \ldots, 4$; $b=1, \ldots, 4$). These also appear, among other terms, on the right, for within the four parentheses on the right, each x_a is combined with each y_b, with a coefficient of ± 1. The other twenty-four terms on the right, which are all of the form $\pm 2\, x_a x_b y_c y_d$, $a<b$, $c<d$, cancel each other pairwise; for on the right the coefficient of

$$
\begin{array}{lll}
2\,x_1 x_2 & \text{is} & y_1 y_2 - y_1 y_2 - y_3 y_4 + y_3 y_4 = 0, \\
2\,x_1 x_3 & \text{is} & y_1 y_3 + y_2 y_4 - y_1 y_3 - y_2 y_4 = 0, \\
2\,x_1 x_4 & \text{is} & y_1 y_4 - y_2 y_3 + y_2 y_3 - y_1 y_4 = 0, \\
2\,x_2 x_3 & \text{is} & y_2 y_3 - y_1 y_4 + y_1 y_4 - y_2 y_3 = 0, \\
2\,x_2 x_4 & \text{is} & y_2 y_4 + y_1 y_3 - y_2 y_4 - y_1 y_3 = 0, \\
2\,x_3 x_4 & \text{is} & y_3 y_4 - y_3 y_4 - y_1 y_2 + y_1 y_2 = 0.
\end{array}
$$

THEOREM 167: *For every $p>2$ there exists an m for which*

$$1 \leq m < p$$

and

$$m\,p = x_1^2 + x_2^2 + x_3^2 + x_4^2$$

is solvable.

142

Remark: Without the condition $m<p$ this would be trivial:

$$p\,p=p^2+0^2+0^2+0^2;$$

but it would also be quite useless.

Proof: The $\dfrac{p+1}{2}$ numbers x^2, $0\leq x\leq\dfrac{p-1}{2}$, are incongruent to each other (mod p) in pairs (for from $x_1{}^2\equiv x_2{}^2$ it would follow that

$$p|(x_1-x_2)(x_1+x_2) \text{ and } x_1\equiv\pm x_2 \pmod{p});$$

the same is true of the $\dfrac{p+1}{2}$ numbers $-1-y^2$, $0\leq y\leq\dfrac{p-1}{2}$. Therefore, since this makes $p+1$ numbers altogether, and since there are only p residue classes mod p, it follows (pigeon-hole principle!) that there exists a pair x, y for which

$$x^2\equiv-1-y^2 \pmod{p}, \ |x|<\frac{p}{2}, \ |y|<\frac{p}{2}.$$

Then we have

$$x^2+y^2+1^2+0^2=m\,p, \ 0<mp<\frac{p^2}{4}+\frac{p^2}{4}+1=\frac{p^2}{2}+1<p^2.$$

(The shortening of the proof referred to above—a very modest one—goes as follows: For $p\equiv1 \pmod 4$ we already know, by Theorem 165, that

$$1\cdot p=x_1{}^2+x_2{}^2+0^2+0^2.$$

For $p\equiv3 \pmod 4$ it follows from Theorem 79 that in the interval $1\leq a\leq p-1$ there exist both a quadratic residue and a quadratic non-residue mod p. Since 1 is a quadratic residue, there must be some a for which

$$\left(\frac{a}{p}\right)=1, \ \left(\frac{a+1}{p}\right)=-1.$$

Then we have $\left(\dfrac{-a-1}{p}\right)=1$, by Theorem 83, so that $a\equiv x^2$ and $-a-1\equiv y^2$ (mod p) for suitable x and y with $|x|<\dfrac{p}{2}$, $|y|<\dfrac{p}{2}$. It follows that

$$x^2+y^2+1\equiv0 \pmod{p}, \ |x|<\frac{p}{2}, \ |y|<\frac{p}{2}.$$

The reader will object that the proof has been shortened by a negative amount; he is correct; but as far as I am concerned, it serves a purpose to emphasize that Theorem 168, which follows, has already been proved earlier in this book for the case $p\equiv1 \pmod 4$.)

Theorem 168: *For every prime p,*

$$p = x_1^2 + x_2^2 + x_3^2 + x_4^2$$

is solvable.

Proof: For $p=2$ this is obvious $(2 = 1^2 + 1^2 + 0^2 + 0^2)$; therefore let $p > 2$. Let $m = m(p)$ be the smallest positive number for which

(94) $$m\,p = x_1^2 + x_2^2 + x_3^2 + x_4^2$$

is solvable. By Theorem 167, $m < p$. We assert that

$$m = 1.$$

In any case, m is odd; for otherwise it would follow from (94) that

$$x_1 + x_2 + x_3 + x_4 \equiv 0 \pmod 2,$$

so that, without loss of generality,

$$x_1 + x_2 \equiv 0, \; x_3 + x_4 \equiv 0 \pmod 2$$

(that is, if the x_k were all odd or all even, this would certainly be true; and if two were odd and two even, it would become true upon suitable renumbering), and therefore

$$\frac{m}{2}p = \left(\frac{x_1 + x_2}{2}\right)^2 + \left(\frac{x_1 - x_2}{2}\right)^2 + \left(\frac{x_3 + x_4}{2}\right)^2 + \left(\frac{x_3 - x_4}{2}\right)^2,$$

where the four parenthesized terms on the right would be integers, contrary to the minimality of m.

Theorem 168 will now be proved indirectly. Let us suppose m to be > 1, and therefore to be odd and ≥ 3. Let numbers y_k be chosen, for $k = 1$, 2, 3, and 4, in such a way that

$$y_k \equiv x_k \pmod m, \; |y_k| < \frac{m}{2}.$$

(This can be done, since $-\dfrac{m-1}{2} \leq y \leq \dfrac{m-1}{2}$ is a complete set of residues.) Then we have

$$\sum_k y_k^2 \equiv \sum_k x_k^2 \equiv m\,p \equiv 0 \pmod m,$$

(95) $$\sum_k y_k^2 = m\,n.$$

In this formula we must have $n > 0$; for otherwise we would have

$$y_k=0, \ m/x_k \text{ for every } k, \ m^2/\sum_k x_k{}^2, \ m^2/m\,p, \ m/p,$$

contradicting $1<m<p$. Furthermore we have $n<m$, for by (95),

$$m\,n<4\,\frac{m^2}{4}=m^2.$$

From (94) and (95) it follows, by (93), that

(96) $m^2np=$right-hand side of (93).

Each parenthesized term on the right-hand side of (93) is $\equiv 0 \pmod m$. For the first one is

$$\sum_k x_k y_k \equiv \sum_k x_k{}^2 \equiv 0 \pmod m,$$

and for the other three terms we merely have to notice, twice for each term, that

$$x_k y_l - x_l y_k \equiv x_k x_l - x_l x_k \equiv 0 \pmod m.$$

From (96) it therefore follows that

$$np=z_1{}^2+z_2{}^2+z_3{}^2+z_4{}^2,$$

which, since $0<n<m$, contradicts the minimality of m.

THEOREM 169 (Lagrange's Theorem): *The diophantine equation*

(97) $$n=x_1{}^2+x_2{}^2+x_3{}^2+x_4{}^2$$

is solvable for every $n\geq 0$.

Proof: For $n=0$ and $n=1$ this is obvious; therefore let $n>1$. By Theorem 166 it follows that the statement is true for $n_1 n_2$ whenever it is true for n_1 and n_2; for if $x_1, \ldots, y_4$ are integers, then each of the four parenthesized terms on the right-hand side of (93) is an integer. Since $n=p_1 p_2 \ldots p_v$, everything thus follows from Theorem 168.

§ 2

Determination of the Number of Solutions

Since the number of solutions of (97) is obviously 1 for $n=0$, we may assume that $n>0$. Let $Q(n)$ denote the number of solutions of (97). The fact that we already know $Q(n)$ to be >0, by § 1, is irrelevant; we shall not use § 1, but we shall indeed use Chap. II (the number of decompositions into two squares).

Throughout the present section (§ 2) the symbols u, u_1, u_2, u_3, u_4, l, m, a, α, b, β, a_1, α_1, b_1 and β_1 will denote positive odd numbers.

THEOREM 170: *Let $A(u)$ be the number of solutions of*

$$(98) \qquad 4u=u_1{}^2+u_2{}^2+u_3{}^2+u_4{}^2,$$

and (as in Part One, Chap. IV) *let $S(u)=\underset{d|u}{\Sigma}d$. Then we have*

$$A(u)=S(u).$$

Example: For $p>2$, the theorem states that

$$4p=u_1{}^2+u_2{}^2+u_3{}^2+u_4{}^2$$

has exactly $p+1$ solutions. For example, for $p=3$ the four solutions are

$$12=3^2+1^2+1^2+1^2=1^2+3^2+1^2+1^2=1^2+1^2+3^2+1^2=1^2+1^2+1^2+3^2.$$

Proof: We obtain all the solutions of (98) when we decompose $4u$ into $2l+2m$ in all possible ways, and then solve

$$2l=u_1{}^2+u_2{}^2, \quad 2m=u_3{}^2+u_4{}^2.$$

(For $u_1{}^2+u_2{}^2\equiv u_3{}^2+u_4{}^2\equiv 2 \pmod 4$.)

If v is odd, then in the equation $2v=x^2+y^2$, x and y must *eo ipso* be odd, so that the number of solutions of this equation equals four times the number of solutions in which x and y are odd, positive numbers; it therefore follows from Theorem 163 that

$$A(u) = \underset{l+m=2u}{\Sigma} \frac{U(2l)}{4}\frac{U(2m)}{4} = \underset{l+m=2u}{\Sigma} \underset{a|2l}{\Sigma}\chi(a)\underset{b|2m}{\Sigma}\chi(b) = \underset{l+m=2u}{\Sigma} \underset{a|l}{\Sigma}\chi(a)\underset{b|m}{\Sigma}\chi(b)$$

$$= \underset{l+m=2u}{\Sigma} \underset{\substack{a|l \\ b|m}}{\Sigma}\chi(ab) = \underset{a\alpha+b\beta=2u}{\Sigma}\chi(ab).$$

146

That is, the last term is summed over all quadruplets (of odd, positive numbers) a, α, b, β for which $a\alpha + b\beta = 2u$.

Let us first count the contribution of the quadruples in which $a = b$. In this case, $a|u$; the equation

$$2\frac{u}{a} = \alpha + \beta$$

clearly has $\frac{u}{a}$ solutions ($\alpha = 1, 3, \ldots, 2\frac{u}{a} - 1$ and the β determined therefrom); since $\chi(aa) = 1$, the contribution of each is thus

$$\sum_{a|u} \frac{u}{a} = \sum_{d|u} d = S(u).$$

It remains to be shown that

$$\sum_{\substack{a\alpha + b\beta = 2u \\ a \geq b}} \chi(ab) = 0.$$

By symmetry, it suffices to show that

$$\sum_{\substack{a\alpha + b\beta = 2u \\ a > b}} \chi(ab) = 0.$$

And for this it suffices to pair off the solutions of

$$a\alpha + b\beta = 2u, \ a > b$$

one to one in such a way that for every pair a, b, α, β; a_1, b_1, α_1, β_1 we have

(99) $$\chi(ab) + \chi(a_1 b_1) = 0.$$

In order to achieve this, I need only specify a rule such that

1) to every quadruple a, b, α, β, a quadruple a_1, b_1, α_1, β_1 is assigned such that

$$a_1\alpha_1 + b_1\beta_1 = 2u, \ a_1 > b_1 ;$$

2) to this latter quadruple the rule assigns the original quadruple a, b, α, β;

3) the equation

(99) $$\chi(ab) + \chi(a_1 b_1) = 0$$

holds.

For the two quadruples would then *eo ipso* be distinct, by (99).

The rule is: Setting

$$n = \left[\frac{b}{a-b}\right] (\geqq 0)$$

for brevity, let

$$a_1 = (n+2)\alpha + (n+1)\beta, \quad \alpha_1 = -n a + (n+1)b, \quad b_1 = (n+1)\alpha + n\beta,$$
$$\beta_1 = (n+1)a - (n+2)b.$$

We have, indeed, that

11) each of these four numbers is odd, since

$$a_1 \equiv n+2+n+1 \equiv 1, \quad \alpha_1 \equiv -n+n+1 \equiv 1, \quad b_1 \equiv n+1+n \equiv 1,$$
$$\beta_1 \equiv n+1-n-2 \equiv 1 \pmod 2;$$

12) each of these numbers is >0: a_1 and b_1, obviously; α_1, since $\frac{b}{a-b} \geqq n$; and β_1, since $n+1 > \frac{b}{a-b}$;

13) $a_1 \alpha_1 + b_1 \beta_1 = -n(n+2)a\alpha - n(n+1)a\beta + (n+1)(n+2)b\alpha$
$$+ (n+1)^2 b\beta$$
$$+ (n+1)^2 a\,\alpha + n(n+1)a\beta - (n+1)(n+2)b\alpha$$
$$- n(n+2)b\beta$$
$$= ((n+1)^2 - n(n+2))(a\alpha + b\beta) = a\alpha + b\beta = 2u;$$

14) $a_1 > b_1$ (obvious).

2) $\left[\frac{b_1}{a_1 - b_1}\right] = \left\lfloor\frac{n(\alpha+\beta)+\alpha}{\alpha+\beta}\right\rfloor = n,$

$(n+2)\alpha_1 + (n+1)\beta_1 = a(-n(n+2)+(n+1)^2) = a,$
$-n a_1 + (n+1)b_1 \quad = \alpha(-n(n+2)+(n+1)^2) = \alpha,$
$(n+1)\alpha_1 + n\beta_1 \quad = b((n+1)^2 - n(n+2)) \quad = b,$
$(n+1)a_1 - (n+2)b_1 = \beta((n+1)^2 - n(n+2)) \quad = \beta.$

(The fourth verification could have been omitted, since $a_1\alpha_1 + b_1\beta_1 = a\alpha + b\beta$.)

3) For odd v and w, we have

$$(v-1)(w-1) \equiv 0 \pmod 4,$$
$$v w \equiv v + w - 1 \pmod 4.$$

Hence we have

$$2 \equiv 2u \equiv a\alpha + b\beta \equiv (a+\alpha-1) + (b+\beta-1) \pmod 4,$$
$$a+b+\alpha+\beta \equiv 0 \pmod 4,$$
$$ab + a_1 b_1 \equiv (a+b-1) + (a_1+b_1-1) \equiv a+b+a_1+b_1+2$$
$$\equiv a+b+(2n+3)\alpha + (2n+1)\beta + 2$$
$$\equiv 2n(\alpha+\beta) + a + b + \alpha + \beta + 2\alpha + 2 \equiv 0 \pmod 4,$$
$$\chi(ab) = -\chi(a_1 b_1).$$

THEOREM 171: $Q(2u)=3Q(u)$.

Proof: In the equation

(100) $$2u=x_1{}^2+x_2{}^2+x_3{}^2+x_4{}^2$$

two of the x_k must be even and two odd, since every perfect square is $\equiv 0$ or 1 mod 4. The number of solutions in which x_1 and x_2 are even and x_3 and x_4 are odd is therefore $\dfrac{1}{6}\,Q(2u)$.

It then follows from (100), if we set

(101) $$y_1=\frac{x_1+x_2}{2},\, y_2=\frac{x_1-x_2}{2},\, y_3=\frac{x_3+x_4}{2},\, y_4=\frac{x_3-x_4}{2},$$

that y_1, y_2, y_3, and y_4 are integers and that

(102) $$u=y_1{}^2+y_2{}^2+y_3{}^2+y_4{}^2,\ y_1+y_2\equiv 0,\ y_3+y_4\equiv 1 \ (\text{mod } 2).$$

Conversely, it follows from (102), if $x_1,\dots,x_4$ are determined from (101), that is, if we set

(103) $$x_1=y_1+y_2,\ x_2=y_1-y_2,\ x_3=y_3+y_4,\ x_4=y_3-y_4,$$

that (100) holds, and that x_1 and x_2 are even, and x_3 and x_4 odd. $\dfrac{1}{6}\,Q(2u)$ is therefore the number of solutions of (102).

$Q(u)$ is the number of solutions of

(104) $$u=y_1{}^2+y_2{}^2+y_3{}^2+y_4{}^2.$$

Hence we have, as asserted, that

$$\frac{1}{6}Q(2u)=\frac{1}{2}Q(u).$$

For in (104) precisely one y_k is odd if $u\equiv 1 \ (\text{mod } 4)$; and this can be only y_3 or y_4 in (102) ; if $u\equiv 3 \ (\text{mod } 4)$, exactly one y_k is even; and this, too, can be only y_3 or y_4 in (102) ; thus (102) has half as many solutions as (104).

THEOREM 172: $Q(u)=8S(u)$,

$\qquad\qquad\qquad\quad Q(2^l u)=24S(u)$ *for* $l>0$.

Remark: This determines $Q(n)$ for $n>0$; to be specific, for odd n, $Q(n)$ must be 8 times the sum, and for even n, 24 times the sum of the odd positive divisors of n.

Proof: For $n>0$, we have

(105)
$$Q(2n)=Q(4n).$$

For

(106)
$$4n=x_1{}^2+x_2{}^2+x_3{}^2+x_4{}^2$$

yields

$$x_1\equiv x_2\equiv x_3\equiv x_4 \pmod 2,$$

so that

(107)
$$2n=y_1{}^2+y_2{}^2+y_3{}^2+y_4{}^2,$$

where the y_k are determined as integers by (101); conversely, (106) follows, from (107), when the x_k are determined by (103).

Furthermore, we have

(108)
$$Q(4u)=16S(u)+Q(u).$$

For in the equation

$$4u=x_1{}^2+x_2{}^2+x_3{}^2+x_4{}^2$$

either all of the x_k are even—this, $Q(u)$ times, since the equation is then equivalent to

$$u=z_1{}^2+z_2{}^2+z_3{}^2+z_4{}^2,\ z_k=\frac{x_k}{2},$$

or else they are all odd—this (because of the signs) $16A(u)=16S(u)$ times, by Theorem 170.

From Theorem 171, (105), and (108), it follows that

$$3Q(u)=Q(2u)=Q(4u)=16S(u)+Q(u),$$

(109)
$$Q(u)=8S(u),$$

and from (109) and Theorem 171 that

(110)
$$Q(2u)=24S(u).$$

For $l>0$, finally, it follows from (105) and (110) that

$$Q(2^l u)=Q(2u)=24S(u).$$

CHAPTER IV

DECOMPOSITION INTO THREE SQUARES

§1

Equivalence of Quadratic Forms

In this chapter I shall assume that the reader is acquainted to a certain extent with the theory of determinants and their applications. That portion of the theory of the so-called quadratic forms which I shall require, involves only two or three variables; it is more expeditious, however, to work it out once, for r variables, instead of twice, for two and for three variables. Consequently, let r be an arbitrary number ≥ 2.

DEFINITION 28: *If $x_1, \ldots, x_r$ are integral variables, and if the numbers a_{kl}, for $1 \leq k \leq l \leq r$, are integral coefficients, then*

$$F = F(x_1, \ldots, x_r) = a_{11}x_1^2 + 2a_{12}x_1x_2 + \cdots + 2a_{1r}x_1x_r + a_{22}x_2^2$$
$$+ 2a_{23}x_2x_3 + \cdots + a_{rr}x_r^2$$

is called a quadratic form—or here, for short, a form.

It is convenient to set

$$a_{kl} = a_{lk} \text{ for } 1 \leq l < k \leq r,$$

so that for $1 \leq k \leq r$ and $1 \leq l \leq r$, we always have

(111) $$a_{kl} = a_{lk} ;$$

then we may simply write

$$F = \sum_{k,l} a_{kl} x_k x_l ;$$

until, later in this section, we specifically set $r = 2$ and $r = 3$, the indices of summation always run from 1 to r.

DEFINITION 29: *The determinant $|a_{kl}|$ is called the discriminant of the form F.*

DEFINITION 30: *If*

$$F(x_1, \ldots, x_r) = \sum_{k,l} a_{kl} x_k x_l, \quad G(x_1, \ldots, x_r) = \sum_{k,l} b_{kl} x_k x_l$$

are forms, then we say that F is equivalent to G, written

$$F \sim G,$$

if there are r^2 integers c_{kl} of determinant

(112)
$$|c_{kl}| = \begin{vmatrix} c_{11} \cdots c_{1r} \\ \cdots \cdots \\ c_{r1} \cdots c_{rr} \end{vmatrix} = 1$$

for which the r equations

(113)
$$x_k = \sum_l c_{kl} y_l$$

formally transform $F(x_1, \ldots, x_r)$ into $G(y_1, \ldots, y_r)$.

That is, we should have identically

$$\sum_{m,n} b_{mn} y_m y_n = \sum_{k,l} a_{kl} \sum_m c_{km} y_m \sum_n c_{ln} y_n = \sum_{m,n} y_m y_n \sum_{k,l} c_{km} a_{kl} c_{ln};$$

since, by (111), $y_m y_n$ and $y_n y_m$ on the right have the same coefficients (because

$$\sum_{k,l} c_{km} a_{kl} c_{ln} = \sum_{k,l} c_{km} a_{lk} c_{ln} = \sum_{l,k} c_{lm} a_{kl} c_{kn} = \sum_{k,l} c_{kn} a_{kl} c_{lm}),$$

this is equivalent to the conditions

$$b_{mn} = \sum_{k,l} c_{km} a_{kl} c_{ln},$$

that is,

(114)
$$b_{kl} = \sum_{m,n} c_{mk} a_{mn} c_{nl}.$$

We say, for brevity: F goes into G under the transformation (c_{kl}).

The following three theorems are analogous to Theorems 45-47 on congruence; they justify the introduction of the concept of equivalence.

THEOREM 173 (Reflexivity): $F \sim F$.

Proof: The so-called identity transformation (of determinant 1)

$$e_{kl} = \begin{cases} 1 \text{ for } k = l, \\ 0 \text{ for } k \gtrless l, \end{cases}$$

that is, the equations

$$x_k = y_k$$

carry F into F.

THEOREM 174 (Symmetry): *If $F \sim G$, then $G \sim F$.*

Proof: By (112), the equations in (113) may be solved for the variables y_k, the solutions having integral coefficients:

$$y_k = \sum_l d_{kl} x_l;$$

and we have

$$|d_{kl}| = 1$$

since

$$y_k = \sum_m d_{km} x_m = \sum_m d_{km} \sum_l c_{ml} y_l = \sum_l y_l \sum_m d_{km} c_{ml},$$

$$\sum_m d_{km} c_{ml} = e_{kl},$$

$$1 = |e_{kl}| = |\sum_m d_{km} c_{ml}| = |d_{kl}||c_{kl}| = |d_{kl}|$$

(the theorem on the multiplication of determinants).

THEOREM 175 (Transitivity): *If $F \sim G$ and $G \sim H$, then $F \sim H$.*

Proof: Suppose F goes into G under (c_{kl}), and G into H under (j_{kl}), so that

$$|c_{kl}| = |j_{kl}| = 1.$$

From

$$x_k = \sum_l c_{kl} y_l, \quad y_k = \sum_l j_{kl} z_l$$

it follows that

$$x_k = \sum_l c_{kl} \sum_m j_{lm} z_m = \sum_m z_m \sum_l c_{kl} j_{lm}.$$

This represents an integral transformation carrying F into H; it has determinant

$$|\sum_m c_{km} j_{ml}| = |c_{kl}||j_{kl}| = 1 \cdot 1 = 1.$$

Theorems 173 to 175 show that the totality of forms fall into classes of equivalent forms.

In addition, we have:

THEOREM 176: *If $F \sim G$, then F and G have the same discriminant.*

All forms having equal discriminants thus fall into classes of equivalent forms.

Proof: By (114) we have

$$|b_{kl}| = |c_{kl}||a_{kl}||c_{kl}| = 1 \cdot |a_{kl}| \cdot 1 = |a_{kl}|.$$

THEOREM 177: *If $F \sim G$, then F and G represent the same numbers.*

Proof: From $G(y_1, \ldots, y_r) = c$, it follows that $F(x_1, \ldots, x_r) = c$ for the *eo ipso* integral x_k given by (113).

DEFINITION 31: *F is called positive definite—or here, for brevity, definite—if $F > 0$ for all integral values of $x_1, \ldots, x_r$ that do not all vanish simultaneously.*

If $F \sim G$, then it of course follows that if F is definite, so is G.

————

Now I shall consider, in somewhat more detail, both binary forms ($r = 2$) and ternary forms ($r = 3$). Their discriminants $|a_{kl}|$ will always be denoted by d. For greater convenience, I shall write the binary forms as $ax^2 + 2bxy + cy^2$, so that

$$d = \begin{vmatrix} a & b \\ b & c \end{vmatrix} = ac - b^2.$$

Such a form is abbreviated as $\{a, b, c\}$.

THEOREM 178: *$F = \{a, b, c\}$ is definite if and only if both $a > 0$ and $d > 0$.*

Proof: 1) If $a \leq 0$, then

$$F(1, 0) = a \leq 0,$$

so that F is not definite.

2) If $a > 0$ and $d \leq 0$, then

$$F(-b, a) = ab^2 - 2b^2 a + ca^2 = -ab^2 + ca^2 = a(ac - b^2) = ad \leq 0,$$

so that F is not definite.

3) If $a > 0$ and $d > 0$, then from

$$aF = a^2 x^2 + 2ab\,xy + ac\,y^2 = (ax + by)^2 + (ac - b^2)y^2 = (ax + by)^2 + d\,y^2,$$

it follows that $F \leq 0$ only when $x = y = 0$. Indeed, it follows from $F \leq 0$ that

$$ax + by = 0 \quad \text{and} \quad y = 0,$$

so that $x = 0$ as well. F is therefore definite.

THEOREM 179 : *Every class of definite binary forms contains at least one form for which*

$$2|b| \leqq a \leqq c.$$

Proof: Let us fix upon a form $\{a_0, b_0, c_0\}$ belonging to the class. Let a be the smallest positive number representable by it (and therefore by any form of the class). Then, for suitable r and t, we have

(115) $$a = a_0 r^2 + 2b_0 rt + c_0 t^2.$$

Here we have $(r, t) = 1$, for otherwise, if we set $(r, t) = v$, since $v^2 | a$, it would then follow that

$$\frac{a}{v^2} = a_0 \left(\frac{r}{v}\right)^2 + 2b_0 \frac{r}{v} \frac{t}{v} + c_0 \left(\frac{t}{v}\right)^2$$

is representable by the form.

Therefore, by Theorem 66, we may choose s and u in such a way that

$$\begin{vmatrix} r & s \\ t & u \end{vmatrix} = ru - st = 1 ;$$

by Theorem 68, the most general such pair, s and u are of the form

$$s = s_0 + hr, \quad u = u_0 + ht,$$

where h is arbitrary.

By (115), the transformation $\begin{pmatrix} r & s \\ t & u \end{pmatrix}$ takes $\{a_0, b_0, c_0\}$ into $\{a, b, c\}$, where the first coefficient is actually our a (by (114), or else by direct computation, or else more elegantly: $G(1, 0) = F(r \cdot 1 + s \cdot 0, t \cdot 1 + u \cdot 0) = F(r, t)$, where G is the new form and F is the old one) ; furthermore (by (114), or else by direct computation), we have

$$b = s(a_0 r + b_0 t) + u(b_0 r + c_0 t)$$
$$= s_0(a_0 r + b_0 t) + u_0(b_0 r + c_0 t) + h(r(a_0 r + b_0 t) + t(b_0 r + c_0 t));$$

consequently, since h has coefficient $a_0 r^2 + 2b_0 rt + c_0 t^2 = a$, b takes on all values in a certain residue class mod a; h can therefore be chosen in such a way that

$$|b| \leqq \frac{a}{2}$$

Since c can also be represented by the form $\{a, b, c\}$ (with $x = 0$ and $y = 1$), we have

$$a \leqq c,$$

so that everything is proved.

THEOREM 180: *In every class of definite binary forms there is at least one form for which*

$$2\,|\,b\,|\leq a\leq\frac{2}{\sqrt{3}}\,\sqrt{d}.$$

Proof: From the inequalities of Theorem 179 it follows that

$$a^2\leq ac=b^2+d\leq\frac{a^2}{4}+d,$$

$$\frac{3}{4}\,a^2\leq d,$$

$$2\,|\,b\,|\leq a\leq\frac{2}{\sqrt{3}}\,\sqrt{d}.$$

THEOREM 181: *Every definite binary form having discriminant 1 is equivalent to the form $x_1^2+x_2^2$.*

Proof: By Theorem 180, every such form is equivalent to a form for which

$$2\,|\,b\,|\leq a\leq\frac{2}{\sqrt{3}},$$

that is,

$$a=1,\ b=0,\ c=1.$$

___

Now for ternary forms!

THEOREM 182: $F=\sum\limits_{k,l=1}^{3} a_{kl}\,x_k\,x_l$ *is definite if and only if all of the following hold:*

$$a_{11}>0,\ b=\begin{vmatrix} a_{11} & a_{12} \\ a_{21} & a_{22} \end{vmatrix}>0,\ d>0.$$

If F is definite, then we have, further, that

(116) $$a_{11}F=(a_{11}\,x_1+a_{12}\,x_2+a_{13}\,x_3)^2+K(x_2,x_3),$$

where $K(x_2,x_3)$ is the definite binary form $\{a_{11}a_{22}-a_{12}{}^2,\ a_{11}a_{23}-a_{12}a_{13},\ a_{11}a_{33}-a_{13}{}^2\}$ with discriminant $a_{11}d$.

Proof (quite inelegant, in order to make it simple for the reader) : (116) holds, in any case, for

$$K(x_2, x_3)=(a_{11}a_{22}-a_{12}^2)x_2^2+2(a_{11}a_{23}-a_{12}a_{13})x_2x_3+(a_{11}a_{33}-a_{13}^2)x_3^2.$$

For

$$a_{11}F=a_{11}^2x_1^2+2a_{11}a_{12}x_1x_2+2a_{11}a_{13}x_1x_3+a_{11}a_{22}x_2^2+2a_{11}a_{23}x_2x_3$$
$$+a_{11}a_{33}x_3^2$$
$$=(a_{11}x_1+a_{12}x_2+a_{13}x_3)^2+(a_{11}a_{22}-a_{12}^2)x_2^2+2(a_{11}a_{23}-a_{12}a_{13})x_2x_3$$
$$+(a_{11}a_{33}-a_{13}^2)x_3^2$$

$$(116) \quad =(a_{11}x_1+a_{12}x_2+a_{13}x_3)^2+K(x_2, x_3).$$

$K(x_2, x_3)$ has discriminant

$$c=(a_{11}a_{22}-a_{12}^2)(a_{11}a_{33}-a_{13}^2)-(a_{11}a_{23}-a_{12}a_{13})^2$$
$$=a_{11}(a_{11}a_{22}a_{33}-a_{11}a_{23}^2+2a_{12}a_{13}a_{23}-a_{12}^2a_{33}-a_{13}^2a_{22})=a_{11}d.$$

1) If $a_{11}\leq0$, then $F(1,0,0)=a_{11}\leq0$, so that F is not definite.

2) If $a_{11}>0$, then clearly $F(x_1, x_2, x_3)$ is definite if and only if $K(x_2, x_3)$ is definite.   For if K is not definite, then $K(x_2, x_3)\leq0$ for some suitable x_2 and x_3 not both 0; and also, therefore, with the additional condition that x_2 and x_3 be divisible by a_{11} (a proportionality factor) ; then x_1 can be determined as an integer from

$$a_{11}x_1+a_{12}x_2+a_{13}x_3=0,$$

and for the resulting triple x_1, x_2, x_3, we have

$$a_{11}F(x_1, x_2, x_3)=0^2+K(x_2, x_3)\leq0,$$
$$F\leq0.$$

On the other hand, if K is definite, then from $F\leq0$ it follows, successively, that

$$K(x_2,x_3)\leq a_{11}F(x_1,x_2,x_3)\leq0, \quad x_2=x_3=0, \quad a_{11}x_1^2\leq0, \quad x_1=0.$$

By Theorem 178, applied to $K(x_2, x_3)$, it follows that in the case where $a_{11}>0$, F is definite if and only if both

$$b=a_{11}a_{22}-a_{12}^2>0, \quad c=a_{11}d>0,$$

that is, if and only if both

$$b>0 \quad \text{and} \quad d>0.$$

Theorem 183:   *If* $(c_{11}, c_{21}, c_{31}) = 1$, *then the six remaining numbers* c_{kl} *can be chosen in such a way that*

$$\lceil c_{kl} \rceil = 1.$$

Proof: Let us set $(c_{11}, c_{21}) = g$, so that $(g, c_{31}) = 1$. Then let us choose c_{12} and c_{22}, by Theorem 66, in such a way that

$$c_{11} c_{22} - c_{12} c_{21} = g;$$

furthermore, let us choose u and v, by Theorem 66, in such a way that

$$g u - c_{31} v = 1.$$

Then we have

$$\begin{vmatrix} c_{11} & c_{12} & \dfrac{c_{11}}{g} v \\[2mm] c_{21} & c_{22} & \dfrac{c_{21}}{g} v \\[2mm] c_{31} & 0 & u \end{vmatrix} = c_{31} \frac{c_{12} c_{21} - c_{11} c_{22}}{g} v + (c_{11} c_{22} - c_{12} c_{21}) u = -c_{31} v + g u = 1.$$

Theorem 184:   *Every class of definite ternary forms contains at least one form for which*

$$a_{11} \leq \frac{4}{3} \sqrt[3]{d}, \ \ 2\,|a_{12}| \leq a_{11}, \ \ 2\,|a_{13}| \leq a_{11}.$$

Proof: Let F be a fixed form belonging to the class. Let a_{11} be the smallest positive number that can be represented by F, and consequently by any form belonging to the class. Then, for suitable c_{11}, c_{21}, c_{31}, we have

$$a_{11} = F(c_{11}, c_{21}, c_{31}).$$

Here we have

$$(c_{11}, c_{21}, c_{31}) = 1,$$

since otherwise $\dfrac{a_{11}}{(c_{11}, c_{21}, c_{31})^2}$ would be representable.

Let $G = \Sigma b_{kl} x_k x_l$ be the form into which F is carried by the transformation (c_{kl}), of determinant 1, constructed in accordance with Theorem 183; then we have

$$b_{11} = G(1, 0, 0) = F(c_{11}, c_{21}, c_{31}) = a_{11}.$$

To G we apply a transformation

$$(d_{kl}) = \begin{pmatrix} 1 & r & s \\ 0 & t & u \\ 0 & v & w \end{pmatrix},$$

where $tw - uv = 1$; then, for arbitrary r and s, we have

$$|d_{kl}| = 1.$$

Now we shall take care of t, u, v, and w. Let G go into H under (d_{kl}). Then in H, the coefficient of $y_1{}^2$ equals $G(d_{11}, d_{21}, d_{31}) = G(1, 0, 0) = a_{11}$; let us set $H = \sum\limits_{k,l} a_{kl} y_k y_l$; then, by (114), we have

(117) $$a_{12} = \sum\limits_{m,n} d_{m1} b_{mn} d_{n2} = \sum\limits_{n} b_{1n} d_{n2} = r a_{11} + t b_{12} + v b_{13},$$

(118) $$a_{13} = \sum\limits_{m,n} d_{m1} b_{mn} d_{n3} = \sum\limits_{n} b_{1n} d_{n3} = s a_{11} + u b_{12} + w b_{13};$$

the transformation

(119) $$x_k = \sum\limits_{l} d_{kl} y_l$$

therefore yields

$$b_{11} x_1 + b_{12} x_2 + b_{13} x_3 = \sum\limits_{k} b_{1k} x_k = \sum\limits_{k} b_{1k} \sum\limits_{l} d_{kl} y_l = \sum\limits_{l} y_l \sum\limits_{k} b_{1k} d_{kl}$$

(120) $$= a_{11} y_1 + a_{12} y_2 + a_{13} y_3.$$

By Theorem 182, we have

$$a_{11} G(x_1, x_2, x_3) = (b_{11} x_1 + b_{12} x_2 + b_{13} x_3)^2 + K(x_2, x_3),$$

$$a_{11} H(y_1, y_2, y_3) = (a_{11} y_1 + a_{12} y_2 + a_{13} y_3)^2 + L(y_2, y_3),$$

where K and L are definite in their respective variables. Since (119) carries the form $G(x_1, x_2, x_3)$ into $H(y_1, y_2, y_3)$, and since (120) also holds, it follows that $K(x_2, x_3)$ is taken into $L(y_2, y_3)$ by the transformation $\begin{pmatrix} t & u \\ v & w \end{pmatrix}$. By Theorem 182, L has the discriminant $a_{11} d$, and its first coefficient is $a_{11} a_{22} - a_{12}{}^2$. Therefore, by Theorem 180, we may dispose of $\begin{pmatrix} t & u \\ v & w \end{pmatrix}$ by arranging matters so that

$$tw - uv = 1, \quad a_{11} a_{22} - a_{12}{}^2 \leq \frac{2}{\sqrt{3}} \sqrt{a_{11} d}.$$

Then, by (117) and (118), r and s can be chosen so that

$$|a_{12}| \leq \frac{a_{11}}{2}, \quad |a_{13}| \leq \frac{a_{11}}{2}.$$

We therefore obtain, since $a_{22} = H(0, 1, 0)$ is representable by H, and is therefore $\geq a_{11}$, that

$$a_{11}^2 \leq a_{11} a_{22} = (a_{11} a_{22} - a_{12}^2) + a_{12}^2 \leq \frac{2}{\sqrt{3}} \sqrt{a_{11} d} + \frac{a_{11}^2}{4},$$

$$a_{11}^2 \leq \frac{8}{3\sqrt{3}} \sqrt{a_{11} d},$$

$$a_{11}^{\frac{3}{2}} \leq \frac{8}{3\sqrt{3}} \sqrt{d},$$

$$a_{11} \leq \frac{4}{3} \sqrt[3]{d},$$

so that everything is proved.

THEOREM 185: *Every definite ternary form with discriminant 1 is equivalent to the form $x_1^2 + x_2^2 + x_3^2$.*

Consequently, every number representable by such a form can be written as a sum of three squares.

Proof: By Theorem 184, the given form is equivalent to a form in which

$$a_{11} \leq \frac{4}{3}, \quad 2|a_{12}| \leq a_{11}, \quad 2|a_{13}| \leq a_{11};$$

from this it follows that

$$a_{11} = 1, \quad a_{12} = 0, \quad a_{13} = 0.$$

The class therefore contains a form

$$G = x_1^2 + a_{22} x_2^2 + 2 a_{23} x_2 x_3 + a_{33} x_3^2,$$

where $K(x_2, x_3) = a_{22} x_2^2 + 2 a_{23} x_2 x_3 + a_{33} x_3^2$ is definite and has discriminant 1. By Theorem 181, $K(x_2, x_3)$ goes into $x_2^2 + x_3^2$ by a suitable transformation $\begin{pmatrix} t\, u \\ v\, w \end{pmatrix}$ of determinant 1; consequently $\begin{pmatrix} 1\ 0\ 0 \\ 0\ t\ u \\ 0\ v\ w \end{pmatrix}$ takes G into $x_1^2 + x_2^2 + x_3^2$.

§ 2

A Necessary Condition for Decomposability into Three Squares

THEOREM 186: *If* $n=x_1^2+x_2^2+x_3^2$, $n>0$, *then n is not of the form* $4^a(8b+7)$, $a\geqq0$, $b\geqq0$.

Proof: 1) $n=8b+7$ cannot be written as the sum of three squares, since every perfect square is $\equiv0$, 1, or 4 mod 8.

2) If the indecomposability of $4^a(8b+7)$ has already been proved for some $a\geqq0$, then it follows for $a+1$. For from

$$4^{a+1}(8b+7)=x_1^2+x_2^2+x_3^2$$

it would follow, because

$$x_1^2+x_2^2+x_3^2\equiv0 \pmod 4,$$

that x_1, x_2, and x_3 must be even. Consequently, we would have

$$4^a(8b+7)=\left(\frac{x_1}{2}\right)^2+\left(\frac{x_2}{2}\right)^2+\left(\frac{x_3}{2}\right)^2.$$

§3

The Necessary Condition is Sufficient

THEOREM 187 : *If $n > 0$ is not of the form $4^a(8b+7)$, $a \geqq 0$, $b \geqq 0$, then n can be written as a sum of three squares.*

Proof: Without loss of generality, we may assume n to be odd (but $\not\equiv 7$ (mod 8)) or else to be equal to twice an odd number. For from the decomposability of n, the same would follow for $4n$, and if we divide out 4 as many times as we can from the given number n, we obtain a number in one of the two forms indicated.

Consequently, let

$$n \equiv 1, 2, 3, 5, \text{ or } 6 \quad (\text{mod } 8).$$

By Theorem 185, it suffices to give, for n, a definite ternary form of discriminant 1 which represents n. By Theorem 182, we therefore have to specify nine numbers a_{11}, a_{12}, a_{13}, a_{22}, a_{23}, a_{33}, x_1, x_2, x_3 which satisfy the four conditions :

$$\begin{cases} n = a_{11}x_1{}^2 + 2a_{12}x_1x_2 + 2a_{13}x_1x_3 + a_{22}x_2{}^2 + 2a_{23}x_2x_3 + a_{33}x_3{}^2, \\ a_{11} > 0, \\ a_{11}a_{22} - a_{12}{}^2 > 0, \\ \begin{vmatrix} a_{11} & a_{12} & a_{13} \\ a_{12} & a_{22} & a_{23} \\ a_{13} & a_{23} & a_{33} \end{vmatrix} = 1. \end{cases}$$

It will even do to take

$$a_{13} = 1, \ a_{23} = 0, \ a_{33} = n, \ x_1 = 0, \ x_2 = 0, \ x_3 = 1.$$

The three remaining unknowns thus have to satisfy the three conditions (the first of the previous conditions is already taken care of) :

$$\begin{cases} a_{11} > 0, \\ b = a_{11}a_{22} - a_{12}{}^2 > 0, \\ a_{22} = bn - 1. \end{cases}$$

(In fact, we have

162

$$\begin{vmatrix} a_{11} & a_{12} & 1 \\ a_{12} & a_{22} & 0 \\ 1 & 0 & n \end{vmatrix} = (a_{11}a_{22} - a_{12}{}^2)\,n - a_{22} = bn - a_{22}.)$$

Here, taking $n > 1$ (which I may do, since $n = 1$ is trivial), $a_{11} > 0$ is a consequence of the other two conditions; for it follows from them that

$$a_{22} > b - 1 \geqq 0,$$
$$a_{11}a_{22} = a_{12}{}^2 + b > 0.$$

We must therefore have

$$\begin{cases} b = a_{11}a_{22} - a_{12}{}^2 > 0, \\ a_{22} = bn - 1. \end{cases}$$

Or, more simply (eliminating the three symbols a_{11}, a_{22}, a_{12}): We must have $b > 0$, and $-b$ must be a quadratic residue mod $bn - 1$.

1) Let

$$n \equiv 2 \text{ or } 6 \pmod 8.$$

Then I shall even show: There is a prime

(121) $$p = bn - 1$$

for which

$$\left(\frac{-b}{p}\right) = 1.$$

We have $(4n, n-1) = 1$. By Dirichlet's Theorem on Arithmetic Progressions, there is a prime

$$p = 4nv + n - 1 = (4v + 1)n - 1.$$

If we set $4v + 1 = b$, then we have $b > 0$, (121) is satisfied and, since $p \equiv 1 \pmod 4$, it follows from Theorems 95 and 92 that

$$\left(\frac{-b}{p}\right) = \left(\frac{p}{b}\right) = \left(\frac{bn-1}{b}\right) = \left(\frac{-1}{b}\right) = 1.$$

2) Let

$$n \equiv 1, 3, \text{ or } 5 \pmod 8.$$

I shall set $c = 1$ if $n \equiv 3 \pmod 8$, and $c = 3$ if $n \equiv 1$ or $5 \pmod 8$. Then, in any case, $\dfrac{cn-1}{2}$ is odd, so that $\left(4n, \dfrac{cn-1}{2}\right) = 1$. By Dirichlet's Theorem, it follows that there is a prime

$$p = 4nv + \frac{cn-1}{2} = \frac{1}{2}\left((8v+c)n-1\right).$$

If we set

$$8v + c = b,$$

then we have

$$b > 0, \quad 2p = bn - 1.$$

We have

$$b \equiv 3 \pmod 8 \text{ and } p \equiv 1 \pmod 4 \text{ for } n \equiv 1 \pmod 8,$$
$$b \equiv 1 \pmod 8 \text{ and } p \equiv 1 \pmod 4 \text{ for } n \equiv 3 \pmod 8,$$
$$b \equiv 3 \pmod 8 \text{ and } p \equiv 3 \pmod 4 \text{ for } n \equiv 5 \pmod 8.$$

In any case, therefore,

$$\left(\frac{-2}{b}\right) = 1,$$

and consequently, by Theorem 95,

$$\left(\frac{-b}{p}\right) = (-1)^{\frac{-b-1}{2}\frac{p-1}{2}}\left(\frac{p}{b}\right) = \left(\frac{p}{b}\right) = \left(\frac{p}{b}\right)\left(\frac{-2}{b}\right) = \left(\frac{-2p}{b}\right) = \left(\frac{1-bn}{b}\right)$$
$$= \left(\frac{1}{b}\right) = 1,$$

so that $-b$ is a quadratic residue mod p. Since $-b \equiv 1^2 \pmod 2$, it follows that $-b$ is a quadratic residue mod $2p$, that is, mod $bn-1$.

From Theorem 187 we obtain an additional proof of Lagrange's Theorem, Theorem 169. By Theorem 187, any positive $n \equiv 1$ or $2 \pmod 4$ can be written as a sum of three squares; and consequently any positive $n \equiv 3 \pmod 4$ as a sum of four squares, by virtue of $n = (n-1)+1^2$. Every positive $n \equiv 0 \pmod 4$ is, however, of the form $4^a(4b+r)$, $r = 1, 2, 3$ and therefore, since $4^a = (2^a)^2$, can be written as a sum of four squares.

PART FOUR

CLASS NUMBER OF BINARY QUADRATIC FORMS

INTRODUCTION

In this part I shall analyze the binary forms of the form $ax^2+bxy+cy^2$. (In the foregoing, because of the analogy with the case of r, rather than 2, variables, it was more convenient to take the middle coefficient to be even.) Here, the number $d=b^2-4ac$ is what will be called the discriminant. (This is customary with binary forms; one should not be misled by the fact that for b even, the number $ac-\dfrac{b^2}{4}=-\dfrac{d}{4}$ was called the discriminant in the preceding part.) Even though our first investigation of equivalence can be carried over to the present part, I should nevertheless like to begin here anew and develop the various details afresh in order that Part Four be readable independently of Part Three.

In Chapter I, I shall begin with somewhat trivial considerations, which will show that only the case in which d is not a perfect square is of interest; in the other case, the form splits into the product of two linear forms. Moreover, we of course have $d\equiv b^2-4ac\equiv0$ or 1 (mod 4). Henceforth we shall always take d to be an arbitrary non-square number $\equiv0$ or 1 (mod 4); then there will certainly be a form belonging to it, namely $\boldsymbol{x^2-\dfrac{d}{4}\,y^2}$ if d is even and $\boldsymbol{x^2+xy-\dfrac{d-1}{4}\,y^2}$ if d is odd.

In Chapters II and III it will turn out that the number of classes into which the forms of discriminant d fall is finite; the determination of this number will immediately reduce to the problem of determining the number of so-called primitive classes, that is, the classes containing a form for which $(a,b,c)=1$ (or, equivalently, in which all the forms have this property); for $d<0$, the only case necessary will be that in which $a>0$ (for one, and therefore for every form of the class).

The determination of the number $h(d)$ of these primitive classes is the task of this fourth part. Here we must interject a few words on the meaning— or, rather, the lack of meaning—of this investigation. The moment the finiteness of the class number has been established, we will have the means at our disposal to calculate $h(d)$ for all d—for $d<0$, I shall actually carry this out, and for $d>0$, I shall not, as being too lengthy and, besides, unnecessary for my purposes; so we shall indicate, using a goodly number of brackets and symbols such as $T(a)$, how to express it explicitly by means of a formula.

If we did not know better, the problem of determining the class number would then already seem to be solved. But we can accomplish still more (unfortunately, or fortunately, depending on one's point of view; I, personally, am happy about it, for the theory in this fourth part, for which we have Gauss and Dirichlet to thank, is one of the most beautiful in all of mathematics); namely, we can find certain simple expressions for $h(d)$. This will come much later on.

Here I would like to tell, but only in anticipation of what will be done later on, how the class number is most easily shown to be finite in the first place, how, in the case $d<0$, the class number is first "determined," and how the final formula for it reads in the case $d=-p$, where $p>3$.

The proof of finiteness is obtained by singling out a certain finite number of forms—let us, for the moment, call them reduced—and showing that each class contains at least one of these forms (and then, the pigeon-hole principle!). A (primitive or imprimitive) form is called reduced if

$$|b|\leqq|a|\leqq|c|.$$

It is easily shown that for any d there is only a finite number of such forms. Consequently the class number, and therefore in particular our $h(d)$, is finite.

In particular, we shall show that in the case $d<0$ every class of forms having $a>0$ contains one and only one form for which

(122) $$-a<b\leqq a<c \quad \text{or} \quad 0\leqq b\leqq a=c.$$

This "determines" the number of classes, and in particular it determines $h(d)$, if of these forms we consider only the primitive ones.

On the other hand, however, our lengthy main procedure will lead to the following final result for $h(d)$, in the special case where $d=-p<-3$:

(123) $$h = \begin{cases} \sum\limits_{r=1}^{\frac{p-1}{2}} \left(\dfrac{r}{p}\right) & \text{for } p\equiv7 \text{ (mod 8)}, \\ \dfrac{1}{3}\sum\limits_{r=1}^{\frac{p-1}{2}} \left(\dfrac{r}{p}\right) & \text{for } p\equiv3 \text{ (mod 8)}; \end{cases}$$

thus h is the excess of the number of quadratic residues mod p between 0 and $\dfrac{p}{2}$ over the number of quadratic non-residues in that interval, or else one third of this excess.

Now I shall submit to the reader two problems of very elementary number theory that I cannot succeed in solving by taking a direct route, although the powerful analytic detours of Part Four of this book will implicitly yield a solution.

First: From (123) it follows, since $h>0$, that for every prime $p\equiv3$ (mod 4) there are more quadratic residues mod p between 0 and $\frac{p}{2}$ than between $\frac{p}{2}$ and p; for there are indeed as many non-residues between 0 and $\frac{p}{2}$ as there are residues between $\frac{p}{2}$ and p, since $\left(\frac{p-r}{p}\right)=-\left(\frac{r}{p}\right)$ for $p\nmid r$. (For $p\equiv1$ (mod 4), on the other hand, there are equally many quadratic residues in both halves of the interval $0<r<p$, since $\left(\frac{p-r}{p}\right)=\left(\frac{r}{p}\right)$ for $p\nmid r$.

But no one has yet been able, using elementary methods, to prove this fact which, with the help of Theorem 79, can be expressed as follows:

For $p\equiv3$ (mod 4), more of the numbers $1^2, 2^2, \ldots, \left(\frac{p-1}{2}\right)^2$ have remainders mod p less than $\frac{p}{2}$ than have remainders mod p greater than $\frac{p}{2}$.

Second: For $p\equiv3$ (mod 4) and $p>3$, it follows from what has been said (since obviously there are only primitive forms here) that the right-hand side of (123) equals the number of solutions of $b^2-4ac=-p$ satisfying the additional condition (122).

But no one has yet succeeded in proving this fact by use of elementary methods; and yet it is a statement that has nothing to do with either class numbers or quadratic forms.

Naturally, the second statement contains the first.

In Chapters IV and V, our longer route will next reduce the determination of $h(d)$ to the problem of finding the sum of the series

$$\sum_{n=1}^{\infty}\left(\frac{d}{n}\right)\frac{1}{n};$$

this is where the theorems of Part One, Chapter VI on the Kronecker symbol, and of Part One, Chapter VII, on Pell's equation, will find application.

Our main difficulties (involving the apparently trivial question of a sign) will then begin, and our most important tool in overcoming these difficulties will be the so-called theory of Gaussian sums, which will be introduced in Chapter VI.

Chapters VII-IX will then quickly bring us to our goal.

CHAPTER I

FACTORABLE AND UNFACTORABLE FORMS

DEFINITION 32: *If a, b, and c are constants, then*

$$F = F(x, y) = a x^2 + b x y + c y^2$$

is called a binary quadratic form, or here, for brevity, a form. It is written: $F = \{a, b, c\}$. *The discriminant of the form is the number* $d = b^2 - 4ac$.

We always have

$$d \equiv 0 \text{ or } 1 \pmod 4,$$

and there is a form for every such d, and even one with $a > 0$, namely, $\left\{ 1, 0, -\dfrac{d}{4} \right\}$ and $\left\{ 1, 1, -\dfrac{d-1}{4} \right\}$, respectively.

We always have

$$4aF = 4a^2x^2 + 4abxy + 4acy^2 = (2ax + by)^2 + (4ac - b^2)y^2$$
$$(124) \qquad\qquad = (2ax + by)^2 - dy^2.$$

THEOREM 188: *If there exists a factorization*

$$(125) \qquad\qquad F = (\varrho x + \sigma y)(\tau x + v y)$$

where ϱ, σ, τ, and v are rational, then there exists a factorization

$$(126) \qquad\qquad F = (r x + s y)(t x + u y)$$

(where r, s, t, and u are integers).

(This statement sounds quite harmless; at the bottom of it, however, lies a deep theorem of Gauss, which appears in Part Nine of *Vorlesungen über Zahlentheorie.*)

Proof: There follows from (125) an equation

$$(127) \qquad\qquad mF = (r x + s y)(t x + u y)$$

in which $m > 0$. Consequently there is an equation of the type (127) in which $m > 0$ and $(m, r, s) = 1$, since otherwise we would merely have to replace m, r, s by the numbers $\dfrac{m}{(m, r, s)}$, $\dfrac{r}{(m, r, s)}$, and $\dfrac{s}{(m, r, s)}$. For the same reason, we may also assume that $(m, t, u) = 1$.

170

From (127), with $m>0$, $(m, r, s)=1$, and $(m, t, u)=1$, however, it follows that $m=1$, in other words (126). For otherwise there would be a prime $p|m$. From

$$ma=rt, \quad mb=ru+st, \quad mc=su$$

it would then follow that

$$p|rt, \quad p|ru+st, \quad p|su;$$

from $p|rt$ it would follow that $p|r$ or $p|t$; without loss of generality (symmetry!) let $p|r$; then we would have $p|st$; from $(m, r, s)=1$ it would follow that $p \nmid s$, so that $p|t$; from $(m, t, u)=1$ it would therefore follow that $p \nmid u$. But $p \nmid s$, $p \nmid u$, and $p|su$ yield a contradiction.

THEOREM 189: *There exists a factorization of the form* (126) *if and only if d is a perfect square.*

Proof: 1) From (126) it follows that

$$a=rt, \quad b=ru+st, \quad c=su,$$
$$d=b^2-4ac=(ru+st)^2-4rstu=(ru-st)^2.$$

2) Let $d=k^2$. Then it follows from (124) that

$$4aF=(2ax+by)^2-k^2y^2=(2ax+(b+k)y)(2ax+(b-k)y).$$

21) If $a \neq 0$, then it follows from this that there exists a factorization of the form (125), and therefore, by Theorem 188, one of the form (126).

22) If $a=0$, then we have at once

$$F=y(bx+cy).$$

CHAPTER II

CLASSES OF FORMS

From now on, throughout the rest of this book, let

d be non-square, and $\equiv 0$ or 1 (mod 4).

Consequently, for every form F having discriminant d, we certainly have $a \neq 0$ and $c \neq 0$.

THEOREM 190: *If $d > 0$, then for suitable x and y, F represents both positive and negative numbers; if $d < 0$ and $a > 0$, then F represents no negative numbers, and represents 0 only for $x = y = 0$; if $d < 0$ and $a < 0$, then F represents no positive numbers, and represents 0 only for $x = y = 0$.*

Hence forms for which $d > 0$ are called indefinite; and those for which $d < 0$ are called definite or—more precisely—positive definite and negative definite, as the case may be.

Geometrically: If $d > 0$ and $k \gtrless 0$, then $F = k$ is a hyperbola (if x and y are construed as any real (not necessarily integral) coordinates); if $d > 0$, then $F = 0$ is a pair of straight lines, namely the pair of asymptotes belonging to all hyperbolas $F = k$ for $k \gtrless 0$; if $d < 0$, then $F = k$ is an ellipse when $ka > 0$, a so-called imaginary pair of lines when $k = 0$, and a so-called imaginary ellipse when $ka < 0$.

Proof: 1) Let $d > 0$. Then we have

$$F(1,0) = a, \quad F(b, -2a) = ab^2 - b \cdot 2ba + c \cdot 4a^2 = a(4ac - b^2) = -da;$$

of these two numbers, certainly one is > 0 and the other is < 0.

2) Let $d < 0$; from (124) it follows that, except when $x = y = 0$, we always have

$$aF > 0,$$

that is, F has the same sign as a; indeed it follows from $aF \leq 0$ that

$$2ax + by = 0, \quad y = 0,$$

and finally that

$$x = 0.$$

172

Since the negative-definite forms, when multiplied by —1, are transformed into positive-definite ones with the same discriminant, and vice versa, we shall only consider positive-definite forms in the case $d<0$.

DEFINITION 33: *$F=\{a, b, c\}$ is said to be equivalent to $G=\{a_1, b_1, c_1\}$, written*

$$F \sim G,$$

if there exist four integers, r, s, t, and u, for which $ru-st=1$, such that the equations

(128) $$x=rX+sY, \quad y=tX+uY$$

formally transform $F(x, y)$ into $G(X, Y)$. We also say: F goes into G under the transformation $\begin{pmatrix} r & s \\ t & u \end{pmatrix}$.

THEOREM 191: *If F has discriminant d, then G also has discriminant d; moreover, if $d<0$ and $a>0$, then we also have $a_1>0$.*

That is, if F is one of our allowable forms, then so is G.

Proof: $$a(rX+sY)^2+b(rX+sY)(tX+uY)+c(tX+uY)^2$$
$$=a_1X^2+b_1XY+c_1Y^2,$$

(129) $$a_1=ar^2+brt+ct^2,$$

(130) $$b_1=2ars+b(ru+st)+2ctu(=2ars+b(1+2st)+2ctu),$$

(131) $$c_1=as^2+bsu+cu^2,$$
$$b_1{}^2-4a_1c_1=(2ars+b(ru+st)+2ctu)^2-4(ar^2+brt+ct^2)(as^2+bsu+cu^2)$$
$$=a^2(4r^2s^2-4r^2s^2)+b^2(r^2u^2+2rstu+s^2t^2-4rstu)+c^2(4t^2u^2-4t^2u^2)$$
$$+4ab(r^2su+rs^2t-r^2su-rs^2t)+4ac(2rstu-r^2u^2-s^2t^2)$$
$$+4bc(rtu^2+st^2u-rtu^2-st^2u)=(b^2-4ac)(ru-st)^2=b^2-4ac=d.$$

(In proving the corresponding statement in Theorem 176, I reasoned somewhat more elegantly.)

Moreover, in case $d<0$ and $a>0$, we may let F represent a_1 by choosing $x=r$ and $y=t$; consequently $a_1>0$, since $r=t=0$ is not possible because of the relation $ru-st=1$.

THEOREMS 192-194: *Reflexivity, symmetry, and transitivity of equivalence.*

Proof: 192) $F \sim F$; for F goes into F by $\begin{pmatrix} 1 & 0 \\ 0 & 1 \end{pmatrix}$, and we have $\begin{vmatrix} 1 & 0 \\ 0 & 1 \end{vmatrix}=1$.

193) From $F \sim G$ it follows that $G \sim F$; for the solution of (128) for X, Y yields (since $ru - st = 1$)

$$X = ux - sy, \quad Y = -tx + ry$$

and we have

$$\begin{vmatrix} u & -s \\ -t & r \end{vmatrix} = ru - st = 1.$$

194) From $F \sim G$ and $G \sim H$ it follows that $F \sim H$. For from (128), $ru - st = 1$, and

$$X = r_1 x' + s_1 y', \quad Y = t_1 x' + u_1 y', \quad r_1 u_1 - s_1 t_1 = 1,$$

it follows that

$$x = r(r_1 x' + s_1 y') + s(t_1 x' + u_1 y') = (rr_1 + st_1) x' + (rs_1 + su_1) y',$$
$$y = t(r_1 x' + s_1 y') + u(t_1 x' + u_1 y') = (tr_1 + ut_1) x' + (ts_1 + uu_1) y',$$

and we have

$$\begin{vmatrix} rr_1 + st_1 & rs_1 + su_1 \\ tr_1 + ut_1 & ts_1 + uu_1 \end{vmatrix} = \begin{vmatrix} r & s \\ t & u \end{vmatrix} \begin{vmatrix} r_1 & s_1 \\ t_1 & u_1 \end{vmatrix} = 1 \cdot 1 = 1.$$

The totality of forms with discriminant d (where, if $d < 0$, we consider only the positive-definite ones) therefore fall into classes of equivalent forms.

Theorem 195: *Equivalent forms represent the same numbers.*

Proof: By (128), it follows from $k = G(X, Y)$ that

$$k = F(rX + sY, tX + uY).$$

CHAPTER III

THE FINITENESS OF THE CLASS NUMBER

Even though the finiteness of the class number will once again come out of what we do later on, we should like nonetheless to prove it beforehand as quickly as possible; in particular, for the case $d < 0$, we establish a deeper result mentioned in the Introduction (the "determinability" of the class number right off the bat).

THEOREM 196: *Every class contains a form for which*

(132)
$$|b| \leq |a| \leq |c|.$$

Proof: Let a form $\{a_0, b_0, c_0\}$ belonging to the class be fixed. Let a be the number smallest in absolute value other than 0, which is representable by $\{a_0, b_0, c_0\}$, or else one of the two such numbers having the smallest absolute value > 0. Then we have

$$a = a_0 r^2 + b_0 r t + c_0 t^2$$

for suitable r and t. We certainly have $(r, t) = 1$, for otherwise $\dfrac{a}{(r,t)^2}$ would already be representable and smaller in absolute value than a. We can therefore find numbers s and u such that

$$r u - s t = 1.$$

By (129), $\begin{pmatrix} r & s \\ t & u \end{pmatrix}$ takes $\{a_0, b_0, c_0\}$ into $\{a, b', c'\}$. The transformation $\begin{pmatrix} 1 & h \\ 0 & 1 \end{pmatrix}$ of determinant 1 (in which h is, for the moment, arbitrary) takes $\{a, b', c'\}$ into $\{a, b, c\}$ by (129) and (130), where

$$b = 2ah + b'.$$

For suitable h it follows from this that

$$|b| \leq |a|.$$

175

Since $c \neq 0$ and since it can be represented by $\{a, b, c\}$ (by setting $x=0$ and $y=1$), it follows from Theorem 195, because of the minimality of $|a|$, that

$$|a| \leq |c|.$$

Theorem 197: *The class number is finite.*

Proof: 1) For $d>0$ it follows from (132) that

$$|ac| \geq b^2 = d + 4ac > 4ac.$$

Hence we have

$$ac < 0,$$
$$4a^2 \leq 4|ac| = -4ac = d - b^2 \leq d,$$
$$|a| \leq \frac{\sqrt{d}}{2},$$
$$|b| \leq |a| \leq \frac{\sqrt{d}}{2}.$$

a and b thus have only a finite set of possible values, and therefore so does c.

2) For $d<0$ it follows from (132), since $a>0$ and $c>0$, that
$$|b| \leq a \leq c,$$
$$4a^2 \leq 4ac = -d + b^2 \leq |d| + a^2,$$
$$|b| \leq a \leq \sqrt{\frac{|d|}{3}},$$

so that c, too, has only a finite number of possible values.

Theorem 198: *For $d<0$, the number of* (positive-definite) *classes of forms equals the number of solutions of*

(133) $\qquad b^2 - 4ac = d, \begin{cases} -a < b \leq a < c \\ or \quad 0 \leq b \leq a = c. \end{cases}$

Proof: We have merely to show that each class contains exactly one such form.

1) By Theorem 196, each class contains at least one form for which

$$-a \leq b \leq a \leq c.$$

In order to remove the extra forms, those for which $b = -a$ and $a<c$, or $-a \leq b < 0$ and $a=c$, it suffices to show that

$$\{a, -a, c\} \sim \{a, a, c\}$$

and

$$\{a, -b, a\} \sim \{a, b, a\}.$$

The former follows from the fact that $\begin{pmatrix} 1 & 1 \\ 0 & 1 \end{pmatrix}$ takes $\{a, -a, c\}$ into the form $a(X+Y)^2 - a(X+Y)Y + cY^2 = aX^2 + aXY + cY^2$. (Moreover, we even could have chosen the number b to lie in the interval $-|a| < b \leq |a|$ in the proof of Theorem 196.)

The latter follows from the fact that the transformation $\begin{pmatrix} 0 & 1 \\ -1 & 0 \end{pmatrix}$ of determinant 1 takes the form $\{a, -b, a\}$ into

$$a Y^2 + b YX + a X^2 = a X^2 + b XY + a Y^2.$$

2) The proof of the fact that every class contains at most one form of type (133) is not so simple. If $\{a, b, c\}$ and $\{a', b', c'\}$ are two such forms, we have to show that $a = a'$, $b = b'$, and $c = c'$.

Without loss of generality, let $a' \leq a$. Let the transformation $\begin{pmatrix} r & s \\ t & u \end{pmatrix}$ for which $ru - st = 1$ take $\{a, b, c\}$ into $\{a', b', c'\}$. Then, by (129) and (130), we have

(134) $$a' = a r^2 + b r t + c t^2,$$

(135) $$b' = 2 a r s + b (r u + s t) + 2 c t u.$$

By (134), we have

(136) $$a' \geq a r^2 - a |rt| + a t^2,$$

so that (since $r^2 + t^2 \geq 2|rt|$)

$$a \geq a' \geq a |rt|,$$

and therefore

(137) $$1 \geq |rt|.$$

Now we have $a = a'$; for otherwise we would have $rt = 0$, and it would follow (since r and t do not both vanish) that

$$a > a' = a r^2 + c t^2 \geq a r^2 + a t^2 \geq a.$$

Now let $c > a$ or $c' > a'$, and therefore (since $a = a'$), by symmetry, $c > a$. Then we have $t = 0$; for otherwise (since $ct^2 > at^2$) the sign $>$ would hold in (136), and therefore also in (137); and we would have $rt = 0$, $r = 0$, and

$$a = c t^2 \geq c.$$

In the case $c > a$ we therefore have $t = 0$ and $ru = 1$, so that, by (135),

$$b' \equiv b \pmod{2a};$$

since

and
$$-a<b\leqq a$$
$$-a=-a'<b'\leqq a'=a,$$

it follows that
$$b=b',$$

and, finally, that
$$c=c'.$$

In the case $c=a$ and $c'=a'$, however, we have
$$c=c', \ a=a',$$
$$b=\pm b',$$

and, since
$$b\geqq 0, \ b'\geqq 0,$$

we therefore also have
$$b=b'.$$

DEFINITION 34: $F=\{a, b, c\}$ is called primitive if $(a, b, c)=1$; otherwise it is called imprimitive.

THEOREM 199: If $F\sim G$, then if F is primitive so is G, and if F is imprimitive so is G.

Proof: From (129), (130), and (131), it follows that $(a, b, c)|$ (a_1, b_1, c_1); by symmetry we also have $(a_1, b_1, c_1)|(a, b, c)$, so that $(a, b, c)=(a_1, b_1, c_1)$.

––––––

The totality of classes of forms thus fall into classes of primitive forms and classes of imprimitive forms—for brevity, primitive and imprimitive classes.

THEOREM 200: If F is imprimitive, so that $(a, b, c)=g>1$, then $g^2|d$, and $\left\{\dfrac{a}{g}, \dfrac{b}{g}, \dfrac{c}{g}\right\}$ is a primitive form of discriminant $\dfrac{d}{g^2}$. And conversely. $\left(\dfrac{a}{g}$ is necessarily >0 if $a>0$; and conversely.$\right)$

Proof: $\left(\dfrac{b}{g}\right)^2-4\dfrac{a}{g}\dfrac{c}{g}=\dfrac{b^2-4ac}{g^2}.$

We thus obtain all of the classes having discriminant d from all of the primitive classes having discriminants of the form $\dfrac{d}{g^2}$, where $g>0$ and $g^2|d$, by multiplying each class by g. Thus, if we had not yet proved the finiteness of the class number, it would nevertheless follow from the fact that, in the sequel, the finiteness of the number $h(d)$ of primitive classes will be proved once again. The number of (primitive and imprimitive) classes for any d is exactly

$$\sum_{\substack{g^2|d \\ g>0}} h\left(\frac{d}{g^2}\right).$$

In any case it suffices, from now on, to consider only primitive forms. Consequently, we shall henceforth take

$$d \text{ non-square and} \equiv 0 \text{ or } 1 \pmod 4,$$

$$b^2-4ac=d, \quad (a, b, c)=1,$$

in case $d<0$; we shall, in addition, take $a>0$.

CHAPTER IV

PRIMARY REPRESENTATIONS BY FORMS

DEFINITION 35: *Let $k \neq 0$. Then*

$$F(x, y) = k$$

is said to be a proper representation of k by the form F if $(x, y) = 1$; an improper representation if $(x, y) > 1$.

THEOREM 201: *Let $k > 0$, and let $F(x, y) = k$ be a proper representation. Then r, s, and l may be chosen in exactly one way so that*

(138) $$\begin{vmatrix} x & r \\ y & s \end{vmatrix} = 1,$$

(139) $$l^2 \equiv d \pmod{4k}, \quad 0 \leq l < 2k,$$

and so that F goes into $\{k, l, m\}$ by the transformation $\begin{pmatrix} x & r \\ y & s \end{pmatrix}$, where m is the number which, in accordance with (139), is determined by

$$l^2 - 4km = d.$$

(We already know, by virtue of (129) and Theorem 191, that the first coefficient of the new form is independent of the choice of r and s satisfying (138), and that the second coefficient, namely l, satisfies the congruence in (139). The theorem therefore is that for exactly one choice of r and s satisfying (138) will the second coefficient belong to the interval $0 \leq l < 2k$. The point is that with each proper representation of k there is associated a well-determined number l belonging to the interval $0 \leq l < 2k$.)

Proof: By Theorem 68, all the solutions of (138) are of the form

$$r = r_0 + hx, \quad s = s_0 + hy,$$

where r_0, s_0 is any solution and h is arbitrary.

Let $F = \{a, b, c\}$; if $\{k, l, m\}$ represents the new form, then it follows from (130) that

$$l = 2axr + b(xs + yr) + 2cys$$
$$= 2axr_0 + b(xs_0 + yr_0) + 2cys_0 + h(2ax^2 + bxy + byx + 2cy^2) = l_0 + 2hk;$$

hence for exactly one h we have $0 \leq l < 2k$; from $l^2 - 4km = d$ it follows, finally, that

$$l^2 \equiv d \pmod{4k}.$$

180

A transformation may take F into F; $\begin{pmatrix} 1 & 0 \\ 0 & 1 \end{pmatrix}$ and $\begin{pmatrix} -1 & 0 \\ 0 & -1 \end{pmatrix}$, for example, certainly do this. The solution to the problem of finding all such transformations is given by

THEOREM 202: *All transformations of $F=\{a, b\ c\}$ into itself are given by the formula*

$$(140) \qquad \begin{pmatrix} \dfrac{t-bu}{2}, & -cu \\[2ex] au\ , & \dfrac{t+bu}{2} \end{pmatrix}$$

where t, u is an arbitrary solution of Pell's Equation,

$$(141) \qquad\qquad t^2-du^2=4.$$

Remarks: 1) $\dfrac{t+bu}{2}$ and $\dfrac{t-bu}{2}$ are clearly integers. For (since $b\equiv d$ (mod 2)) we have, by (141),

$$t\pm bu\equiv t+du\equiv t^2-du^2\equiv 4\equiv 0 \ (\text{mod } 2).$$

2) The determinant of the transformation (140) is clearly 1; for by (141) we have

$$\frac{t-bu}{2}\frac{t+bu}{2}+acu^2=\frac{t^2-b^2u^2}{4}+acu^2=\frac{t^2-(b^2-4ac)u^2}{4}=\frac{t^2-du^2}{4}=1.$$

3) The trivial solutions $t=\pm 2$, $u=0$ of equation (141) (we know that no others exist for $d<-4$) yield the above-mentioned transformations $\begin{pmatrix} 1 & 0 \\ 0 & 1 \end{pmatrix}$ and $\begin{pmatrix} -1 & 0 \\ 0 & -1 \end{pmatrix}$.

Proof: 1) In order to show that (140) takes F into itself, it suffices to show that the first two coefficients are left unaltered. Indeed, by (129) and (130), the first two new coefficients are

$$a_1=a\left(\frac{t-bu}{2}\right)^2+b\frac{t-bu}{2}au+ca^2u^2$$

$$=a\frac{t^2}{4}-ab\frac{tu}{2}+ab^2\frac{u^2}{4}+ab\frac{tu}{2}-ab^2\frac{u^2}{2}+a^2cu^2=\frac{a}{4}(t^2-(b^2-4ac)u^2)=a,$$

$$b_1=-2a\frac{t-bu}{2}cu+b(1-2acu^2)+2cau\frac{t+bu}{2}$$

$$=-actu+abcu^2+b-2abcu^2+actu+abcu^2=b.$$

2) In order to show that every transformation $\begin{pmatrix} r & s \\ m & n \end{pmatrix}$ (satisfying $rn-sm=1$) which takes F into F is of the form (140), I begin by observing that, by virtue of (129) and (130),

$$
(142) \qquad
\begin{aligned}
a &= ar^2 + brm + cm^2, \\
b &= 2ars + b(1+2sm) + 2cmn ;
\end{aligned}
$$

hence we have

$$
(143) \qquad 0 = ars + bsm + cmn.
$$

From (142) and (143) we now eliminate b, on the one hand, and c, on the other. This gives, on the one hand,

$$
(144) \qquad as = csm^2 - crmn = cm(sm - rn) = -cm,
$$

and on the other hand,

$$
(145) \qquad
\begin{aligned}
an &= ar^2n + brmn - arsm - bsm^2 = ar + bm, \\
a(n-r) &= bm.
\end{aligned}
$$

From (144) and (145) it follows that

$$
a/cm, \; a/bm;
$$

since $(a, b, c) = 1$ (we now—finally—make use of the assumption of primitivity), it follows that

$$
a/m,
$$
$$
m = au.
$$

We therefore have, from (144) and (145), that

$$
s = -cu, \; n-r = bu.
$$

Furthermore, it follows that

$$
(n+r)^2 = (n-r)^2 + 4nr = b^2u^2 + 4(1+sm) = b^2u^2 + 4(1-acu^2) = du^2 + 4,
$$

and therefore, if we set

$$
n+r = t,
$$

that

$$
(141) \qquad t^2 - du^2 = 4,
$$
$$
r = \frac{t-bu}{2}, \; n = \frac{t+bu}{2}.
$$

Definition 36: *A representation of $k>0$ by $F=\{a, b, c\}$, where $a>0$, is called primary:*

if $d<0$, in every case;
if $d>0$, provided that

(146) $$2ax+(b-\sqrt{d})y>0, \quad 1\leq\frac{2ax+(b+\sqrt{d})y}{2ax+(b-\sqrt{d})y}<\varepsilon^2,$$

where ε is defined as in Theorem 111.

$\Big($Namely

$$\varepsilon=\frac{t_0+u_0\sqrt{d}}{2},$$

where t_0, u_0 is the smallest positive solution of (141); we had $\varepsilon>1$, and all the solutions of (141) were given by

$$\frac{t+u\sqrt{d}}{2}=\pm\varepsilon^n.\Big)$$

To orient the reader: 1) If we set

$$2ax+(b+\sqrt{d})y=L, \quad 2ax+(b-\sqrt{d})y=\bar{L}$$

(the bar has nothing to do with the usual notation for the conjugate of a complex number), then (146) reads

(147) $$\bar{L}>0, \quad 1\leq\frac{L}{\bar{L}}<\varepsilon^2;$$

we therefore have

$$L\geq\bar{L}>0.$$

2) If a representation of k by $\{a, b, c\}$ is improper and primary, and if we set $(x, y)=g$, then $\dfrac{k}{g^2}$ has a proper and primary representation by $\{a, b, c\}$, using $\dfrac{x}{g}$, $\dfrac{y}{g}$ in place of x, y; also conversely. In fact, the inequalities in (146) admit a positive proportionality factor in x and y. It follows that there are exactly as many primary representations by F for any $k>0$ (assuming finiteness has been proved; it will come out of Theorem 203) as there are proper primary ones by F for $\dfrac{k}{g^2}$, where $g>0$ and $g^2|k$.

THEOREM 203: *Let $k>0$ be properly representable by $F=\{a, b, c\}$, where $a>0$ (I require this even if $d>0$). Then for every l such that*

$$(139) \qquad l^2 \equiv d \pmod{4k}, \quad 0 \leq l < 2k,$$

which corresponds, in the sense of Theorem 201, to at least one such representation, there exist exactly two such representations if $d < -4$, exactly four if $d = -4$, and exactly six if $d = -3$; if $d > 0$, then there is exactly one primary representation of this kind.

If we set

$$w = \begin{cases} 1 & \text{for } d > 0, \\ 2 & \text{for } d < -4, \\ 4 & \text{for } d = -4, \\ 6 & \text{for } d = -3 \end{cases}$$

for the rest of Part Four (we know from Part One, Chapter VII that if $d < 0$ this w represents the number of solutions of equation (141)), then we may express this uniformly: *For each such l there are exactly w proper primary representations of k.*

Remark: Since there are only a finite number of l to begin with, it follows that in all cases the number of primary representations of k by F is finite.

Proof: Since $l^2 \equiv d \pmod{4k}$, it follows that there is exactly one m for which

$$l^2 - 4km = d,$$

and we shall assume that $F = \{a, b, c\}$ goes into $G = \{k, l, m\}$ under at least one transformation $\begin{pmatrix} x_0 \, r_0 \\ y_0 \, s_0 \end{pmatrix}$. We wish to find all such transformations $\begin{pmatrix} x \, r \\ y \, s \end{pmatrix}$ and to show that the first column x, y of this matrix represents exactly w pairs of values—unconditionally, if $d < 0$, and provided the additional conditions (146) are satisfied, if $d > 0$.

Let $\begin{pmatrix} x_1 \, r_1 \\ y_1 \, s_1 \end{pmatrix}$ be any transformation that takes F into F. (We are acquainted with all such transformations, by virtue of Theorem 202; but this theorem will not be applied until afterwards.) I shall first show that the most general matrix $\begin{pmatrix} x \, r \\ y \, s \end{pmatrix}$ is given by

$$(148) \qquad \begin{pmatrix} x \, r \\ y \, s \end{pmatrix} = \begin{pmatrix} x_1 x_0 + r_1 y_0, & x_1 r_0 + r_1 s_0 \\ y_1 x_0 + s_1 y_0, & y_1 r_0 + s_1 s_0 \end{pmatrix}.$$

(In order to avoid matrix calculations, I shall take considerable pains with my choice of notation.)

Indeed: 1) The right side of (148) takes F into G; for by the formulas in the proof of Theorem 194, it yields the same as what we get by first transforming F by $\begin{pmatrix} x_1 & r_1 \\ y_1 & s_1 \end{pmatrix}$—this gives F—and then transforming the result (namely F)by $\begin{pmatrix} x_0 & r_0 \\ y_0 & s_0 \end{pmatrix}$—this gives G.

2) Let $\begin{pmatrix} x & r \\ y & s \end{pmatrix}$ take F into G. By the formulas in the proof of Theorem 193, G goes into F by means of $\begin{pmatrix} s_0 & -r_0 \\ -y_0 & x_0 \end{pmatrix}$. Consequently, the transformation

$$\begin{pmatrix} x\,s_0 - r\,y_0, & -x\,r_0 + r\,x_0 \\ y\,s_0 - s\,y_0, & -y\,r_0 + s\,x_0 \end{pmatrix}$$

takes F into F, via G. If we set it equal to $\begin{pmatrix} x_1 & r_1 \\ y_1 & s_1 \end{pmatrix}$, that is, if we set

$$x_1 = x\,s_0 - r\,y_0,\ \ r_1 = -x\,r_0 + r\,x_0,\ \ y_1 = y\,s_0 - s\,y_0,\ \ s_1 = -y\,r_0 + s\,x_0\,,$$

then we do in fact have

$$x_1\,x_0 + r_1\,y_0 = x,\ \ x_1\,r_0 + r_1\,s_0 = r,\ \ y_1\,x_0 + s_1\,y_0 = y,\ \ y_1\,r_0 + s_1\,s_0 = s.$$

If we take into account the form, given to us by Theorem 202, of all of the matrices $\begin{pmatrix} x_1 & r_1 \\ y_1 & s_1 \end{pmatrix}$, then we see that our general x and y are given by the formulas

(149)
$$\begin{cases} x = \dfrac{t - b\,u}{2}\,x_0 - c\,u\,y_0, \\[2mm] y = a\,u\,x_0 + \dfrac{t + b\,u}{2}\,y_0, \end{cases}$$

where t, u is any solution of (141). Distinct pairs t, u correspond to distinct pairs x, y; for the determinant of the coefficients of t and u on the right-hand side of (149) is

$$\frac{1}{4}\begin{vmatrix} x_0, & -(b\,x_0 + 2\,c\,y_0) \\ y_0, & 2\,a\,x_0 + b\,y_0 \end{vmatrix} = \frac{1}{4}(2\,a\,x_0^2 + b\,x_0\,y_0 + b\,x_0\,y_0 + 2\,c\,y_0^2) = \frac{k}{2} \neq 0.$$

For $d < 0$, everything has been taken care of.

For $d > 0$, I have to show that for exactly one admissible pair of values t, u, that is, for exactly one sign and one accompanying n in the formula

$$\frac{t + u\sqrt{d}}{2} = \pm\,\varepsilon^n$$

the inequalities

(147)
$$\overline{L}>0,\ 1\leq\frac{L}{\overline{L}}<\varepsilon^2$$

hold; here x and y are defined as in (149).

By (149), we have

$$4ax+2(b+\sqrt{d})y=2a(t-bu)x_0-4acuy_0+2abux_0+(t+bu)by_0$$
$$+\sqrt{d}(2aux_0+(t+bu)y_0)$$
$$=t(2ax_0+by_0)+duy_0+\sqrt{d}(2aux_0+buy_0+ty_0)$$
$$=(2ax_0+(b+\sqrt{d})y_0)(t+u\sqrt{d}),$$
$$2ax+(b+\sqrt{d})y=(2ax_0+(b+\sqrt{d})y_0)\frac{t+u\sqrt{d}}{2},$$

so that if we set

$$L_0=2ax_0+(b+\sqrt{d})y_0,$$

we have

$$L=\pm L_0\varepsilon^n.$$

From the fact that $L>0$, it now follows that the sign on the right must be that of L_0. (L_0 does not vanish; for otherwise we would have $2ax_0+by_0=y_0=0$, and therefore $x_0=y_0=0$.) We therefore have to show that in the formula

$$L=|L_0|\varepsilon^n,$$

there is exactly one choice of n for which (147) will hold.

We first note that, by (124),

$$4ak=(2ax+(b+\sqrt{d})y)(2ax+(b-\sqrt{d})y)=L\overline{L},$$

so that, since $L>0$, *eo ipso* $\overline{L}=\dfrac{4ak}{L}>0$. By virtue of the fact that

$$\frac{L}{\overline{L}}=\frac{L^2}{4ak}=\frac{|L_0|^2\varepsilon^{2n}}{4ak},$$

it follows that we need precisely

$$1\leq\frac{|L_0|^2\varepsilon^{2n}}{4ak}<\varepsilon^2;$$

this coincides with

$$\frac{2\sqrt{ak}}{|L_0|}\leq\varepsilon^n<\frac{2\sqrt{ak}}{|L_0|}\varepsilon,$$

and the latter clearly has exactly one solution n, since the interval runs precisely from a number ξ (inclusive) to $\xi\varepsilon$ (exclusive), where $\xi>0$.

DEFINITION 37: *A representative system of the* (primitive) *classes of forms* (where, if $d<0$, we take $a>0$) *shall mean a set of representatives, one from each class, having $a>0$.*

Such a representative, having $a>0$, certainly exists in the case $d>0$, for every form represents a positive number, and therefore represents some particular positive number properly, and is therefore equivalent to a form having this number as its first coefficient.

THEOREM 204: *Let $k>0$, and let $(k,d)=1$. Then the number $\psi(k)$ of primary representations of k by all the forms belonging to a representative system is finite, and its value is given by*

$$\psi(k)=w\sum_{n|k}\left(\frac{d}{n}\right)$$

(Kronecker symbol!).

Proof: We first consider the proper primary representations. By the Remark in Theorem 97, the conditions

(139) $l^2\equiv d\,(\mathrm{mod}\,4\,k),\ \ 0\leq l<2\,k$

have exactly

$$\sum_{f|k}\left(\frac{d}{f}\right)$$

solutions, where f runs through all the square-free positive divisors of k. (Here the condition $(k,d)=1$ was made use of.) For every such l, the form $\{k,l,m\}$, where m is determined from $l^2-4km=d$, is equivalent to exactly one form of the representative system. By means of this form, we obtain by Theorem 203 exactly w proper primary representations belonging to l. The number of proper primary representations of k by forms belonging to the representative system is therefore

$$w\sum_{f|k}\left(\frac{d}{f}\right).$$

By the second of the two remarks that precede Theorem 203, it follows that the number of primary representations of k by forms belonging to the representative system is

$$\psi(k)=w\sum_{\substack{g^2|k\\g>0}}\sum_{f|\frac{k}{g^2}}\left(\frac{d}{f}\right)$$

(since $(k,d)=1$, we indeed have $\left(\dfrac{k}{g^2},d\right)=1$ if $g^2|k$). It follows from Theorem 96, since $(g^2,d)=1$, that

$$\psi(k)=w \sum_{\substack{g^2|k \\ g>0}} \sum_{f|\frac{k}{g^2}} \left(\frac{d}{fg^2}\right)=w \sum_{n|k}\left(\frac{d}{n}\right);$$

for every $n>0$ can be uniquely written in the form fg^2, where f is square-free and $g>0$; and then $n|k$ implies $g^2|k$, $f|\frac{k}{g^2}$, and conversely.

THEOREM 205: *If, for $\tau>1$, we set*

$$H(\tau)=\sum_{\substack{1\leq k\leq\tau \\ (k,\,d)=1}} \psi(k),$$

(the number of primary representations, by forms belonging to the representative system, of all of the natural numbers up to τ that are relatively prime to d), *then*

$$\lim_{\tau=\infty}\frac{H(\tau)}{\tau}$$

exists, and we have

$$\lim_{\tau=\infty}\frac{H(\tau)}{\tau}=w\frac{\varphi(|d|)}{|d|}\sum_{n=1}^{\infty}\left(\frac{d}{n}\right)\frac{1}{n}.$$

Remark: By Theorem 141, this series

$$\sum_{n=1}^{\infty}\left(\frac{d}{n}\right)\frac{1}{n}$$

certainly converges, since $\left(\dfrac{d}{n}\right)$ is a character of the second kind mod $|d|$, according to the closing remark of Part Two, Chap. III, § 2. From now on its sum will be denoted by $K=K(d)$.

Two Proofs: 1) By Theorem 204, we have

$$\frac{H(\tau)}{w}=\sum_{\substack{1\leq k\leq\tau \\ (k,\,d)=1}} \sum_{n|k}\left(\frac{d}{n}\right)=\sum_{1\leq k\leq\tau} \sum_{n|k}\left(\frac{d}{n}\right)\left(\frac{d}{\frac{k}{n}}\right)^2;$$

this follows from the fact that, if $n|k$ and $n>0$, we have

$$\left(\frac{d}{n}\right)\left(\frac{d}{\frac{k}{n}}\right)^2=\begin{cases}\left(\dfrac{d}{n}\right) & \text{for } (k,d)=1, \\ 0 & \text{for } (k,d)>1,\end{cases}$$

for in the former case $\left(\dfrac{k}{n},d\right)=1$ and in the latter case either $(n,d)>1$ or $\left(\dfrac{k}{n},d\right)>1$.

Consequently, if it is tacitly understood in the following formulas that $n \geq 1$ and $m \geq 1$, we have

$$\frac{H(\tau)}{w} = \sum_{nm \leq \tau} \left(\frac{d}{n}\right)\left(\frac{d}{m}\right)^2,$$

so that (and the reader should draw a figure for this similar to the one he drew for the Proof of Theorem 152; here, in the (n, m)-plane he should draw the curvilinear triangle bounded by the positive branch of the hyperbola $nm = \tau$ and the lines $n=1$ and $m=1$, and in addition he should draw the line $n = \sqrt{\tau}$. Arithmetically: if $nm \leq \tau$, then either $n \leq \sqrt{\tau}$, so that we have $m \leq \dfrac{\tau}{n}$; or else $n > \sqrt{\tau}$, so that we have $m \leq \sqrt{\tau}$, $\sqrt{\tau} < n \leq \dfrac{\tau}{m}$)

$$(150) \qquad \frac{H(\tau)}{w} = \sum_{n \leq \sqrt{\tau}} \left(\frac{d}{n}\right) \sum_{m \leq \frac{\tau}{n}} \left(\frac{d}{m}\right)^2 + \sum_{m \leq \sqrt{\tau}} \left(\frac{d}{m}\right)^2 \sum_{\sqrt{\tau} < n \leq \frac{\tau}{m}} \left(\frac{d}{n}\right).$$

Now, for $\xi > 0$,

$$\sum_{m \leq \xi} \left(\frac{d}{m}\right)^2$$

is the number of positive integers up to ξ that are relatively prime to d, that is, the number of positive integers $\leq \xi$ belonging to a certain collection of $\varphi(|d|)$ residue classes mod $|d|$. Consequently, by Theorem 118, we have

$$(151) \qquad \left| \sum_{m \leq \xi} \left(\frac{d}{m}\right)^2 - \frac{\varphi(|d|)}{|d|} \xi \right| < \varphi(|d|) \leq |d|.$$

It follows further, by Theorem 139, for $1 \leq \xi < \eta$, that

$$(152) \qquad \left| \sum_{\xi < n \leq \eta} \left(\frac{d}{n}\right) \right| \leq \frac{\varphi(|d|)}{2} < |d|.$$

From (150), (151), and (152), we obtain

$$\left| \frac{H(\tau)}{w} - \frac{\varphi(|d|)}{|d|} \tau \sum_{n \leq \sqrt{\tau}} \left(\frac{d}{n}\right) \frac{1}{n} \right|$$

$$= \left| \sum_{n \leq \sqrt{\tau}} \left(\frac{d}{n}\right) \left(\sum_{m \leq \frac{\tau}{n}} \left(\frac{d}{m}\right)^2 - \frac{\varphi(|d|)}{|d|} \frac{\tau}{n} \right) + \sum_{m \leq \sqrt{\tau}} \left(\frac{d}{m}\right)^2 \sum_{\sqrt{\tau} < n \leq \frac{\tau}{m}} \left(\frac{d}{n}\right) \right|$$

$$\leq \sum_{n \leq \sqrt{\tau}} |d| + \sum_{m \leq \sqrt{\tau}} |d| \leq 2|d|\sqrt{\tau},$$

$$(153) \qquad \left| \frac{H(\tau)}{\tau} - w \frac{\varphi(|d|)}{|d|} \sum_{n \leq \sqrt{\tau}} \left(\frac{d}{n}\right) \frac{1}{n} \right| \leq \frac{2|d|w}{\sqrt{\tau}},$$

from which, by virtue of the convergence of the series

$$\sum_{n=1}^{\infty} \left(\frac{d}{n} \right) \frac{1}{n} = K(d),$$

our conclusion, namely

$$\lim_{\tau=\infty} \frac{H(\tau)}{\tau} = w \frac{\varphi(|d|)}{|d|} K(d),$$

follows.

2) Various ideas in the first proof will be useful to us for other purposes. If our goal is merely Theorem 205, then we can reach it more quickly, albeit somewhat more forcibly, in the following way.

By Theorem 204, we have

$$(154) \qquad \frac{1}{w} \frac{H(\tau)}{\tau} = \frac{1}{\tau} \sum_{\substack{1 \leq k \leq \tau \\ (k,d)=1}} \sum_{n|k} \left(\frac{d}{n} \right) = \sum_{n=1}^{\infty} \left(\frac{d}{n} \right) \frac{A(\tau; d, n)}{\tau},$$

where $A(\tau; d, n)$ represents the number of positive integers up to $\frac{\tau}{n}$ that are relatively prime to d. It is clear that

$$(155) \qquad \frac{A(\tau; d, n)}{\tau} \leq \frac{1}{n}$$

and that, for fixed n,

$$(156) \qquad \lim_{\tau=\infty} \frac{A(\tau; d, n)}{\tau} = \frac{\varphi(|d|)}{|d|} \frac{1}{n}.$$

By (155), Theorem 139, and Theorem 140, it follows that

$$\left| \sum_{n=u}^{v} \left(\frac{d}{n} \right) \frac{A(\tau; d, n)}{\tau} \right| \leq \frac{|d|}{u}$$

for $v \geq u \geq 1$, since $A(\tau; d, n)$ does not increase for increasing n, and therefore that the series on the right-hand side of (154) is uniformly convergent for $\tau > 1$. Therefore, by (156), the conclusion follows.

CHAPTER V

REPRESENTATIONS OF $h(d)$ IN TERMS OF $K(d)$

We should now like to investigate

$$H(\tau, F) = \sum_{\substack{1 \leq k \leq \tau \\ (k, d) = 1}} \psi(k, F) \qquad (\tau > 1),$$

where $\psi(k, F)$ is the number of primary representations of k by a fixed form F of the representative system; we ask whether—analogously to Theorem 205—

$$(157) \qquad \lim_{\tau = \infty} \frac{H(\tau, F)}{\tau}$$

exists. We shall find that:

1) It does.
2) The limit is independent of F; thus it depends only on d.
3) It is > 0.
4) It can be written explicitly.

If, for the moment, we denote it by $M(d)$, then the following is a consequence of what has just been stated.

If $F_1, F_2, \ldots, F_{h_0}$ are representatives of a finite number of distinct classes (we behave as though we did not already know the class number to be finite), then we clearly have

$$\sum_{n=1}^{h_0} H(\tau, F_n) \leq H(\tau),$$

so that, by Theorem 205,

$$h_0 M(d) = \sum_{n=1}^{h_0} \lim_{\tau = \infty} \frac{H(\tau, F_n)}{\tau} = \lim_{\tau = \infty} \frac{\sum_{n=1}^{h_0} H(\tau, F_n)}{\tau} \leq \lim_{\tau = \infty} \frac{H(\tau)}{\tau} = w \frac{\varphi(|d|)}{|d|} K(d).$$

Consequently, h_0 is bounded, so that the class number is finite. Call it $h = h(d)$. Now, if F_n runs over the entire representative system, we have

$$\sum_{n=1}^{h} H(\tau, F_n) = H(\tau),$$

and therefore

$$(158) \qquad h(d) M(d) = w \frac{\varphi(|d|)}{|d|} K(d).$$

This is precisely the goal of this chapter. The class number will once more be "determined"; to be sure, the heralded proof of our assertion regarding the limit in (157) will be somewhat tedious.

But (158) is far from being our final formula; for we shall manage to express the series

$$K(d) = \sum_{n=1}^{\infty} \left(\frac{d}{n}\right) \frac{1}{n}$$

in closed form. This, however, will take three full chapters more!

THEOREM 206: *If x and y each run through a complete set of residues* mod $|d|$, *then exactly* $|d|\varphi(|d|)$ *of the d^2 numbers $F(x, y)$ which result are relatively prime to d.*

Remark: That the number is independent of the choice of the sets of residues is clear to begin with; for from $x \equiv x'$ and $y \equiv y'$, it follows that $F(x, y) \equiv F(x', y')$.

Proof: It suffices to show, for $p^l | d$, $l > 0$, that if x and y each run through a complete set of residues mod p^l, then $p \nmid F(x, y)$ exactly $p^l \varphi(p^l)$ times. For if the canonical decomposition of $|d|$ is $|d| = \prod_{p||d|} p^l$, then, since $(F, d) = 1$ is equivalent to $p \nmid F$ for all $p||d|$, by Theorem 71 there are exactly $\prod_{p||d|} p^l \varphi(p^l) = |d| \varphi(|d|)$ pairs of classes $x \equiv x_0 \pmod{|d|}$, $y \equiv y_0 \pmod{|d|}$.

Since $(a, b, c) = 1$ and $b^2 - 4ac = d$, we cannot have both $p|a$ and $p|c$ if $p|d$. Without loss of generality, let $p \nmid a$. (For, $a > 0$ is not used in the following proof.)

1) Let $p > 2$. Then, since $(p, 4a) = 1$, it depends precisely on $4aF = (2ax + by)^2 - dy^2$ not being divisible by p, that is, since $p|d$, on

$$2ax + by \not\equiv 0 \pmod{p}.$$

For each of our p^l values of y, since $p \nmid 2a$, all of the x belonging to a certain set of $p-1$ residue classes mod p have this property, that is, exactly

$$p^{l-1}(p-1) = \varphi(p^l)$$

of our x.

2) Let $p = 2$, so that $2|d$ and $2|b$. The condition

$$ax^2 + bxy + cy^2 \equiv 1 \pmod 2$$

implies that

$$x + cy \equiv 1 \pmod 2.$$

For each of our 2^l values of y, all of the x belonging to one residue class mod 2 have this property, that is, exactly $2^{l-1} = \varphi(2^l)$ of our x.

THEOREM 207: *Let $m > 0$. Suppose given an ellipse or a sector of an hyperbola* (the curvilinear triangle bounded by an arc of the hyperbola and two rays drawn from its endpoints to the center of the hyperbola) ; *let I be its area. Suppose the figure stretched by an amount $\sqrt{\tau}$, $\tau > 0$* (that is, suppose we consider the set of points $\xi\sqrt{\tau}$, $\eta\sqrt{\tau}$ instead of the original set of points ξ, η). *Let $U(\tau)$ denote the number of points with integral coordinates* (so-called lattice points) *within the extended figure* (with each boundary point either counted or not, as we please) *which satisfy the additional conditions:*

$$x \equiv x_0 \pmod{m}, \quad y \equiv y_0 \pmod{m}.$$

Then we have

$$\lim_{\tau=\infty} \frac{U(\tau)}{\tau} = \frac{I}{m^2}.$$

Proof: In the plane of the original figure, let us lay out two mutually perpendicular systems of parallel lines, spaced $\dfrac{m}{\sqrt{\tau}}$ units apart, around the point $\xi = \dfrac{x_0}{\sqrt{\tau}}$, $\eta = \dfrac{y_0}{\sqrt{\tau}}$; that is, let us draw all of the lines

$$\xi = \frac{x_0 + rm}{\sqrt{\tau}}, \quad \eta = \frac{y_0 + sm}{\sqrt{\tau}}.$$

Let $W(\tau)$ be the number of squares in this net which are contained in the ellipse or in the sector of the hyperbola, as the case may be; a square only part of which is contained in the figure should be counted if and only if its "southwestern" corner (that is, the corner in which both ξ and η are minimal) is counted in the corresponding stretched-out figure. Then we clearly have

$$U(\tau) = W(\tau).$$

Since $\dfrac{m^2}{\tau}$ is the area of each square of our net, it follows from the basic theorems of integral calculus that

$$I = \int\int d\xi \, d\eta = \lim_{\tau=\infty} \left(\frac{m^2}{\tau} W(\tau) \right),$$

which proves our theorem.

THEOREM 208: *The following formulas hold for the function $H(\tau, F)$, defined above:*

$$\lim_{\tau=\infty} \frac{H(\tau, F)}{\tau} = \begin{cases} \dfrac{2\pi}{\sqrt{|d|}} \dfrac{\varphi(|d|)}{|d|} & \textit{for } d<0, \\[2mm] \dfrac{\log \varepsilon}{\sqrt{d}} \dfrac{\varphi(d)}{d} & \textit{for } d>0, \end{cases}$$

where ε is defined as in Theorem 111.

Proof: By Theorem 206, it is sufficient to prove that the number of solutions $U(\tau)=U(\tau, F, x_0, y_0)$ of

$$0\leq F(x, y)\leq \tau, \quad x\equiv x_0 \;(\mathrm{mod}\; |d|), \quad y\equiv y_0 \;(\mathrm{mod}\; |d|),$$

which, in case $d>0$, also satisfy conditions (146), has the property that

$$\lim_{\tau=\infty} \frac{U(\tau)}{\tau} = \begin{cases} \dfrac{2\pi}{\sqrt{|d|}} \dfrac{1}{d^2} & \text{for } d<0, \\[2mm] \dfrac{\log \varepsilon}{\sqrt{d}} \dfrac{1}{d^2} & \text{for } d>0. \end{cases}$$

($F(x, y)=0$ is allowed, since this equation can only be satisfied by $x=y=0$, because of the irrationality of $\sqrt{d}$.)

1) Let $d<0$. By Theorem 207, we need only note that the ellipse

$$a\xi^2+b\xi\eta+c\eta^2\leq 1$$

(from which, after stretching, we obtain $F(x, y)\leq\tau$) has area $\dfrac{2\pi}{\sqrt{|d|}}$. The reader certainly knows this.

2) Let $d>0$. By Theorem 207, it suffices to prove, using the abbreviations

$$\Lambda=2a\xi+(b+\sqrt{d})\eta, \quad \bar{\Lambda}=2a\xi+(b-\sqrt{d})\eta,$$

that the hyperbola sector

(159) $$a\xi^2+b\xi\eta+c\eta^2\leq 1, \quad \bar{\Lambda}>0, \quad 1\leq \frac{\Lambda}{\bar{\Lambda}}<\varepsilon^2$$

has area $\dfrac{\log \varepsilon}{\sqrt{d}}$. (The condition $0 \leq a\xi^2 + b\xi\eta + c\eta^2$ may be omitted, since it

follows from $a\xi^2 + b\xi\eta + c\eta^2 = \dfrac{\Lambda\bar{\Lambda}}{4a}$ and $\Lambda \geq \bar{\Lambda} > 0$.) (159) is a sector

of an hyperbola; for (please draw this!) the asymptotes of the hyperbola

$a\xi^2 + b\xi\eta + c\eta^2 = \dfrac{\Lambda\bar{\Lambda}}{4a} = 1$ are the lines $\Lambda = 0$ and $\bar{\Lambda} = 0$, so that the half-

rays $\Lambda = \bar{\Lambda} > 0$ (this is, incidentally, the positive ξ-axis) and $\Lambda = \varepsilon^2 \bar{\Lambda} > 0$

intersect the same branch of the hyperbola (within the region $\Lambda > 0$, $\bar{\Lambda} > 0$).
The area of the hyperbola sector (159) is

$$I = \iint d\xi\, d\eta$$

over the region $\Lambda\bar{\Lambda} \leq 4a$, $\bar{\Lambda} > 0$, $1 \leq \dfrac{\Lambda}{\bar{\Lambda}} < \varepsilon^2$. Let

$$\frac{\Lambda}{2\sqrt{a}} = \varrho, \frac{\bar{\Lambda}}{2\sqrt{a}} = \sigma$$

be chosen as new variables; since

$$\begin{vmatrix} \dfrac{\partial \varrho}{\partial \xi} & \dfrac{\partial \varrho}{\partial \eta} \\ \dfrac{\partial \sigma}{\partial \xi} & \dfrac{\partial \sigma}{\partial \eta} \end{vmatrix} = \frac{1}{2\sqrt{a}}\frac{1}{2\sqrt{a}} \begin{vmatrix} 2a, & b+\sqrt{d} \\ 2a, & b-\sqrt{d} \end{vmatrix} = -\sqrt{d},$$

we have

$$I = \frac{1}{\sqrt{d}} \iint d\varrho\, d\sigma,$$

over the hyperbola sector $\varrho\sigma \leq 1$, $\sigma \geq 0$, $\sigma \leq \varrho \leq \varepsilon^2\sigma$ (please draw a new diagram; or else use the old one in case the hyperbola originally drawn happened to be an equilateral one) having the vertices $0, 0$; $\varepsilon, \dfrac{1}{\varepsilon}$; $1, 1$. Consequently, we have

$$\sqrt{d}\,I = \int_0^\varepsilon d\varrho \int_{\frac{\varrho}{\varepsilon^2}}^{\mathrm{Min}\left(\varrho, \frac{1}{\varrho}\right)} d\sigma = \int_0^1 d\varrho \int_{\frac{\varrho}{\varepsilon^2}}^{\varrho} d\sigma + \int_1^\varepsilon d\varrho \int_{\frac{\varrho}{\varepsilon^2}}^{\frac{1}{\varrho}} d\sigma$$

$$= \int_0^1 \left(\varrho - \frac{\varrho}{\varepsilon^2}\right) d\varrho + \int_1^\varepsilon \left(\frac{1}{\varrho} - \frac{\varrho}{\varepsilon^2}\right) d\varrho = \int_0^1 \varrho\, d\varrho + \int_1^\varepsilon \frac{d\varrho}{\varrho} - \int_0^\varepsilon \frac{\varrho}{\varepsilon^2} d\varrho = \log \varepsilon.$$

THEOREM 209:

$$h(d) = \begin{cases} \dfrac{w\sqrt{|d|}}{2\pi} K(d) & \text{for } d<0, \\[3mm] \dfrac{\sqrt{d}}{\log \varepsilon} K(d) & \text{for } d>0. \end{cases}$$

Proof: It follows from Theorem 205 and Theorem 208 (cf. 158)) that

$$h(d) \cdot \left\{ \begin{matrix} 2\pi \\ \log \varepsilon \end{matrix} \right\} \cdot \frac{1}{\sqrt{|d|}} \, \frac{\varphi(|d|)}{|d|} = w \frac{\varphi(|d|)}{|d|} K(d) \quad \text{for } d \begin{cases} <0, \\ >0. \end{cases}$$

Now we may forget completely the meaning of h, as well as the quadratic forms, and we have merely (merely!) to find the sum of the series

$$K(d) = \sum_{n=1}^{\infty} \left(\frac{d}{n} \right) \frac{1}{n}.$$

CHAPTER VI

GAUSSIAN SUMS

I shall assume that the reader is familiar with the following theorem from the classical theory of Fourier series:

THEOREM 210: *Let $f(\xi)$ be defined for $0 \leq \xi \leq 1$* (as a real or a complex function; the case in which $f(\xi)$ is complex follows immediately from the real case) ; *moreover, let $f(\xi)$ be continuous and let $f'(\xi)$ also exist and be continuous. If we set*

$$\alpha_h = 2 \int_0^1 f(\eta) \cos 2\pi h\eta \, d\eta, \quad \beta_h = 2 \int_0^1 f(\eta) \sin 2\pi h\eta \, d\eta,$$

then we have

$$\frac{\alpha_0}{2} + \sum_{h=1}^{\infty} (\alpha_h \cos 2\pi h\xi + \beta_h \sin 2\pi h\xi) = \begin{cases} f(\xi) & \text{for } 0 < \xi < 1, \\ \dfrac{f(0) + f(1)}{2} & \text{for } \xi = 0. \end{cases}$$

In particular, therefore (since $\alpha_{-h} = \alpha_h$ and $\beta_{-h} = -\beta_h$), we have

$$\frac{f(0) + f(1)}{2} = \frac{\alpha_0}{2} + \sum_{h=1}^{\infty} \alpha_h = \frac{1}{2} \lim_{N=\infty} \sum_{h=-N}^{N} \alpha_h = \frac{1}{2} \lim_{N=\infty} \sum_{h=-N}^{N} (\alpha_h + \beta_h i)$$

$$(160) \qquad = \lim_{N=\infty} \sum_{h=-N}^{N} \int_0^1 f(\eta) e^{2\pi i h\eta} d\eta.$$

THEOREM 211: *Let $n > 0$. Then*

$$\sum_{s=0}^{n-1} e^{2\pi i \frac{s^2}{n}} = \begin{cases} (1+i)\sqrt{n} & \text{for } n \equiv 0 \\ \sqrt{n} & \text{for } n \equiv 1 \\ 0 & \text{for } n \equiv 2 \\ i\sqrt{n} & \text{for } n \equiv 3 \end{cases} \pmod{4}.$$

Remark: There are proofs that are more elementary (*cf.* the Appendix to this chapter) ; the reader cannot, however, become accustomed early enough to the use of analysis; moreover, the following proof (using 160)) is the shortest of the many proofs of this theorem, which was one of Gauss's greatest discoveries. All that is required, incidentally, for the determination of the class number, is the special case of Theorem 211 in which $n = p > 2$, which will lead directly to Theorem 212. Nevertheless, I should not like to prove the formula

$$\sum_{s=0}^{p-1} e^{2\pi i\frac{s^2}{p}} = \begin{cases} \sqrt{p} & \text{for } p\equiv 1 \\ i\sqrt{p} & \text{for } p\equiv 3 \end{cases} \pmod 4$$

for prime numbers only, since it follows for all positive odd numbers with just as little trouble, or rather (today!) with just as much ease.

Proof: Since

$$e^{2\pi i\frac{0^2}{n}} = 1 = e^{2\pi i\frac{n^2}{n}},$$

it follows that

$$\sum_{s=0}^{n-1} e^{2\pi i\frac{s^2}{n}} = \sum_{s=0}^{n-1} \frac{e^{2\pi i\frac{s^2}{n}} + e^{2\pi i\frac{(s+1)^2}{n}}}{2}.$$

By (160), with

$$f(\xi) = e^{2\pi i\frac{(s+\xi)^2}{n}} = f_s(\xi),$$

we have

$$\sum_{s=0}^{n-1} e^{2\pi i\frac{s^2}{n}} = \sum_{s=0}^{n-1} \frac{f_s(0)+f_s(1)}{2} = \sum_{s=0}^{n-1} \lim_{N=\infty} \sum_{h=-N}^{N} \int_0^1 e^{2\pi i\left(\frac{(s+\eta)^2}{n}+h\eta\right)} d\eta$$

$$= \lim_{N=\infty} \sum_{h=-N}^{N} \sum_{s=0}^{n-1} \int_0^1 e^{2\pi i\left(\frac{(s+\eta)^2}{n}+h\eta\right)} d\eta$$

$$= \lim_{N=\infty} \sum_{h=-N}^{N} \sum_{s=0}^{n-1} \int_s^{s+1} e^{2\pi i\left(\frac{\eta^2}{n}+h\eta\right)} d\eta$$

$$(161) \quad = \lim_{N=\infty} \sum_{h=-N}^{N} \int_0^n e^{2\pi i\left(\frac{\eta^2}{n}+h\eta\right)} d\eta = n \lim_{N=\infty} \sum_{h=-N}^{N} \int_0^1 e^{2\pi i n(\xi^2+h\xi)} d\xi$$

(setting $\eta=n\xi$).

Now it is well known that

$$\gamma = \int_{-\infty}^{\infty} e^{2\pi i\xi^2} d\xi$$

converges; it is not necessary for us to know the value of γ, since it will come out of what follows. Hence, if we set $\xi=\sqrt{n}\eta$, we have, on the one hand,

$$\frac{\gamma}{\sqrt{n}} = \int_{-\infty}^{\infty} e^{2\pi i n \eta^2} d\eta = \sum_{k=-\infty}^{\infty} \int_k^{k+1} e^{2\pi i n \eta^2} d\eta = \sum_{k=-\infty}^{\infty} \int_0^1 e^{2\pi i n (\xi+k)^2} d\xi$$

$$= \sum_{k=-\infty}^{\infty} \int_0^1 e^{2\pi i n (\xi^2 + 2k\xi)} d\xi,$$

and on the other hand,

$$\frac{\gamma}{\sqrt{n}} = \sum_{k=-\infty}^{\infty} \int_{k-\frac{1}{2}}^{k+\frac{1}{2}} e^{2\pi i n \eta^2} d\eta = \sum_{k=-\infty}^{\infty} \int_0^1 e^{2\pi i n \left(\xi+k-\frac{1}{2}\right)^2} d\xi$$

$$= \sum_{k=-\infty}^{\infty} e^{2\pi i n \left(k-\frac{1}{2}\right)^2} \int_0^1 e^{2\pi i n (\xi^2 + (2k-1)\xi)} d\xi$$

$$= i^n \sum_{k=-\infty}^{\infty} \int_0^1 e^{2\pi i n (\xi^2 + (2k-1)\xi)} d\xi$$

(since

$$e^{2\pi i n \left(k-\frac{1}{2}\right)^2} = e^{2\pi i n \left(k^2 - k + \frac{1}{4}\right)} = e^{\frac{\pi i n}{2}} = i^n).$$

Hence, because of (161), we have

$$\frac{\gamma}{\sqrt{n}}(1+i^{-n}) = \sum_{k=-\infty}^{\infty} \int_0^1 e^{2\pi i n (\xi^2 + 2k\xi)} d\xi + \sum_{k=-\infty}^{\infty} \int_0^1 e^{2\pi i n (\xi^2 + (2k-1)\xi)} d\xi$$

$$= \sum_{h=-\infty}^{\infty} \int_0^1 e^{2\pi i n (\xi^2 + h\xi)} d\xi = \frac{1}{n} \sum_{s=0}^{n-1} e^{2\pi i \frac{s^2}{n}},$$

(162)
$$\sum_{s=0}^{n-1} e^{2\pi i \frac{s^2}{n}} = \gamma \sqrt{n} \, (1+i^{-n}).$$

The absolute constant γ is determined by setting $n=1$ in (162):

$$1 = \gamma \, (1-i),$$

$$\gamma = \frac{1}{1-i} = \frac{1+i}{2}.$$

It therefore follows from (162) that

$$\sum_{s=0}^{n-1} e^{2\pi i \frac{s^2}{n}} = \sqrt{n} \frac{(1+i)(1+i^{-n})}{2},$$

and in this formula we have

$$\frac{(1+i)(1+i^{-n})}{2} = \begin{cases} 1+i & \text{for } n \equiv 0 \\ 1 & \text{for } n \equiv 1 \\ 0 & \text{for } n \equiv 2 \\ i & \text{for } n \equiv 3 \end{cases} \pmod 4.$$

THEOREM 212:

$$\sum_{r=1}^{p-1}\left(\frac{r}{p}\right) e^{\frac{2\pi i r}{p}} = \begin{cases} \sqrt{p} & \text{for } p\equiv 1 \ (\text{mod } 4), \\ i\sqrt{p} & \text{for } p\equiv 3 \ (\text{mod } 4). \end{cases}$$

Remark: Except for sign, this is quite easily proven (only after years of effort did Gauss succeed in determining the sign).

Namely, if we set

$$e^{\frac{2\pi i}{p}} = \varrho, \quad \sum_{r=1}^{p-1}\left(\frac{r}{p}\right)\varrho^r = \lambda$$

for the sake of abbreviation, then $\left(\text{since } \left(\dfrac{r}{p}\right) \text{ and } \varrho^r \text{ have period } p \text{ for } p \nmid r\right)$ we have

$$\lambda = \sum_r \left(\frac{r}{p}\right)\varrho^r,$$

the sum being taken over a reduced set of residues; hence, if s also runs through such a set, we have

$$\lambda^2 = \sum_r \left(\frac{r}{p}\right)\varrho^r \ \sum_s \left(\frac{s}{p}\right)\varrho^s;$$

rt also runs through a reduced set of residues when t does; hence we have

$$\lambda^2 = \sum_r \left(\frac{r}{p}\right)\varrho^r \ \sum_t \left(\frac{rt}{p}\right)\varrho^{rt} = \sum_{r,t}\left(\frac{t}{p}\right)\varrho^{(1+t)r} = \sum_{t=1}^{p-1}\left(\frac{t}{p}\right)\sum_{r=1}^{p-1}\varrho^{(1+t)r}$$

$$= \sum_{t=1}^{p-1}\left(\frac{t}{p}\right)\sum_{r=0}^{p-1}\varrho^{(1+t)r},$$

since

$$\sum_{t=1}^{p-1}\left(\frac{t}{p}\right)=0$$

(by Theorem 79). Now we have

$$\sum_{r=0}^{p-1}\varrho^{(1+t)r} = \begin{cases} p & \text{for } t=p-1, \\ \dfrac{1-\varrho^{(1+t)p}}{1-\varrho^{1+t}}=0 & \text{for } 1\leq t\leq p-2; \end{cases}$$

it follows that

$$\lambda^2 = \left(\frac{p-1}{p}\right)p = (-1)^{\frac{p-1}{2}}\,p,$$

$$\lambda = \begin{cases} \pm\sqrt{p} & \text{for } p\equiv 1 \ (\text{mod } 4), \\ \pm i\sqrt{p} & \text{for } p\equiv 3 \ (\text{mod } 4). \end{cases}$$

These remarks, incidentally, are not made use of in the following complete proof of Theorem 212.

Proof: If a runs over the quadratic residues and b over the quadratic non-residues mod p in the interval $0<x<p$, then we have

$$\lambda = \sum_{r=1}^{p-1} \left(\frac{r}{p}\right) e^{\frac{2\pi i r}{p}} = \sum_a \varrho^a - \sum_b \varrho^b.$$

On the other hand, we have

$$1 + \sum_a \varrho^a + \sum_b \varrho^b = \sum_{s=0}^{p-1} \varrho^s = \frac{1-\varrho^p}{1-\varrho} = 0,$$

so that

$$\lambda = \sum_a \varrho^a + 1 + \sum_a \varrho^a = 1 + 2\sum_a \varrho^a.$$

By Theorem 79, the a coincide with the remainders of $1^2, 2^2, \ldots, \left(\frac{p-1}{2}\right)^2$ upon division by p. The remainders of s^2, for $1 \leq s \leq p-1$, therefore yield each of the a exactly twice. Consequently, by Theorem 211,

$$\lambda = 1 + \sum_{s=1}^{p-1} \varrho^{s^2} = \sum_{s=0}^{p-1} \varrho^{s^2} = \begin{cases} \sqrt{p} & \text{for } p \equiv 1 \pmod{4}, \\ i\sqrt{p} & \text{for } p \equiv 3 \pmod{4}. \end{cases}$$

APPENDIX

INTRODUCTION

Because of the importance of Theorem 211, I should now like to present three more proofs, at least for odd n, which are quite different from the above and from each other.

The first, due to Kronecker, makes use of complex function theory, in particular of Cauchy's Theorem; it also yields a proof, incidentally, for even n.

The second proof is due to I. Schur and makes use of matrix algebra.

The third proof is due to Mertens, and its calculations involve only (though extensively) finite trigonometric sums.

Incidentally, Theorem 211 is trivial for $n \equiv 2 \pmod 4$; for then we have

$$e^{2\pi i \frac{\left(s+\frac{n}{2}\right)^2}{n}} = e^{2\pi i \frac{s^2+sn+\frac{n^2}{4}}{n}} = e^{2\pi i \frac{s^2}{n}} \cdot e^{\pi i \frac{n}{2}} = -e^{2\pi i \frac{s^2}{n}},$$

so that the terms in the sum cancel each other out in pairs.

The case $n \equiv 0 \pmod 4$ could be reduced to the case $4 \nmid n$ in an elementary manner; but I shall omit the lengthy proof of this statement since, in any case, it is only Theorem 212, that is, Theorem 211 for odd (and indeed prime) n which is later made use of.

§1

Kronecker's Proof

Let $n>0$. For $0<\varrho<\frac{1}{4}$, $\omega>1$, let us consider the integral

$$I=I(n,\varrho,\omega)=\int \frac{e^{\frac{2\pi i}{n}\xi^2}}{1-e^{2\pi i\xi}}\,d\xi,$$

which is taken in the positive direction around the rectangle with vertices $\pm\omega i$, $\frac{n}{2}\pm\omega i$ in which—in order to avoid the points 0 (a pole of the integrand) and $\frac{n}{2}$ (a pole, in case n is even)—semicircular indentations have been made, the semicircles being of radius ϱ with centers at 0 and $\frac{n}{2}$, respectively. The integrand is regular along this path, and inside the path has the poles s, where $1\leq s\leq\frac{n-1}{2}$. (For $n=1$ or 2 there are no poles at all inside.) I is therefore independent of ϱ and ω (that is, it depends only on n); since the residue of the integrand at s is clearly $-\frac{1}{2\pi i}e^{\frac{2\pi i}{n}s^2}$, it follows from Cauchy's Theorem that

$$I=-\sum_{1\leq s\leq\frac{n-1}{2}}e^{\frac{2\pi i}{n}s^2}=-\frac{1}{2}\sum_{s=1}^{n-1}{}' e^{\frac{2\pi i}{n}s^2},$$

where the symbol Σ' indicates that if n is even, then the term for which $s=\frac{n}{2}$ (which would, incidentally, be i^n) is omitted from the sum.

The sum of the integrals over both of the straight-line segments of the boundary on the left $\xi=i\eta$, $\omega\geq\eta\geq\varrho$ and $\xi=-i\eta$, $\varrho\leq\eta\leq\omega$, is

$$i\int_{\omega}^{\varrho}\frac{e^{-\frac{2\pi i}{n}\eta^2}}{1-e^{-2\pi\eta}}\,d\eta-i\int_{\varrho}^{\omega}\frac{e^{-\frac{2\pi i}{n}\eta^2}}{1-e^{2\pi\eta}}\,d\eta=-i\int_{\varrho}^{\omega}e^{-\frac{2\pi i}{n}\eta^2}\left(\frac{e^{2\pi\eta}}{e^{2\pi\eta}-1}-\frac{1}{e^{2\pi\eta}-1}\right)d\eta$$

$$=-i\int_{\varrho}^{\omega}e^{-\frac{2\pi i}{n}\eta^2}\,d\eta;$$

203

as $\omega \to \infty$, this expression approaches

$$- i \int_\varrho^\infty e^{-\frac{2\pi i}{n}\eta^2}\, d\eta$$

(since, as is well known, this integral converges).

Since

$$e^{\frac{2\pi i}{n}\left(\frac{n}{2}\mp i\eta\right)^2} = e^{\frac{2\pi i}{n}\left(\frac{n^2}{4}\mp ni\eta-\eta^2\right)} = i^n e^{\pm 2\pi\eta} e^{-\frac{2\pi i}{n}\eta^2}$$

and

$$e^{2\pi i\left(\frac{n}{2}\mp i\eta\right)} = (-1)^n e^{\pm 2\pi\eta},$$

the sum of the integrals over both of the straight boundary segments $\xi = \frac{n}{2} - i\eta,\ \omega \geq \eta \geq \varrho$ and $\xi = \frac{n}{2} + i\eta,\ \varrho \leq \eta \leq \omega$ on the right is

$$- i^{1+n}\int_\omega^\varrho \frac{e^{2\pi\eta}\, e^{-\frac{2\pi i}{n}\eta^2}}{1-(-1)^n e^{2\pi\eta}}\, d\eta + i^{1+n}\int_\varrho^\omega \frac{e^{-2\pi\eta}\, e^{-\frac{2\pi i}{n}\eta^2}}{1-(-1)^n e^{-2\pi\eta}}\, d\eta$$

$$= i^{1+n}\int_\varrho^\omega e^{-\frac{2\pi i}{n}\eta^2}\left(\frac{e^{2\pi\eta}}{1-(-1)^n e^{2\pi\eta}} + \frac{1}{e^{2\pi\eta}-(-1)^n}\right) d\eta$$

$$= i^{1+n}(-1)^n\int_\varrho^\omega e^{-\frac{2\pi i}{n}\eta^2}\left(\frac{(-1)^n e^{2\pi\eta}}{1-(-1)^n e^{2\pi\eta}} + \frac{1}{(-1)^n e^{2\pi\eta}-1}\right) d\eta$$

$$= -i^{1+n}(-1)^n\int_\varrho^\omega e^{-\frac{2\pi i}{n}\eta^2}\, d\eta = -i(-i)^n\int_\varrho^\omega e^{-\frac{2\pi i}{n}\eta^2}\, d\eta;$$

as $\omega \to \infty$, this expression approaches

$$-i(-i)^n\int_\varrho^\infty e^{-\frac{2\pi i}{n}\eta^2}\, d\eta.$$

The integrals over the horizontal segments of the boundary approach 0 as $\omega \to \infty$; since for $\xi = \tau + \omega i,\ \frac{n}{2} \geq \tau \geq 0$ we have

$$\left| \frac{e^{\frac{2\pi i}{n}\xi^2}}{1-e^{2\pi i\xi}} \right| \leqq \frac{e^{-\frac{4\pi\tau\omega}{n}}}{1-e^{-2\pi\omega}} \leqq \frac{e^{-\frac{4\pi\tau\omega}{n}}}{1-e^{-2\pi}},$$

so that

$$\left| \int_{\frac{n}{2}+\omega i}^{\omega i} \frac{e^{\frac{2\pi i}{n}\xi^2}}{1-e^{2\pi i\xi}}d\xi \right| \leqq \frac{1}{1-e^{-2\pi}} \int_0^{\frac{n}{2}} e^{-\frac{4\pi\tau\omega}{n}}d\tau < \frac{1}{1-e^{-2\pi}} \int_0^{\infty} e^{-\frac{4\pi\tau\omega}{n}}d\tau$$

$$= \frac{1}{1-e^{-2\pi}} \frac{1}{\omega} \int_0^{\infty} e^{-\frac{4\pi x}{n}}dx,$$

and for $\xi = \tau - \omega i,\ 0 \leqq \tau \leqq \dfrac{n}{2}$ we have

$$\left| \frac{e^{\frac{2\pi i}{n}\xi^2}}{1-e^{2\pi i\xi}} \right| \leqq \frac{e^{\frac{4\pi\tau\omega}{n}}}{e^{2\pi\omega}-1},$$

so that

$$\left| \int_{-\omega i}^{\frac{n}{2}-\omega i} \frac{e^{\frac{2\pi i}{n}\xi^2}}{1-e^{2\pi i\xi}}d\xi \right| \leqq \frac{1}{e^{2\pi\omega}-1} \int_0^{\frac{n}{2}} e^{\frac{4\pi\tau\omega}{n}}d\tau = \frac{1}{e^{2\pi\omega}-1} \left\{ \frac{n}{4\pi\omega} e^{\frac{4\pi\tau\omega}{n}} \right\}_0^{\frac{n}{2}}$$

$$= \frac{1}{e^{2\pi\omega}-1} \frac{n}{4\pi\omega} (e^{2\pi\omega}-1) = \frac{n}{4\pi\omega}.$$

We therefore have

$$-\frac{1}{2}\sum_{s=1}^{n-1}{}' e^{\frac{2\pi i}{n}s^2} = -i(1+(-i)^n)\int_\varrho^{\infty} e^{-\frac{2\pi i}{n}\eta^2}d\eta + I_1 + I_2,$$

where I_1 and I_2 denote the integrals over the semicircles around 0 and $\dfrac{n}{2}$, respectively.

We now consider the limit as $\varrho \to 0$. We have

$$\int_\varrho^{\infty} e^{-\frac{2\pi i}{n}\eta^2}d\eta \to \int_0^{\infty} e^{-\frac{2\pi i}{n}\eta^2}d\eta;$$

furthermore, if $f(\xi)$ has a pole of order one with residue a at $\xi = \xi_0$, then by integrating in the negative direction around a semicircle $\mathfrak{H}(\varrho)$ with center at ξ and radius ϱ we have

$$\lim_{\varrho=0} \int_{\mathfrak{H}(\varrho)} f(\xi)d\xi = -\pi i \alpha;$$

for

$$f(\xi) = \frac{\alpha}{\xi - \xi_0} + g(\xi),$$

where $g(\xi)$ is regular at ξ_0; and therefore, since

$$\lim_{\varrho=0} \int_{\mathfrak{H}(\varrho)} g(\xi)d\xi = 0$$

(length of path $\pi\varrho$, and integrand uniformly bounded for small ϱ), we have

$$\lim_{\varrho=0} \int_{\mathfrak{H}(\varrho)} f(\xi)d\xi = \alpha \lim_{\varrho=0} \int_{\mathfrak{H}(\varrho)} \frac{d\xi}{\xi - \xi_0} = \alpha \lim_{\varrho=0} (-\pi i) = -\pi i \alpha.$$

Consequently (in case n is odd $\dfrac{n}{2}$ is a regular point and we have simply $\lim\limits_{\varrho=0} I_2 = 0$),

$$-i(1+(-i)^n)\int_0^\infty e^{-\frac{2\pi i}{n}\eta^2}\,d\eta = -\frac{1}{2}\sum_{s=1}^{n-1}{}' e^{\frac{2\pi i}{n}s^2} - \frac{1}{2}e^{\frac{2\pi i}{n}0^2}$$

$$-\begin{cases} 0 & \text{in case } 2 \nmid n, \\ \dfrac{1}{2}e^{\frac{2\pi i}{n}\left(\frac{n}{2}\right)^2} & \text{in case } 2 \mid n, \end{cases}$$

so that, in any case,

$$= -\frac{1}{2}\sum_{s=0}^{n-1} e^{\frac{2\pi i}{n}s^2},$$

$$\sum_{s=0}^{n-1} e^{2\pi i\frac{s^2}{n}} = 2i(1+(-i)^n)\int_0^\infty e^{-\frac{2\pi i}{n}\eta^2}\,d\eta = 2i(1+(-i)^n)\sqrt{n}\int_0^\infty e^{-2\pi i\lambda^2}\,d\lambda.$$

The integral on the right can be evaluated by the specialization $n=1$; we have

$$1 = 2i(1-i)\int_0^\infty e^{-2\pi i\lambda^2}\,d\lambda,$$

so that

$$\sum_{s=0}^{n-1} e^{2\pi i\frac{s^2}{n}} = \frac{1+(-i)^n}{1-i}\sqrt{n};$$

these are the four values of our theorem, depending on the residue class mod 4.

§2

Schur's Proof

I shall not take for granted any knowledge of matrix calculus, and shall develop:

1) The concept: A matrix is a square array

$$\mathfrak{A} = \begin{pmatrix} \alpha_{11} \cdots \alpha_{1n} \\ \cdots\cdots\cdots \\ \alpha_{n1} \cdots \alpha_{nn} \end{pmatrix} = (\alpha_{kl})$$

of n^2 elements. (The numbering may of course also run, say, from 0 to $n-1$.)

2) The definition of multiplication:

$$(\alpha_{kl})(\beta_{kl}) = (\sum_m \alpha_{km}\beta_{ml}).$$

3) The definition

$$\mathfrak{A}^2 = \mathfrak{A}\mathfrak{A}.$$

4) The notation

$$e_{kl} = \begin{cases} 1 & \text{for } k=l, \\ 0 & \text{for } k \neq l. \end{cases}$$

5) The definition of the characteristic function of a matrix $\mathfrak{A}=(\alpha_{kl})$; it is the determinant

$$\Phi(\xi) = |\xi e_{kl} - \alpha_{kl}|:$$

$\Phi(\xi)$ is a polynomial of exactly n-th degree with leading coefficient 1, and therefore $= \prod_{r=1}^{n}(\xi-\xi_r)$; the ξ_r are called the characteristic roots of the matrix. The coefficient of ξ^{n-1} is $-\sum_k \alpha_{kk}$, so that

$$\sum_{r=1}^{n} \xi_r = \sum_k \alpha_{kk}.$$

$\sum_k \alpha_{kk}$ is called the trace of the matrix.

6) The THEOREM: *The characteristic roots of $\mathfrak{A}^2$ are the ξ_r^2, and therefore those of $(\mathfrak{A}^2)^2$ are the ξ_r^4.*

Proof: The statement reads:

$$\left| \xi e_{kl} - \sum_m \alpha_{km}\alpha_{ml} \right| = \prod_{r=1}^{n}(\xi - \xi_r^2).$$

Indeed, let η be a number for which $\eta^2 = \xi$. Then the matrix product

$$(\eta e_{kl} + \alpha_{kl})(\eta e_{kl} - \alpha_{kl}) = \left(\sum_m (\eta e_{km} + \alpha_{km})(\eta e_{ml} - \alpha_{ml}) \right)$$

$$= \left(\eta^2 \sum_m e_{km}e_{ml} + \eta \sum_m \alpha_{km}e_{ml} - \eta \sum_m e_{km}\alpha_{ml} - \sum_m \alpha_{km}\alpha_{ml} \right)$$

$$= \left(\eta^2 e_{kl} + \eta \alpha_{kl} - \eta \alpha_{kl} - \sum_m \alpha_{km}\alpha_{ml} \right) = \left(\xi e_{kl} - \sum_m \alpha_{km}\alpha_{ml} \right).$$

so that

$$\left| \eta e_{kl} + \alpha_{kl} \right| \left| \eta e_{kl} - \alpha_{kl} \right| = \left| \xi e_{kl} - \sum_m \alpha_{km}\alpha_{ml} \right|,$$

and in this we have

$$\left| \eta e_{kl} - \alpha_{kl} \right| = \Phi(\eta) = \prod_{r=1}^{n} (\eta - \xi_r),$$

$$\left| \eta e_{kl} + \alpha_{kl} \right| = (-1)^n \left| -\eta e_{kl} - \alpha_{kl} \right| = (-1)^n \Phi(-\eta) = (-1)^n \prod_{r=1}^{n} (-\eta - \xi_r)$$

$$= \prod_{r=1}^{n} (\eta + \xi_r),$$

so that

$$\left| \xi e_{kl} - \sum_m \alpha_{km}\alpha_{ml} \right| = \prod_{r=1}^{n} (\eta^2 - \xi_r^2) = \prod_{r=1}^{n} (\xi - \xi_r^2).$$

———

Now let $n > 0$ be odd, and let

$$S = \sum_{s=0}^{n-1} e^{2\pi i \frac{s^2}{n}}.$$

We first show that

$$|S| = \sqrt{n};$$

this will still be easy.

$$|S|^2 = S\bar{S} = \sum_{s,t=0}^{n-1} e^{\frac{2\pi i}{n}(s^2 - t^2)} = \sum_{s,t} e^{\frac{2\pi i}{n}(s^2 - t^2)},$$

the sum being taken over any two complete sets of residues mod n. Since, when t is fixed, $s+t$ also runs through such a set when s does, we have

$$|S|^2 = \sum_{s,t} e^{\frac{2\pi i}{n}((s+t)^2 - t^2)} = \sum_{s,t} e^{\frac{2\pi i}{n}(s^2 + 2st)} = \sum_{s=0}^{n-1} e^{\frac{2\pi i}{n}s^2} \sum_{t=0}^{n-1} e^{\frac{4\pi i s}{n}t}.$$

In this formula,

$$\sum_{t=0}^{n-1} e^{\frac{4\pi i s}{n} t} = \begin{cases} n & \text{for } n/2s, \text{ that is, } n/s, \\ 0 & \text{otherwise,} \end{cases}$$

so that

$$|S|^2 = n,$$
$$|S| = \sqrt{n}.$$

Now we set

$$\varepsilon = e^{\frac{2\pi i}{n}},$$

and we consider the n-by-n matrix

$$\mathfrak{A} = (\varepsilon^{kl}) \quad (k \text{ and } l = 0,1,\ldots, n-1).$$

If $\xi_1, \ldots, \xi_n$ are its characteristic roots, then our

$$S = \sum_{k=0}^{n-1} \varepsilon^{kk} = \sum_{r=1}^{n} \xi_r$$

is the trace of $\mathfrak{A}$.

We have

$$\mathfrak{A}^2 = \left(\sum_{m=0}^{n-1} \varepsilon^{km+ml} \right) = \left(\sum_{m=0}^{n-1} \varepsilon^{(k+l)m} \right) = (s_{k+l}),$$

where

$$s_j = \sum_{m=0}^{n-1} \varepsilon^{jm} = \begin{cases} n & \text{for } n/j, \\ 0 & \text{otherwise.} \end{cases}$$

It follows further from this that

$$(\mathfrak{A}^2)^2 = \left(\sum_{m=0}^{n-1} s_{k+m} s_{m+l} \right) = (n^2 e_{kl});$$

for if $k=l$ we have

$$\sum_{m=0}^{n-1} s_{k+m} s_{m+l} = \sum_{m=0}^{n-1} s_{k+m}^2 = n^2$$

(since n divides $k+m$ for exactly one m) ; for $k \neq l$ we have

$$\sum_{m=0}^{n-1} s_{k+m} s_{m+l} = 0,$$

since we never have $n/k+m$ and $n/m+l$ simultaneously.

$(\mathfrak{A}^2)^2$ has the ξ_r^4 as its roots, by 6). Moreover, $(\mathfrak{A}^2)^2$ has the characteristic function

$$|\xi e_{kl} - n^2 e_{kl}| = (\xi - n^2)^n.$$

Consequently, $(\mathfrak{A}^2)^2$ has its n roots all $= n^2$. We therefore have

$$\xi_r = i^{a_r} \sqrt{n}; \ a_r = 0, 1, 2, \text{ or } 3.$$

If $i^a \sqrt{n}$ $(a = 0, 1, 2, 3)$ has multiplicity m_a, then

$$S = \sum_{r=1}^{n} \xi_r = \sqrt{n} \ (m_0 - m_2 + i \ (m_1 - m_3)).$$

From

$$|S|^2 = n$$

it follows that

$$(m_0 - m_2)^2 + (m_1 - m_3)^2 = 1.$$

We therefore have

$$m_0 - m_2 = 0, \ m_1 - m_3 = \pm 1. \quad \text{or} \quad m_0 - m_2 = \pm 1, \ m_1 - m_3 = 0,$$

$$S = v \, \eta \, \sqrt{n}, \text{ where } v = \pm 1, \text{ and } \eta = 1 \text{ or } i.$$

Since $\mathfrak{A}^2$ has trace

$$\sum_{r=0}^{n-1} s_{2r} = n,$$

it follows that

$$n \ (m_0 - m_1 + m_2 - m_3) = \sum_{r=1}^{n} \xi_r^2 = n;$$

we therefore have the four equations

$$m_0 + m_1 + m_2 + m_3 = n,$$
$$m_0 + i m_1 - m_2 - i m_3 = v \eta,$$
$$m_0 - m_1 + m_2 - m_3 = 1,$$
$$m_0 - i m_1 - m_2 + i m_3 = v \eta^{-1}$$

for m_0, m_1, m_2, and m_3. From this it follows that

$$2 \ (m_1 - m_3) = v i \ (\eta^{-1} - \eta),$$
$$4 m_2 = n + 1 - v \ (\eta + \eta^{-1}).$$

Since m_2 is an integer, we must have

$$\eta = \begin{cases} 1 & \text{for } n \equiv 1 \ (\text{mod } 4), \\ i & \text{for } n \equiv 3 \ (\text{mod } 4), \end{cases}$$

so that in any case

$$\eta = i^{\left(\frac{n-1}{2}\right)^2}.$$

It remains to be shown that we must have

$$v = 1.$$

This is achieved by computing

$$|\mathfrak{A}| = |\varepsilon^{kl}|$$

in two different ways. On the one hand, since

$$|\xi e_{kl} - \varepsilon^{kl}| = \prod_{r=1}^{n} (\xi - \xi_r),$$

we have, setting $\xi = 0$,

$$|\mathfrak{A}| = (-1)^n \ | -\varepsilon^{kl}| = \prod_{r=1}^{n} \xi_r = n^{\frac{n}{2}} \ i^{m_1 - 2m_2 - m_3};$$

since

$$m_1 - m_3 = \begin{cases} 0 & \text{for } n \equiv 1 \ (\text{mod } 4), \\ v & \text{for } n \equiv 3 \ (\text{mod } 4), \end{cases}$$

and

$$2m_2 = \begin{cases} \dfrac{n+1}{2} - v & \text{for } n \equiv 1 \ (\text{mod } 4), \\[2mm] \dfrac{n+1}{2} & \text{for } n \equiv 3 \ (\text{mod } 4), \end{cases}$$

$$i^v = vi,$$

it follows that

$$|\mathfrak{A}| = n^{\frac{n}{2}} i^{v - \frac{n+1}{2}} = n^{\frac{n}{2}} vi \ i^{-\frac{n+1}{2}} = n^{\frac{n}{2}} vi^{\frac{1-n}{2}} = n^{\frac{n}{2}} vi^{\frac{n^2-n}{2}} = n^{\frac{n}{2}} vi^{\frac{n(n-1)}{2}}.$$

On the other hand, by a well-known formula in determinants, we have

$$|\mathfrak{A}| = \begin{vmatrix} 1 & 1 & \cdots & 1 \\ 1 & \varepsilon & \cdots & \varepsilon^{n-1} \\ \cdots & \cdots & \cdots & \cdots \\ 1 & \varepsilon^{n-1} & \cdots & \varepsilon^{(n-1)(n-1)} \end{vmatrix} = \prod_{0 \le l < k \le n-1} (\varepsilon^k - \varepsilon^l) = \prod_{l<k} e^{\frac{\pi i (k+l)}{n}} \left(e^{\frac{\pi i (k-l)}{n}} - e^{\frac{\pi i (l-k)}{n}} \right)$$

$$= e^{\frac{\pi i}{n} \sum_{l<k} (k+l)} \prod_{l<k} \left(2i \sin \frac{\pi (k-l)}{n} \right) = \prod_{l<k} \left(2i \sin \frac{\pi (k-l)}{n} \right),$$

since

$$\sum_{l<k}(k+l) = \sum_{k=1}^{n-1}\sum_{l=0}^{k-1}(k+l) = \sum_{k=1}^{n-1}\left(k^2+\frac{(k-1)k}{2}\right)$$

$$=\sum_{k=1}^{n-1}\left(-\frac{k(k-1)^2}{2}+\frac{(k+1)k^2}{2}\right)=\frac{n(n-1)^2}{2}=2n\left(\frac{n-1}{2}\right)^2$$

is divisible by $2n$.

We therefore have

$$|\mathfrak{A}| = i^{\frac{n(n-1)}{2}}\prod_{l<k}\left(2\sin\frac{\pi(k-l)}{n}\right);$$

since, in this product, every sine is positive, it follows by comparison with the other formula that

$$v=1.$$

§3

Mertens' Proof

For this proof we must first establish the fact that

$$S = \pm i^{\frac{n-1}{2}} \sqrt{n} = \begin{cases} \pm \sqrt{n} & \text{for } n \equiv 1 \ (\text{mod } 4), \\ \pm i \sqrt{n} & \text{for } n \equiv 3 \ (\text{mod } 4) \end{cases}$$

This is more difficult than the proof given earlier in § 2 of the mere fact that

$$|S| = \sqrt{n};$$

for $n = p$, to be sure, we know from the Remark preceding Theorem 212 and from the proof of that theorem that the determination of the value of S, up to sign, is quite simple. (As already noted, the case $n = p$ would have sufficed for the applications to be made later.)

We first show that if, for $n > 0$, we set

$$\varphi(m, n) = \sum_{s=0}^{n-1} e^{2\pi i \frac{m s^2}{n}} = \sum_{s} e^{2\pi i \frac{m s^2}{n}}$$

over any complete set of residues mod n, then

$$\varphi(m n_2, n_1)\, \varphi(m n_1, n_2) = \varphi(m, n_1 n_2) \text{ for } n_1 > 0, n_2 > 0, (n_1, n_2) = 1.$$

Indeed, we have

$$\varphi(m n_2, n_1)\, \varphi(m n_1, n_2) = \sum_{s_1, s_2} e^{2\pi i \left(\frac{m n_2 s_1^2}{n_1} + \frac{m n_1 s_2^2}{n_2} \right)} = \sum_{s_1, s_2} e^{2\pi i \frac{m (n_2^2 s_1^2 + n_1^2 s_2^2)}{n_1 n_2}}$$

$$= \sum_{s_1, s_2} e^{2\pi i \frac{m (n_2 s_1 + n_1 s_2)^2}{n_1 n_2}} = \sum_{s=0}^{n_1 n_2 - 1} e^{2\pi i \frac{m s^2}{n_1 n_2}} = \varphi(m, n_1 n_2)$$

by Theorem 73.

213

For $n=1$ we have

$$\varphi(m, 1) = 1.$$

If $n > 1$ and $n = \underset{p|n}{\varPi} p^l$ is its canonical decomposition, then repeated application of the above functional relation yields

$$\varphi(1, n) = \underset{p|n}{\varPi} \varphi\left(\frac{n}{p^l}, \, p^l\right).$$

For $l \geqq 2$ and $p \nmid 2m$, we now have

$$\varphi(m, p^l) = p \, \varphi(m, p^{l-2}).$$

For,

$$\varphi(m, p^l) = \sum_{s=0}^{p^l-1} e^{2\pi i \frac{m\,s^2}{p^l}} = \sum_{t=0}^{p^{l-1}-1} \sum_{z=0}^{p-1} e^{2\pi i \frac{m\,(p^{l-1}z+t)^2}{p^l}}$$

$$= \sum_{t=0}^{p^{l-1}-1} e^{2\pi i \frac{m\,t^2}{p^l}} \sum_{z=0}^{p-1} e^{2\pi i \frac{2\,m\,t\,z}{p}}.$$

In this formula, the inner sum is p, in case $p|2mt$, that is, in case $p|t$; otherwise it is 0. Consequently

$$\varphi(m, p^l) = p \sum_{v=0}^{p^{l-2}-1} e^{2\pi i \frac{m\,v^2}{p^{l-2}}} = p\varphi(m, p^{l-2}).$$

From this it follows, for $p \nmid 2m$ and $l \geqq 1$, that

$$\varphi(m, p^l) = \begin{cases} p^{\frac{l}{2}} \, \varphi(m, 1) = p^{\frac{l}{2}} & \text{for } l \text{ even.} \\ p^{\frac{l-1}{2}} \, \varphi(m, p) & \text{for } l \text{ odd.} \end{cases}$$

It follows, for odd $n > 1$, that

$$\varphi(1, n) = P_n \, \varPi \varphi\left(\frac{n}{p^l}, \, p\right),$$

where $P_n > 0$ and the product is taken over those primes p that go an odd number of times into n.

Now we can easily show that

$$(\varphi(m,p))^2 = \left(\frac{-1}{p}\right) p \text{ for } p \nmid 2m.$$

For if

$$\varrho = e^{\frac{2\pi i m}{p}},$$

and if a runs over the quadratic residues in the interval $0 < x < p$, then we have

$$\varphi(m,p) = \sum_{s=0}^{p-1} e^{2\pi i \frac{m s^2}{p}} = 1 + 2 \sum_a \varrho^a;$$

and from here on, everything continues as in the proof of Theorem 212, together with the Remark preceding it, except only that here ϱ represents any primitive p-th root of unity, while there it represented a particular one.

Thus

$$(\varphi(1,n))^2 = Q_n \prod_{\substack{p|n \\ 2\nmid l}} \left(\frac{-1}{p}\right) = Q_n \left(\frac{-1}{n}\right) = Q_n (-1)^{\frac{n-1}{2}}, \quad Q_n > 0,$$

so that

$$S^2 = (\varphi(1,n))^2 = (-1)^{\frac{n-1}{2}} n,$$

since we have already established directly, in § 2, that

$$|S| = |\varphi(1,n)| = \sqrt{n}.$$

(It also follows directly, of course, since

$$P_n = \frac{\sqrt{n}}{\prod\limits_{\substack{p|n \\ 2\nmid l}} \sqrt{p}}, \quad Q_n = P_n^2 \prod_{\substack{p|n \\ 2\nmid l}} p,$$

that

and

$$Q_n = n$$

$$S = \pm i^{\frac{n-1}{2}} \sqrt{n}$$

without

$$|S| = \sqrt{n}$$

first being shown.)

Consequently: Let $n > 0$ be odd. We already know that

$$S = \pm i^{\frac{n-1}{2}} \sqrt{n} = \pm \frac{1+i}{1+i^n} \sqrt{n},$$

and we should like to show that the upper sign always holds.

Let us define R by

$$(1+i)\,R = \sum_{s=0}^{2n-1} e^{\frac{\pi i s^2}{2n}}.$$

Then we have

$$(1+i)\,R = \sum_{r=0}^{n-1} e^{\frac{\pi i (2r)^2}{2n}} + \sum_{r=0}^{n-1} e^{\frac{\pi i (2r+1)^2}{2n}}$$

$$= \sum_{r=0}^{n-1} e^{\frac{2\pi i r^2}{n}} + \sum_{t=-\frac{n-1}{2}}^{\frac{n-1}{2}} e^{\frac{\pi i \left(2\left(\frac{n-1}{2}+t\right)+1\right)^2}{2n}} = S + \sum_{t=-\frac{n-1}{2}}^{\frac{n-1}{2}} e^{\frac{\pi i (n+2t)^2}{2n}}$$

$$= S + \sum_{t=-\frac{n-1}{2}}^{\frac{n-1}{2}} e^{\frac{\pi i (n^2+4tn+4t^2)}{2n}} = S + i^n \sum_{t=-\frac{n-1}{2}}^{\frac{n-1}{2}} e^{\frac{2\pi i t^2}{n}} = (1+i^n)\,S,$$

$$R = \frac{1+i^n}{1+i}\,S = \pm\sqrt{n}.$$

R is therefore real, and we have to show merely (merely! this is where the computation really begins in earnest) that

$$R > 0.$$

Let us set

$$\frac{\pi}{64\,n} = \omega$$

for the sake of brevity. Then we have

$$\sum_{s=0}^{8n-1} e^{8s^2 i\omega} = \sum_{s=0}^{8n-1} e^{\frac{\pi i s^2}{8n}} = \sum_{s=0}^{4n-1} e^{\frac{\pi i s^2}{8n}} + \sum_{s=4n}^{8n-1} e^{\frac{\pi i s^2}{8n}}.$$

Here, on the one hand, we have

$$\sum_{s=4n}^{8n-1} e^{\frac{\pi i s^2}{8n}} = \sum_{t=0}^{4n-1} e^{\frac{\pi i (4n+t)^2}{8n}} = \sum_{t=0}^{4n-1} e^{\frac{\pi i (16n^2+8nt+t^2)}{8n}} = \sum_{t=0}^{4n-1} (-1)^t\, e^{\frac{\pi i t^2}{8n}},$$

and on the other hand,

$$\sum_{s=4n}^{8n-1} e^{\frac{\pi i s^2}{8n}} = \sum_{u=1}^{4n} e^{\frac{\pi i (8n-u)^2}{8n}} = \sum_{u=1}^{4n} e^{\frac{\pi i (64n^2-16nu+u^2)}{8n}} = \sum_{u=1}^{4n} e^{\frac{\pi i u^2}{8n}} = \sum_{u=0}^{4n-1} e^{\frac{\pi i u^2}{8n}},$$

so that, on the one hand, we have

$$\sum_{s=0}^{8n-1} e^{8s^2i\omega} = \sum_{s=0}^{4n-1}(1+(-1)^s)\, e^{\frac{\pi i s^2}{8n}} = 2\sum_{\substack{s=0\\2/s}}^{4n-1} e^{\frac{\pi i s^2}{8n}} = 2\sum_{v=0}^{2n-1} e^{\frac{\pi i v^2}{2n}} = 2(1+i)R,$$

and on the other hand,

$$\sum_{s=0}^{8n-1} e^{8s^2i\omega} = 2\sum_{s=0}^{4n-1} e^{\frac{\pi i s^2}{8n}},$$

and consequently

$$(1+i)R = \sum_{s=0}^{4n-1} e^{\frac{\pi i s^2}{8n}} = \sum_{s=0}^{4n-1} e^{8s^2i\omega};$$

since R is real, it follows that

$$R = \sum_{s=0}^{4n-1} \cos 8\, s^2\omega = \sum_{s=1}^{4n-1} \sin 8\, s^2\omega.$$

Now

$$\sin(\alpha+\beta)\sin(\alpha-\beta) = (\sin\alpha\cos\beta+\cos\alpha\sin\beta)(\sin\alpha\cos\beta-\cos\alpha\sin\beta)$$
$$=\sin^2\alpha\cos^2\beta-\cos^2\alpha\sin^2\beta=\sin^2\alpha(1-\sin^2\beta)-(1-\sin^2\alpha)\sin^2\beta=\sin^2\alpha-\sin^2\beta;$$

setting

$$\alpha=(2s+1)^2\omega,\ \ \beta=(2s-1)^2\omega,$$

we have, since

$$\alpha+\beta=(8s^2+2)\omega,\ \ \alpha-\beta=8s\omega,$$

that

$$\frac{\sin^2((2s+1)^2\omega)-\sin^2((2s-1)^2\omega)}{\sin 8\,s\omega}=\sin(8s^2+2)\omega$$
$$=\sin 8\,s^2\omega\cos 2\,\omega+\cos 8\,s^2\omega\sin 2\,\omega$$

for $1\leq s\leq 4n-1$ $\left(\text{we have }\sin 8s\omega>0\text{ since }0<8s\omega<32n\omega=\dfrac{\pi}{2}\right)$; it follows, by summation over $s=1,2,\ldots,4n-1$, that

$$R\cos 2\,\omega+(R-1)\sin 2\,\omega = \sum_{s=1}^{4n-1} \frac{\sin^2((2s+1)^2\omega)-\sin^2((2s-1)^2\omega)}{\sin 8s\omega},$$

so that, by so-called summation by parts,

$$R\left(\cos 2\omega + \sin 2\omega\right) = \sin 2\omega - \frac{\sin^2 \omega}{\sin 8\omega}$$

$$+ \sum_{s=1}^{4n-2} \sin^2((2s+1)^2\omega)\left(\frac{1}{\sin 8s\omega} - \frac{1}{\sin 8(s+1)\omega}\right) + \frac{\sin^2((8n-1)^2\omega)}{\sin(8(4n-1)\omega)}.$$

The right-hand side is positive; for, first of all, we have

$$\sin 2\omega - \frac{\sin^2 \omega}{\sin 8\omega} = \frac{\sin 2\omega \sin 8\omega - \sin \omega \sin \omega}{\sin 8\omega} > 0;$$

and second, in the sum, every term

$$\frac{1}{\sin 8s\omega} - \frac{1}{\sin 8(s+1)\omega} > 0,$$

since the sine function is increasing in the first quadrant; and third,

$$\sin 8(4n-1)\omega > 0.$$

Moreover, $\cos 2\omega + \sin 2\omega$ is > 0; and we therefore have

$$R > 0.$$

CHAPTER VII

REDUCTION TO FUNDAMENTAL DISCRIMINANTS

DEFINITION 38: *Let d continue to be non-square and* $\equiv 0$ *or* 1 (mod 4). *d is called a fundamental discriminant if it is not divisible by the square of any odd prime and is either odd or* $\equiv 8$ *or* 12 (mod 16).

THEOREM 213: *Every* $d \equiv 0$ *or* 1 (mod 4) *which is non-square can be written, and written uniquely, in the form* fm^2, *where* $m > 0$ *and* f *is a fundamental discriminant.*

Proof: 1) Let d be odd. If $d = fm^2$ at all, in the sense of the theorem, then m^2 must be the greatest square that divides d. Then f is actually a fundamental discriminant; for, first, $f \equiv d \equiv 1$ (mod 4), second, f is non-square, and third, f is square-free.

2) Let d be even.

21) I shall first show that d may be written in the form fm^2. In any case, we have $d = qr^2$, where $r > 0$ and q is square-free and non-square.

If $q \equiv 1$ (mod 4), then q is a fundamental discriminant.

If $q \equiv 2$ or 3 (mod 4), then r is even (since $4|d$), so that $d = 4q \left(\frac{r}{2} \right)^2$, and $4q$ is a fundamental discriminant; for $4q$ is first of all $\equiv 0$ (mod 4), second, non-square, third, not divisible by the square of any odd prime, and fourth, $\equiv 8$ or 12 (mod 16).

22) I shall now prove uniqueness. From the fact that $d = fm^2$, $m > 0$, and f is a fundamental discriminant, it follows that m^2 is divisible by the greatest odd square contained in d.

If f is odd, then f is square-free, so that m is the above r, and f is the above q.

If f is even, so that $f \equiv 8$ or 12 (mod 16), then $4 \nmid \frac{f}{4}$, so that $2m$ is the above r, and f is the above $4q$.

THEOREM 214: *Let* $d = fm^2$ *be the decomposition of our d in accordance with Theorem 213. Then we have*

$$K(d) = \prod_{p|m} \left(1 - \left(\frac{f}{p} \right) \frac{1}{p} \right) K(f).$$

Remark: Since the product on the right contains only a finite number of factors, it follows that the determination of $K(d)$ is reduced to the determination of $K(f)$, so that in the next chapter we may restrict our attention to fundamental discriminants.

Proof: If $\sum\limits_{n=1}^{\infty} b_n$ converges and if $a_1 + \ldots + a_u$ is a finite sum, then we certainly have

$$(a_1 + \cdots + a_u)(b_1 + \cdots \text{ad inf.}) = (a_1 b_1 + a_1 b_2 + \cdots) + (0 + a_2 b_1 + 0 + a_2 b_2 + \cdots)$$

$$+ (0 + 0 + a_3 b_1 + 0 + 0 + a_3 b_2 + \cdots) + \cdots + (0 + 0 + \cdots + a_u b_1 + \cdots)$$

$$= \sum_{\substack{s=1 \\ r|s \\ r \leq u}}^{\infty} \sum_{r} a_r b_s \, .$$

The right-hand side of our assertion, namely

$$\sum_{r|m} \mu(r) \left(\frac{f}{r}\right) \frac{1}{r} \cdot \sum_{n=1}^{\infty} \left(\frac{f}{n}\right) \frac{1}{n} \, ,$$

is therefore

$$= \sum_{\substack{s=1 \\ r|s \\ r|m}}^{\infty} \sum \mu(r) \left(\frac{f}{r}\right) \frac{1}{r} \left(\frac{f}{\frac{s}{r}}\right) \frac{1}{\frac{s}{r}} = \sum_{\substack{s=1 \\ r|(s,\,m)}}^{\infty} \sum \mu(r) \left(\frac{f}{s}\right) \frac{1}{s}$$

$$= \sum_{s=1}^{\infty} \left(\frac{f}{s}\right) \frac{1}{s} \sum_{r|(s,\,m)} \mu(r) = \sum_{\substack{s=1 \\ (s,\,m)=1}}^{\infty} \left(\frac{f}{s}\right) \frac{1}{s} = \sum_{s=1}^{\infty} \left(\frac{f m^2}{s}\right) \frac{1}{s} = \sum_{s=1}^{\infty} \left(\frac{d}{s}\right) \frac{1}{s} = K(d).$$

CHAPTER VIII

THE DETERMINATION OF $K(d)$ FOR
FUNDAMENTAL DISCRIMINANTS

Let d always represent a fundamental discriminant throughout Chapters VIII and IX.

If $\xi > 0$, then by $\sqrt{\xi}$ I always mean the positive number whose square is ξ. In this chapter, by way of exception, if $\xi < 0$, the symbol $\sqrt{\xi}$ will be given a definite value, namely $i\sqrt{|\xi|}$.

THEOREM 215: *If $n > 0$ and if r runs through a complete set of positive residues* mod $|d|$, *then*

$$\sum_r \left(\frac{d}{r}\right) e^{\frac{2\pi i}{|d|} nr} = \left(\frac{d}{n}\right) \sqrt{d}.$$

Remark: The fact that this sum is independent of the choice of residue classes follows immediately from the fact that $\left(\dfrac{d}{r}\right)$ (by Theorem 99, 4)) and $e^{\frac{2\pi i}{|d|} nr}$ each have period $|d|$ (with respect to the positive variable r).

Proof: The numbers -4, 8, -8, and $(-1)^{\frac{p-1}{2}} p$, where $p > 2$, are all fundamental discriminants; let them for the moment be called prime discriminants.

It clearly suffices to prove all of the following four statements:

1) d may be written in the form Πq, where the q are prime discriminants and every pair of factors is relatively prime. (That is, at most one of the numbers -4, 8, -8 appears, and each $(-1)^{\frac{p-1}{2}} p$ appears at most once.)

2) Every non-empty Πq, where the q are prime discriminants which are pairwise relatively·prime, is a fundamental discriminant.

3) If the theorem is true for two fundamental discriminants d_1 and d_2 for which $(d_1, d_2) = 1$, then it holds for $d_1 d_2$ (which, by 1) and 2), is certainly a fundamental discriminant).

4) The theorem is true for prime discriminants.

Proof of 1): If d is odd, then $d \equiv 1 \pmod 4$ and is square-free, so that

$$d = \prod_{p|d} (-1)^{\frac{p-1}{2}} p,$$

where every $p > 2$.

If $d \equiv 8 \pmod{16}$, then $\dfrac{d}{8}$ is odd and square-free, so that for a suitable choice of sign we have

$$d = \pm 8 \prod_{\substack{p|d \\ p>2}} (-1)^{\frac{p-1}{2}} p$$

If $d \equiv 12 \pmod{16}$, then $\dfrac{d}{4} \equiv -1 \pmod 4$ and is square-free, so that

$$d = (-4) \prod_{\substack{p|d \\ p>2}} (-1)^{\frac{p-1}{2}} p.$$

Proof of 2): $\prod q$ is not divisible by the square of any odd prime, is non-square, and is $\equiv 1 \pmod 4$ or $\equiv 8$ or $12 \pmod{16}$.

Proof of 3): From

$$\sum_{r_1} \left(\frac{d_1}{r_1}\right) e^{\frac{2\pi i}{|d_1|} n r_1} = \left(\frac{d_1}{n}\right) \sqrt{d_1}, \quad \sum_{r_2} \left(\frac{d_2}{r_2}\right) e^{\frac{2\pi i}{|d_2|} n r_2} = \left(\frac{d_2}{n}\right) \sqrt{d_2}$$

it follows that

(163)
$$\sum_{r_1,r_2} \left(\frac{d_1}{r_1}\right)\left(\frac{d_2}{r_2}\right) e^{\frac{2\pi i n}{|d_1 d_2|}(r_1|d_2|+r_2|d_1|)} = \left(\frac{d_1}{n}\right)\left(\frac{d_2}{n}\right) \sqrt{d_1} \sqrt{d_2}.$$

For $p \nmid d_1 d_2$ and $p > 2$, it follows from Theorem 81 that

$$\left(\frac{d_1}{p}\right)\left(\frac{d_2}{p}\right) = \left(\frac{d_1 d_2}{p}\right);$$

for $p \nmid d_1 d_2$ and $p = 2$, it follows from Definition 20 that

$$\left(\frac{d_1}{p}\right)\left(\frac{d_2}{p}\right) = \left(\frac{2}{|d_1|}\right)\left(\frac{2}{|d_2|}\right) = \left(\frac{2}{|d_1| |d_2|}\right) = \left(\frac{d_1 d_2}{p}\right);$$

for $p | d_1 d_2$ it follows from Definition 20 that

$$\left(\frac{d_1}{p}\right)\left(\frac{d_2}{p}\right) = 0 = \left(\frac{d_1 d_2}{p}\right).$$

For every p we therefore have

$$\left(\frac{d_1}{p}\right)\left(\frac{d_2}{p}\right)=\left(\frac{d_1 d_2}{p}\right).$$

Consequently, by Definition 20, we have

$$\left(\frac{d_1}{n}\right)\left(\frac{d_2}{n}\right)=\left(\frac{d_1 d_2}{n}\right),$$

so that by (163) and Theorem 99, 3), we have

$$(164)\ \sum_{r_1,r_2}\left(\frac{d_1}{r_1\,|d_2|}\right)\left(\frac{d_2}{r_2\,|d_1|}\right)e^{\frac{2\pi i n}{|d_1 d_2|}(r_1|d_2|+r_2|d_1|)}=\left(\frac{d_1}{|d_2|}\right)\left(\frac{d_2}{|d_1|}\right)\left(\frac{d_1 d_2}{n}\right)\sqrt{d_1}\,\sqrt{d_2}.$$

By Theorem 73, $r_1|d_2|+r_2|d_1|$ runs through a complete positive system of residues $r \bmod |d_1 d_2|$; by Theorem 99, 4) we have

$$\left(\frac{d_1}{r_1\,|d_2|}\right)=\left(\frac{d_1}{r_1\,|d_2|+r_2\,|d_1|}\right),\ \left(\frac{d_2}{r_2\,|d_1|}\right)=\left(\frac{d_2}{r_1\,|d_2|+r_2\,|d_1|}\right).$$

(164) therefore yields

$$\sum_r\left(\frac{d_1 d_2}{r}\right)e^{\frac{2\pi i n}{|d_1 d_2|}r}=\sum_r\left(\frac{d_1}{r}\right)\left(\frac{d_2}{r}\right)e^{\frac{2\pi i n}{|d_1 d_2|}r}=\left(\frac{d_1}{|d_2|}\right)\left(\frac{d_2}{|d_1|}\right)\left(\frac{d_1 d_2}{n}\right)\sqrt{d_1}\,\sqrt{d_2}.$$

It therefore suffices to prove only that

$$\left(\frac{d_1}{|d_2|}\right)\left(\frac{d_2}{|d_1|}\right)\sqrt{d_1}\,\sqrt{d_2}=\sqrt{d_1 d_2}.$$

Since

$$\sqrt{d_1}\,\sqrt{d_2}=\begin{cases}-\sqrt{d_1 d_2} & \text{for } d_1<0,\ d_2<0,\\ \sqrt{d_1 d_2} & \text{otherwise,}\end{cases}$$

I therefore have to show that

$$\left(\frac{d_1}{|d_2|}\right)\left(\frac{d_2}{|d_1|}\right)=\begin{cases}-1 & \text{for } d_1<0,\ d_2<0,\\ 1 & \text{otherwise.}\end{cases}$$

Since $(d_1, d_2) = 1$, let d_1 be odd, without loss of generality. Then, by Theorem 98, 1), we have

$$\left(\frac{d_1}{|d_2|}\right)\left(\frac{d_2}{|d_1|}\right) = \left(\frac{|d_2|}{|d_1|}\right)\left(\frac{d_2}{|d_1|}\right).$$

For $d_2 > 0$, this reads

$$\left(\frac{d_2}{|d_1|}\right)^2 = 1;$$

for $d_2 < 0$, it reads

$$\left(\frac{|d_2|}{|d_1|}\right)(-1)^{\frac{|d_1|-1}{2}}\left(\frac{|d_2|}{|d_1|}\right) = (-1)^{\frac{|d_1|-1}{2}} = \begin{cases} 1 & \text{in case } d_1 > 0, \\ -1 & \text{in case } d_1 < 0. \end{cases}$$

Proof of 4): Let d be a prime discriminant. We shall investigate the cases $(n, d) > 1$ and $(n, d) = 1$; in the latter case it suffices to carry out the proof for $n = 1$, that is, to show that

$$\sum_r \left(\frac{d}{r}\right) e^{\frac{2\pi i r}{|d|}} = \sqrt{d};$$

for, if we set $e^{\frac{2\pi i}{|d|}} = \varrho$, then for $(n, d) = 1$ we have

$$\left(\frac{d}{n}\right)\sum_r\left(\frac{d}{r}\right)\varrho^r = \left(\frac{d}{n}\right)\sum_r\left(\frac{d}{nr}\right)\varrho^{nr} = \sum_r\left(\frac{d}{n^2 r}\right)\varrho^{nr} = \sum_r\left(\frac{d}{r}\right)\varrho^{nr}.$$

In case $(n, d) > 1$, the statement of the theorem reads

$$\sum_r \left(\frac{d}{r}\right)\varrho^{nr} = 0.$$

41) For $d = -4$, we have

$$\sum_r \left(\frac{d}{r}\right)\varrho^{nr} = \sum_r\left(\frac{-4}{r}\right)i^{nr} = i^n - i^{3n} = \begin{cases} (-1)^m - (-1)^{3m} = 0 & \text{in case } n = 2m, \\ i - i^3 = 2i = \sqrt{-4} & \text{in case } n = 1. \end{cases}$$

42) For $d = \pm 8$, it follows from Theorem 93 $\left(\text{since } \varrho^2 = i, \ \varrho = \dfrac{1+i}{\sqrt 2}\right)$ that

$$\sum_r \left(\frac{d}{r}\right)\varrho^{nr} = \sum_r\left(\frac{\pm 8}{r}\right)\varrho^{nr} = \sum_r\left(\frac{\pm 2}{r}\right)\varrho^{nr} = \varrho^n \mp \varrho^{3n} - \varrho^{5n} \pm \varrho^{7n}$$

$$= \varrho^n\,(1 \mp i^n - i^{2n} \pm i^{3n}).$$

This reads

$$\varrho^n(1\mp(-1)^m-1\pm(-1)^{3m})=0 \qquad \text{in case } n=2m,$$

$$\frac{1+i}{\sqrt{2}}(1\mp i+1\mp i)=\frac{1+i}{\sqrt{2}}2(1\mp i)\begin{cases} =2\sqrt{2}=\sqrt{8} & \text{in case } n=1,\ d=8, \\ =2i\sqrt{2}=\sqrt{-8} & \text{in case } n=1,\ d=-8. \end{cases}$$

43) For $d=(-1)^{\frac{p-1}{2}}p$, we have

in case $(n,d)>1$, since $p|n$ and because $\left(\dfrac{d}{r}\right)$ is a character of the second kind mod $|d|$:

$$\sum_r \left(\frac{d}{r}\right)\varrho^{nr}=\sum_r\left(\frac{d}{r}\right)=0,$$

in case $n=1$, by Theorem 98, 1) and Theorem 212:

$$\sum_r \left(\frac{d}{r}\right)\varrho^{nr}=\sum_r\left(\frac{d}{r}\right)\varrho^r=\sum_r\left(\frac{r}{|d|}\right)\varrho^r=\sum_r\left(\frac{r}{p}\right)\varrho^r=\sum_{r=1}^{p-1}\left(\frac{r}{p}\right)e^{\frac{2\pi i r}{p}}$$

$$=\sqrt{(-1)^{\frac{p-1}{2}}p}.$$

(The entire machinery of Chapter VI was necessary only for subcase 43) of the fourth statement.)

THEOREM 216: *For $0<\varphi<2\pi$, we have*

(165) $$\sum_{n=1}^{\infty}\frac{\sin n\varphi}{n}=\frac{\pi}{2}-\frac{\varphi}{2},$$

(166) $$\sum_{n=1}^{\infty}\frac{\cos n\varphi}{n}=-\log\left(2\sin\frac{\varphi}{2}\right).$$

Proof: This I assume known from analysis. Otherwise, the inexperienced reader may derive (165) from the Fourier expansion of the very well-behaved right-hand side; (166) preferably not in this way, because of the singularities $\varphi=0$ and $\varphi=2\pi$, but rather from the fact that for $|\xi|\leq1$, with the exception of $\xi=1$ (ξ complex), we have, by suitable normalization of the imaginary part of the logarithm (this normalization being arbitrary, since it drops out immediately),

$$\sum_{n=1}^{\infty}\frac{\xi^n}{n}=-\log(1-\xi),$$

from which, if we set $\xi=e^{\varphi i}$, our result follows by comparison of the real parts.

THEOREM 217: *If d is a fundamental discriminant, then*

$$K(d) = \begin{cases} -\dfrac{1}{\sqrt{d}} \sum\limits_{r=1}^{d-1} \left(\dfrac{d}{r}\right) \log \sin \dfrac{\pi r}{d} & \text{for } d>0, \\[4mm] -\dfrac{\pi}{|d|^{\frac{3}{2}}} \sum\limits_{r=1}^{|d|-1} \left(\dfrac{d}{r}\right) r & \text{for } d<0. \end{cases}$$

Proof: By Theorem 215, we have

$$\sqrt{d}\,K(d) = \sum_{n=1}^{\infty} \left(\frac{d}{n}\right) \sqrt{d}\,\frac{1}{n} = \sum_{n=1}^{\infty} \frac{1}{n} \sum_{r=1}^{|d|-1} \left(\frac{d}{r}\right) e^{\frac{2\pi i}{|d|} nr}$$

(167)
$$= \sum_{r=1}^{|d|-1} \left(\frac{d}{r}\right) \sum_{n=1}^{\infty} \frac{1}{n} e^{\frac{2\pi i}{|d|} nr}$$

(since $\sum\limits_{n=1}^{\infty}$ on the right converges, by Theorem 216, since $0 < \dfrac{2\pi r}{|d|} < 2\pi$).

1) Let $d>0$. By (166), it follows from (167), since the left-hand side is real, that

$$\sqrt{d}\,K(d) = \sum_{r=1}^{d-1} \left(\frac{d}{r}\right) \sum_{n=1}^{\infty} \frac{\cos\left(n\dfrac{2\pi r}{d}\right)}{n} = -\sum_{r=1}^{d-1} \left(\frac{d}{r}\right) \log\left(2 \sin \frac{\pi r}{d}\right)$$

$$= -\sum_{r=1}^{d-1} \left(\frac{d}{r}\right) \log \sin \frac{\pi r}{d}$$

since

$$\log 2 \sum_{r=1}^{d-1} \left(\frac{d}{r}\right) = 0.$$

2) Let $d<0$. By (165), it follows from (167), since the left-hand side is pure imaginary, that

$$\sqrt{|d|}\,K(d) = \sum_{r=1}^{|d|-1} \left(\frac{d}{r}\right) \sum_{n=1}^{\infty} \frac{\sin\left(n\dfrac{2\pi r}{|d|}\right)}{n} = \sum_{r=1}^{|d|-1} \left(\frac{d}{r}\right) \left(\frac{\pi}{2} - \frac{\pi r}{|d|}\right)$$

(168)
$$= -\frac{\pi}{|d|} \sum_{r=1}^{|d|-1} \left(\frac{d}{r}\right) r.$$

CHAPTER IX

FINAL FORMULAS FOR THE CLASS NUMBER

THEOREM 218: *Let d be a fundamental discriminant. Then we have*

$$\varepsilon^{h(d)} = \frac{\prod\limits_{t} \sin \dfrac{\pi t}{d}}{\prod\limits_{s} \sin \dfrac{\pi s}{d}} \quad \text{for } d>0,$$

(169)
$$h(d) = \frac{w}{2|d|}(\Sigma\, t - \Sigma\, s) \quad \text{for } d<0,$$

where s runs through the numbers in the interval $0<r<|d|$ *for which* $\left(\dfrac{d}{r}\right)=1$ *and t through those numbers in the same interval for which* $\left(\dfrac{d}{r}\right)=-1.$

Remarks: 1) for $d=(-1)^{\frac{p-1}{2}} p$, where $p>2$, it follows from Theorem 98, 1) that this means that s runs through the quadratic residues and t through the quadratic non-residues mod p between 0 and p.

2) In case $d>0$, it follows from Theorem 101 that the right-hand side of the statement also

$$= \left(\frac{\prod\limits_{t<\frac{d}{2}} \sin \dfrac{\pi t}{d}}{\prod\limits_{s<\frac{d}{2}} \sin \dfrac{\pi s}{d}} \right)^{2}.$$

Proof: 1) Let $d>0$. By Theorems 209 and 217, we have

$$h(d) = -\frac{\sqrt{d}}{\log \varepsilon}\frac{1}{\sqrt{d}}\sum_{r=1}^{d-1}\left(\frac{d}{r}\right)\log\sin\frac{\pi r}{d} = \frac{1}{\log \varepsilon}\left(\Sigma\log\sin\frac{\pi t}{d} - \Sigma\log\sin\frac{\pi s}{d}\right).$$

2) Let $d<0$. By Theorems 209 and 217, we have

$$h(d) = -w\frac{\sqrt{|d|}}{2\pi}\frac{\pi}{|d|^{\frac{3}{2}}}\sum_{r=1}^{|d|-1}\left(\frac{d}{r}\right)r = \frac{w}{2|d|}(\Sigma\, t - \Sigma\, s).$$

227

For $d<0$ I shall develop—for general purposes, first of all, and secondly to carry out what was promised in the Introduction—still another, and even simpler, formula for $h(d)$, and—since the elementary transformation of (169) could be carried out, to be sure, but would be quite laborious—I shall do this by once again bringing in the series $K(d)$.

Theorem 219: *Let $d<0$ be a fundamental discriminant. Then*

$$h(d)= \frac{w}{2\left(2-\left(\frac{d}{2}\right)\right)} \sum_{r=1}^{\left[\frac{|d|}{2}\right]} \left(\frac{d}{r}\right).$$

Remark: For $d=-p$, $p\equiv3$ (mod 4) and $p>3$, this is precisely what was asserted in (123), since

$$\left(\frac{d}{r}\right) = \left(\frac{r}{p}\right), \quad \left[\frac{|d|}{2}\right]=\frac{p-1}{2}, \quad \frac{w}{2}=1, \quad 2-\left(\frac{d}{2}\right)= \begin{cases} 3 \text{ for } p\equiv3 \text{ (mod 8)}, \\ 1 \text{ for } p\equiv7 \text{ (mod 8)}. \end{cases}$$

Proof: By (165) we have, for $2\pi<\varphi<4\pi$,

$$\sum_{n=1}^{\infty}\frac{\sin n\varphi}{n} = \sum_{n=1}^{\infty}\frac{\sin n(\varphi-2\pi)}{n} = \frac{\pi}{2}-\frac{\varphi-2\pi}{2} = \frac{\pi}{2}-\frac{\varphi}{2}+\pi.$$

The series on the left converges for $\varphi=2\pi$ as well; by Theorem 215 (with $2n$ in place of n), we therefore have

$$\sqrt{d}\,K(d)\left(\frac{d}{2}\right) = \sum_{n=1}^{\infty}\left(\frac{d}{2n}\right)\sqrt{d}\,\frac{1}{n} = \sum_{n=1}^{\infty}\frac{1}{n}\sum_{r=1}^{|d|-1}\left(\frac{d}{r}\right)e^{\frac{2\pi i}{|d|}2nr},$$

$$\sqrt{|d|}\,K(d)\left(\frac{d}{2}\right) = \sum_{n=1}^{\infty}\frac{1}{n}\sum_{r=1}^{|d|-1}\left(\frac{d}{r}\right)\sin\left(n\frac{4\pi r}{|d|}\right) = \sum_{r=1}^{|d|-1}\left(\frac{d}{r}\right)\sum_{n=1}^{\infty}\frac{\sin\left(n\frac{4\pi r}{|d|}\right)}{n}$$

$$= \sum_{1\leq r\leq\frac{|d|}{2}}\left(\frac{d}{r}\right)\left(\frac{\pi}{2}-\frac{2\pi r}{|d|}\right) + \sum_{\frac{|d|}{2}<r<|d|}\left(\frac{d}{r}\right)\left(\frac{\pi}{2}-\frac{2\pi r}{|d|}+\pi\right)$$

(I have, to be sure, replaced $\sum_n$ by the incorrect value $-\frac{\pi}{2}$ instead of 0, for $r=\frac{|d|}{2}$; this is harmless, however, since for d even we certainly have $\left(\frac{d}{\frac{|d|}{2}}\right)=0$, since $4|d$). It therefore follows, by (168), that

$$\sqrt{|d|}\,K(d)\left(\frac{d}{2}\right) = -\frac{2\pi}{|d|}\sum_{r=1}^{|d|-1}\left(\frac{d}{r}\right)r + \pi\sum_{\frac{|d|}{2}<r<|d|}\left(\frac{d}{r}\right)$$

$$= 2\sqrt{|d|}\,K(d) + \pi\sum_{\frac{|d|}{2}<r<|d|}\left(\frac{d}{r}\right) = 2\sqrt{|d|}\,K(d) - \pi\sum_{0<r\leq\frac{|d|}{2}}\left(\frac{d}{r}\right),$$

$$\sqrt{|d|}\left(2-\left(\frac{d}{2}\right)\right)K(d) = \pi\sum_{0<r\leq\frac{|d|}{2}}\left(\frac{d}{r}\right),$$

so that, by Theorem 209, we have

$$h(d) = \frac{w\sqrt{|d|}}{2\pi}\frac{\pi}{\sqrt{|d|}}\frac{1}{2-\left(\frac{d}{2}\right)}\sum_{0<r\leq\frac{|d|}{2}}\left(\frac{d}{r}\right) = \frac{w}{2\left(2-\left(\frac{d}{2}\right)\right)}\sum_{r=1}^{\left[\frac{|d|}{2}\right]}\left(\frac{d}{r}\right).$$

APPENDIX

EXERCISES

EXERCISES FOR PART ONE

Exercises for Chapter I

1. Suppose $b>0$ and $b \nmid a$. Put $r_0=a$ and $r_1=b$ and determine $r_2, r_3, \ldots,$ r_n by the relations:

$$r_0=r_1 q_1+r_2, \qquad 0<r_2<r_1,$$
$$r_1=r_2 q_2+r_3, \qquad 0<r_3<r_2,$$

$$\cdots$$

$$r_{n-2}=r_{n-1}q_{n-1}+r_n, \quad 0<r_n<r_{n-1},$$
$$r_{n-1}=r_n q_n, \qquad 0=r_{n+1}.$$

Show that r_n, the last non-zero remainder, is the greatest common divisor of a and b. This process for finding the greatest common divisor is known as the Euclidean Algorithm.

2. For arbitrary a and b, not both zero, consider all numbers of the form $ax+by$, where x and y take on all integer values. Let d be the smallest positive number in this collection. Show that $d=(a, b)$.

3. Prove that $(ma, mb)=m(a, b)$, where $m>0$ and a and b are not both zero.

4. Deduce Theorem 15 from either Theorem 14 or Ex. 3.

5. Show that the greatest common divisor of $a+b$ and $a-b$ is either 1 or 2 if $(a, b)=1$.

6. Suppose $F_n=2^{2^n}+1$, for $n=0, 1, 2, \ldots$. Show that if $k>0$, then $F_n|(F_{n+k}-2)$. Infer that any two of the numbers $F_0, F_1, F_2, \ldots$ are relatively prime.

7. Show that if $ad-bc=1$, then $(a+b, c+d)=1$.

8. Prove that if n is odd, then $n(n^2-1)$ is divisible by 24.

9. Show that in the so-called Fibonacci series, $1, 2, 3, 5, 8, \ldots$, in which each term is the sum of the two preceding terms, two consecutive terms are always relatively prime.

10. Show that the sum $1+\dfrac{1}{2}+\dfrac{1}{3}+\ldots+\dfrac{1}{n}$ is not an integer if $n>1$.

(HINT: Let 2^l be the highest power of 2 not exceeding n. Then there is no other number between 1 and n inclusive which is divisible by 2^l.)

Exercises for Chapter II

1. Prove that if $a \geq 3$ and $n \geq 2$, then $a^n - 1$ is composite.

2. Prove that $T(a)$ is odd if and only if a is a perfect square.

3. Suppose $n > 0$. Show that $T(2^n - 1) \geq T(n)$ and $T(2^n + 1) > T^*(n)$, where $T^*(n)$ is the number of odd positive divisors of n.

4. Use Ex. 6 of Chap. I to give another proof of Theorem 18.

5. Suppose k to be a given integer greater than 2.

   a) If $q_1 - 1, q_2 - 1, \ldots, q_v - 1$ are divisible by k, show that $q_1 q_2 \ldots q_v - 1$ is divisible by k.

   b) If $n > 0$, show that there is a prime p such that $k \nmid (p - 1)$ and $p \mid (nk - 1)$.

   c) By the method of proof of Theorem 18, show that there are infinitely many primes p such that $k \nmid (p - 1)$.

6. If $f(n)$ is a non-constant polynomial in n with integral coefficients, then $f(n)$ is composite for infinitely many values of n.

   (HINT: Let a be such that $A = |f(a)| > 1$. Then $A \mid f(Ax + a)$ for every x.)

7. Prove that if ξ and η are real, then $[\xi + \eta] \geq [\xi] + [\eta]$.

8. Use Theorem 27 and Ex. 7 to prove that if $m > 0$ and $n > 0$, then $(m + n)!$ is divisible by $m! \, n!$. Infer that the product of any n consecutive integers is always divisible by $n!$.

9. If $1 \leq r \leq p^n$, $p^k \mid r$, and $p^{k+1} \nmid r$, show that $p^n! \{ r! (p^n - r)! \}^{-1}$ is divisible by p^{n-k} but not by p^{n-k+1}.

Exercises for Chapter III

1. Suppose $r \geq 2$, $a_1 > 0, \ldots, a_r > 0$, and let v be the least positive common multiple of $a_1, \ldots, a_r$. Show that if we write $a_1' = \frac{v}{a_1}, \ldots, a_r' = \frac{v}{a_r}$, then $(a_1', \ldots, a_r') = 1$.

2. Suppose $r \geq 2$ and $a_1, \ldots, a_r$ are not all zero, say $a_1 \neq 0$, Let $d_1 = a_1$ and $d_n = (a_n, d_{n-1})$ for $2 \leq n \leq r$. Show that $d_r = (a_1, \ldots, a_r)$.

3. If $r \geq 2$ and $a_1 > 0, \ldots, a_r > 0$, let us denote (temporarily) the least positive common multiple of $a_1, \ldots, a_r$ by $\{a_1, \ldots, a_r\}$. Show that if $a > 0$, $b > 0$, and $c > 0$, then

   a) $(a, \{b, c\}) = \{(a, b), (a, c)\}$;

   b) $\{a, (b, c)\} = (\{a, b\}, \{a, c\})$;

   c) $(\{a, b\}, \{a, c\}, \{b, c\}) = \{(a, b), (a, c), (b, c)\}$.

Exercises for Chapter IV

1. If $a>0$ and $b>1$, show that $\dfrac{S(a)}{a}<\dfrac{S(ab)}{ab}\leq\dfrac{S(a)S(b)}{ab}$.

2. Show that an odd integer divisible by no more than two primes cannot be a perfect number.

(HINT: Show that $S(a)<2a$ for such an odd number a.)

3. Prove that the sum of the reciprocals of the positive divisors of a perfect number is equal to 2.

4. If n is an odd perfect number, show that $n=p^r m^2$, where $p\equiv r\equiv1$ (mod 4) and $p\nmid m$. If m is given, show that there is at most one prime-power p^r such that $p\nmid m$ and $p^r m^2$ is perfect.

5. It is implicit in the proof of Theorem 31 that if $a>0$, $b>0$, and $(a,b)=1$, then $S(ab)=S(a)S(b)$. Prove more generally that if $a>0$ and $b>0$, then $S(a)S(b)=\displaystyle\sum_{d|(a,b)}d\,S(\tfrac{ab}{d^2})$.

(HINT: First treat the case where a and b are powers of the same prime.)

6. The number-theoretic function $\lambda(a)$ (Liouville function) is defined thus:

$\lambda(a)=1$ if $a=1$ or if a is the product of an even number of primes (not necessarily distinct), while $\lambda(a)=-1$ if a is the product of an odd number of primes (not necessarily distinct). Prove the following:

a) If $a>0$ and $b>0$, then $\lambda(ab)=\lambda(a)\lambda(b)$.

b) $\displaystyle\sum_{d|a}\lambda(d)=\begin{cases}1 \text{ if } a=b^2 \text{ for some } b\neq0,\\ 0 \text{ if } a>1,\ a\neq b^2 \text{ for all } b.\end{cases}$

c) For $\xi\geq1$ we have $\displaystyle\sum_{n=1}^{[\xi]}\lambda(n)\left[\frac{\xi}{n}\right]=[\xi^{\frac{1}{2}}]$.

d) For $x\geq1$ we have $\left|\displaystyle\sum_{n=1}^{x}\frac{\lambda(n)}{n}\right|<2$.

7. If $a>0$, show that $\displaystyle\sum_{d|a}\mu(d)S\left(\frac{a}{d}\right)=a$.

8. Show that $\Lambda(a)=\displaystyle\sum_{d|a}\mu(d)\log\left(\frac{a}{d}\right)=-\sum_{d|a}\mu(d)\log d$.

9. Let $G(a)$ be any number-theoretic function. Denote by $F(a)$ the number-theoretic function

$$F(a)=\sum_{d|a}\mu(d)G\left(\frac{a}{d}\right).$$

Show that $G(a)=\displaystyle\sum_{d|a}F(d)$.

10. Let $f(a)$ be a number-theoretic function which never takes the value zero. Denote by $g(a)$ the number-theoretic function

$$g(a) = \prod_{d|a} f(d).$$

Show that we have

$$f(a) = \prod_{d|a} g\left(\frac{a}{d}\right)^{\mu(d)}.$$

11. Show that $\varphi(5186) = \varphi(5187) = \varphi(5188) = 2592$.

12. If $n > 0$, show that $\varphi(n)|n$ if and only if n is of one of the forms 1, 2^a, $2^a 3^b$, where $a > 0$, $b > 0$.

13. Prove that if $a > 0$ and $b > 0$, then $\varphi(ab) = \varphi(a)\varphi(b)c(\varphi(c))^{-1}$, where c is the product of those primes that divide both a and b.

14. If $n > 0$, then $T(1) + T(2) + \ldots + T(n) = \left[\frac{n}{1}\right] + \left[\frac{n}{2}\right] + \ldots + \left[\frac{n}{n}\right]$.

(Hint: Count in two ways the number of solutions of $xy \leq n$, $x > 0$, $y > 0$.)

15. If $n > 0$ and $k = [\sqrt{n}]$, show that

$$T(1) + T(2) + \ldots + T(n) = 2\left(\left[\frac{n}{1}\right] + \left[\frac{n}{2}\right] + \ldots + \left[\frac{n}{k}\right]\right) - k^2.$$

(Hint: If $xy \leq n$, $x > 0$, and $y > 0$, then either $x \leq k$ or $y \leq k$, and possibly both.)

Exercises for Chapter V

1. If $a = c_0 + c_1 g + \ldots + c_n g^n$, prove that

$$a \equiv c_0 + c_1 + \ldots + c_n \pmod{g - 1}.$$

(In particular, any number is congruent modulo 9 to the sum of its decimal digits; cf. Theorem 8.)

2. If $a > 4$ and a is not a prime, show that $(a-1)! \equiv 0 \pmod{a}$.

3. If $k > 0$ and $n(k-1)$ is even, show that there exist integers x and y relatively prime to k such that $x + y \equiv n \pmod{k}$.

(Hint: First consider the case in which k is a power of a prime and then use Theorem 70.)

4. Given that $a>0$, $b>0$, $(a, b)=1$, and $aa'+bb'=1$. Show that if $n\geq0$ the diophantine equation $ax+by=n$ has

$$1+\left[\frac{b'n}{a}\right]+\left[\frac{a'n}{b}\right]$$

solutions in non-negative integers x and y.

5. Given that $a>0$, $b>0$, $(a, b)=1$. Show that if $n>ab—a—b$ there exist non-negative integers x and y such that $ax+by=n$, but that if $n=ab—a—b$, this is not the case.

6. Show that

$$(a+b)^p\equiv a^p+b^p \pmod p.$$

7. Prove that if $m^p+n^p\equiv0 \pmod p$, where $p>2$, then

$$m^p+n^p\equiv0 \pmod{p^2}.$$

8. Given that $r>1$, $s>1$, and $rs>p$. Then if $p\nmid a$, we can find integers x and y such that

$$ax\equiv y \pmod p,\ 1\leq|x|<r,\ 1\leq|y|<s.$$

(HINT: Consider the numbers $au—v$, where $0\leq u\leq r—1$ and $0\leq v\leq s—1$. Since $rs>p$, two of these numbers must be congruent modulo p.)

9. Given that $p>3$.

a) Prove that $p!$ and $(p—1)!—1$ are relatively prime.

b) Prove that if $n>0$ and $n\equiv(p—1)!—1 \pmod{p!}$, then the $p—2$ integers preceding n and the p integers following n are composite.

10. If $p>2$, use Wilson's Theorem to show that

$$\left\{\left[\frac{p—1}{2}\right]!\right\}^2\equiv(-1)^{\frac{p+1}{2}} \pmod p.$$

11. If $1\leq j\leq p—2$ and if s_j is the sum of the products of the numbers $1, 2, \ldots, p—1$ taken j at a time, show that $s_j\equiv0 \pmod p$.

12. If $l>2$ show that

$$a^{2^{l-2}}\equiv1 \pmod{2^l}$$

for a odd.

(HINT: Use mathematical induction.)

13. If $p>2$ and $l\geq0$ or if $p=2$ and $0\leq l\leq2$, define $\varkappa(p^l)=\varphi(p^l)$. If $p=2$ and $l>2$, define $\varkappa(p^l)=\frac{1}{2}\varphi(p^l)$. If $m>1$ and if $m=p_1^{l_1}\cdots p_r^{l_r}$ is its canonical factorization, define $\varkappa(m)$ as the least common multiple of $\varkappa(p_1^{l_1})$, $\ldots$, $\varkappa(p_r^{l_r})$. Show that if $(a, m)=1$ then $a^{\varkappa(m)}\equiv1 \pmod m$. (For this reason $\varkappa(m)$ is sometimes called the universal exponent of m.)

14. Given that $m>1$ and m is odd. Consider the following four statements:

(i) m is prime,
(ii) $\varphi(m)|(m-1)$,
(iii) $\varkappa(m)|(m-1)$,
(iv) $2^{m-1}\equiv1\pmod{m}$.

a) Show that if one of these four statements holds, then those that follow it also hold.

b) Show that if $m=341, 645, 1387$, or 1905, then (iv) holds but (iii) does not. Show that if $m=561, 1105$, or 1729, then (iii) holds but (ii) does not. (There are no known examples in which (ii) holds but (i) does not.)

c) Show that if (iv) holds when $m=k$, then it also holds when $m=2^k-1$.

Exercises for Chapter VI

1. Show that the congruence $ax^2+bx+c\equiv0\pmod{p}$, where p is odd and $p\nmid a$, has a solution if and only if b^2-4ac is a quadratic residue modulo p.

2. If $\left(\dfrac{n}{p}\right)=-1$, show that $\sum\limits_{d|n}d^{\frac{p-1}{2}}\equiv0\pmod{p}$.

3. Show that $\sum\limits_{n=1}^{p-1}\left(\dfrac{n}{p}\right)=0$.

4. If $p>2$, show that the product of the quadratic residues in a given reduced residue system modulo p is congruent to $-\left(\dfrac{-1}{p}\right)$.

(HINT: Proceed as in the first proof of Wilson's Theorem.)

5. If $p\equiv3\pmod4$ and r is the number of quadratic non-residues among the numbers $1, 2, \ldots, \dfrac{p-1}{2}$, then $\left(\dfrac{p-1}{2}\right)!\equiv(-1)^r\pmod{p}$.

6. Show that the conclusion of Theorem 86 can be written

$$\left(\frac{p}{q}\right)=\left(\frac{(-1)^{\frac{q-1}{2}}q}{p}\right).$$

7. If $p>2$, show that the number of solutions of the congruence $x^8\equiv16\pmod{p}$ is 8 if $p\equiv1\pmod8$, 4 if $p\equiv5\pmod8$, and 2 if $p\equiv3, 7\pmod8$.

(HINT: Use the identity

$$x^8-16=\{x^2-2\}\{x^2+2\}\{(x-1)^2+1\}\{(x+1)^2+1\}.)$$

8. Show that for every prime p the congruence

$$x^6-11x^4+36x^2-36\equiv0 \pmod{p}$$

is solvable. How many solutions are there?

9. Use Gauss's Lemma directly to show that -3 is a quadratic residue of primes congruent to 1 modulo 6 and a quadratic non-residue of primes congruent to 5 modulo 6.

10. Prove that $\sum\limits_{r=1}^{p-2}\left(\dfrac{r(r+1)}{p}\right)=-1$, provided $p>2$.

(HINT: For each r for which $1\leq r\leq p-2$ there is a unique s for which $1\leq s\leq p-2$ and $rs\equiv1 \pmod{p}$. Accordingly

$$\left(\frac{r(r+1)}{p}\right)=\left(\frac{rs(rs+s)}{p}\right)=\left(\frac{s+1}{p}\right).\ )$$

11. Let $p>2$ and let N be the number of integers n in the interval $1\leq n\leq p-2$ such that n and $n+1$ are both quadratic residues modulo p. Show that $N=\dfrac{1}{4}\left(p-4-\left(\dfrac{-1}{p}\right)\right)$.

$$\left(\text{HINT}:\ N=\frac{1}{4}\sum_{n=1}^{p-2}\left(1+\left(\frac{n}{p}\right)\right)\left(1+\left(\frac{n+1}{p}\right)\right).\ \right)$$

12. If $n\geq1$, show that $\left(\dfrac{n}{4n-1}\right)=1$, $\left(\dfrac{-n}{4n-1}\right)=-1$ (Jacobi symbols).

13. If k is even, $k>0$, h is odd, and $(h,k)=1$, prove the following relation for the Jacobi symbol:

$$(-1)^{\frac{(h+1)k}{4}}\left(\frac{k}{h+k}\right)=\left(\frac{k}{h}\right).$$

14. Show that the Jacobi symbol can be expressed in terms of the Kronecker symbol in either of the following two ways:
If $m>0$, m is odd, and $(n,m)=1$, then

$$\left(\frac{n}{m}\right)=\begin{cases}1 \text{ if } m \text{ is a square,}\\ \left(\dfrac{m}{|n|}\right) \text{ if } m\equiv1 \pmod 4 \text{ and } m \text{ is not a square,}\\ \dfrac{n}{|n|}\left(\dfrac{-m}{|n|}\right) \text{ if } m\equiv3 \pmod 4,\end{cases}$$

$$\left(\frac{n}{m}\right)=\begin{cases}1 \text{ if } n \text{ is a square,}\\ \left(\dfrac{4n}{m}\right) \text{if } n \text{ is not a square.}\end{cases}$$

15. Show that the Kronecker symbol may be expressed in terms of the Jacobi symbol as follows: If $d \equiv 0$ or $1 \pmod 4$ and is not a square and $m > 0$, then

$$\left(\frac{d}{m}\right) = \begin{cases} 0 \text{ if } (m, d) > 1, \\ \left(\dfrac{m}{|d|}\right) \text{if } (m, d) = 1, d \equiv 1 \pmod 4, \\ \left(\dfrac{d}{\frac{4}{m}}\right) \text{if } (m, d) = 1, d \equiv 0 \pmod 4. \end{cases}$$

16. a) Show that the fifth assertion of Theorem 99 may be modified to read: $\left(\dfrac{d}{p}\right) = -1$ for suitable p.

b) If n is not a square, show that there are an infinite number of odd p such that $\left(\dfrac{n}{p}\right) = -1$.

(HINT: Apply a) with $d = h^2 n$, where h is the product of the first r primes, r being an arbitrary positive integer.)

c) If the congruence $x^2 \equiv n \pmod p$ is solvable for all sufficiently large p, show that n is a square.

Exercises for Chapter VII

1. Let a, b, and c be given and either $b^2 - ac < 0$ or $b^2 - ac = a$ positive square. Show that for any given k the equation $ax^2 + 2bxy + cy^2 = k$ has only a finite number of solutions.

2. Let a, b, and c be given and either $b^2 - ac = 0$ or $b^2 - ac$ positive and not a square. Show that there exists a non-zero k such that the equation $ax^2 + 2bxy + cy^2 = k$ has an infinite number of solutions, unless $a = b = c = 0$.

3. If k is given, show that there are an infinite number of positive values of d for which the equation $x^2 - dy^2 = k$ is solvable.

4. If d is divisible by 4 or by any prime congruent to 3 modulo 4, show that the equation $x^2 - dy^2 = -1$ has no solutions.

5. Let d be positive and not a square and suppose that the equation $x^2 - dy^2 = -1$ has solutions. If x_0, y_0 is that solution for which y_0 has the smallest positive value and $x_0 > 0$, show that the general solution of $x^2 - dy^2 = -1$ is given by the formula

$$\pm (x_0 + y_0 \sqrt{d})^{2n+1} = x + y\sqrt{d},$$

while the general solution of $x^2 - dy^2 = 1$ is given by the formula

$$\pm (x_0 + y_0 \sqrt{d})^{2n} = x + y\sqrt{d}.$$

6. Show that the equation $x^2-34y^2=-1$ has no solutions.

(HINT: The equation $x^2-34y^2=1$ has the solution $x=35$, $y=6$.)

7. If d is divisible by any prime congruent to 3 modulo 4, show that the equation $x^2-dy^2=-4$ has no solutions.

8. Suppose $d>0$, $d\equiv0$, 1 (mod 4), d not a square and suppose the equation $x^2-dy^2=-4$ has solutions. If x_0, y_0 is that solution for which y_0 has the smallest positive value and $x_0>0$, show that the general solution of $x^2-dy^2=-4$ is given by the formula

$$\pm\left(\frac{x_0+y_0\sqrt{d}}{2}\right)^{2n+1}=\frac{x+y\sqrt{d}}{2},$$

while the general solutions of $x^2-dy^2=4$ is given by the formula

$$\pm\left(\frac{x_0+y_0\sqrt{d}}{2}\right)^{2n}=\frac{x+y\sqrt{d}}{2}.$$

9. Suppose $d\equiv0$ (mod 4). Show that any solution of the equation $x^2-dy^2=4$ is of the form $x=2u$, $y=v$, where $u^2-\frac{1}{4}dv^2=1$. Similarly for the equation $x^2-dy^2=-4$, if it has solutions.

10. Suppose $d\equiv1$ (mod 8). Show that any solution of the equation $x^2-dy^2=4$ is of the form $x=2u$, $y=2v$, where $u^2-dv^2=1$. Similarly for the equation $x^2-dy^2=-4$, if it has solutions.

11. Suppose $d\equiv5$ (mod 8). If x_0, y_0 is that solution of $x^2-dy^2=4$ for which y_0 has the smallest value and $x_0>0$, and if x_0', y_0' is that solution of $x^2-dy^2=1$ for which y_0' has the smallest positive value and $x_0'>0$, show that

$$x_0'+y_0'\sqrt{d}=\frac{x_0+y_0\sqrt{d}}{2}$$

if x_0 and y_0 are even, but that

$$x_0'+y_0'\sqrt{d}=\left(\frac{x_0+y_0\sqrt{d}}{2}\right)^3$$

if x_0 and y_0 are odd. Similarly for the equation $x^2-dy^2=-4$, if it has solutions.

EXERCISES FOR PART TWO

Exercises for Chapter I

1. Show that there is a positive constant a such that there is a prime number between n and an for every positive n.

2. If $\varepsilon > 0$ show that $\Sigma p^{-1} (\log p)^{-\varepsilon}$ converges, the sum being extended over all prime numbers in increasing order.

3. Show that if m runs through the composite numbers in increasing order, then $\Sigma \{m - \varphi(m)\}^{-2}$ converges.

(HINT: If m has a prime factor $\leq m^{\frac{1}{3}}$, then $m - \varphi(m) > m^{\frac{2}{3}}$. If not, then m is either the square of a prime number or the product of two distinct prime numbers.)

4. (a) Show that $\Sigma \{\log (1 - \frac{1}{p}) + \frac{1}{p}\}$ converges, the sum being extended over all prime numbers in increasing order.

(b) If $\xi \geq 3$ show that

$$\sum_{p \leq \xi} \frac{1}{p} \geq \log \log \xi + \Sigma \{\log (1 - \frac{1}{p}) + \frac{1}{p}\}.$$

(*Cf.* the second proof of Theorem 114.)

5. For $\xi > 0$ define

$$\vartheta(\xi) = \sum_{p \leq \xi} \log p.$$

Show that there are positive constants a' and a'' such that $a'\xi < \vartheta(\xi) < a''\xi$ for $\xi \geq 2$.

(HINT: Use the fact that $\{\pi(\xi) - \pi(\sqrt{\xi})\} \log \sqrt{\xi} \leq \vartheta(\xi) \leq \pi(\xi) \log \xi$.)

6. Show that

$$|\sum_{p \leq n} p^{-1} \log p - \log n|$$

is bounded for $n \geq 1$.

(HINT: Use Theorem 27 to show that

$$n \sum_{p \leq n} p^{-1} \log p - \sum_{p \leq n} \log p \leq \log n! \leq n \sum_{p \leq n} p^{-1} \log p$$

$$+ n \sum_{p \leq n} \{p(p-1)\}^{-1} \log p,$$

and then use Ex. 5 and the obvious inequalities $e^n > n^n (n!)^{-1} \geq 1$.)

7. In the notation of Ex. 5 show that

$$\lim_{\xi \to \infty} \pi(\xi) (\log \xi) \{\vartheta(\xi)\}^{-1} = 1.$$

(HINT: Show that

$$\vartheta(\xi) \log^{-1}\xi \leq \pi(\xi) \leq \omega + \vartheta(\xi) \log^{-1}\omega$$

if $2 \leq \omega \leq \xi$, and then take $\omega = \xi \log^{-2}\xi$ for large ξ.)

8. If $\varepsilon > 0$ show that the number of distinct prime factors of n is less than $(1+\varepsilon) \log n \log^{-1} \log n$ for all sufficiently large n.

(HINT: If n has r distinct prime factors, where $r > 2$, then $n \geq p_1 p_2 \ldots p_r$ and accordingly $\log n \log^{-1} \log n \geq \vartheta(p_r) \log^{-1}\vartheta(p_r)$.)

9. If $t > 0$ and $\xi \geq 2$ show that

$$\prod_{t < p \leq \xi} \left(1 - \frac{t}{p}\right) < \log^{-t} \xi \prod_{p \leq t} \left(1 - \frac{1}{p}\right)^{-t}$$

(Cf. the proof of the second part of Theorem 115.)

Exercises for Chapter II

1. Suppose given a set of N objects and certain properties $A_1, A_2, \ldots,$ A_r pertaining to them. Let $N(A_i)$ of the objects have property A_i, $N(A_i, A_j)$ of the objects have both properties A_i and A_j, $N(A_i, A_j, A_k)$ of the objects have the three properties A_i, A_j, and $A_k, \ldots, N(A_1, A_2, \ldots, A_r)$ have all r properties $A_1, A_2, \ldots, A_r$. Let Z be the number of the objects that have none of the properties $A_1, A_2, \ldots, A_r$. Show that

$$Z = N + \sum_{n=1}^{r}(-1)^n N_n,$$

where

$$N_n = \sum N(A_{i_1}, A_{i_2}, \ldots, A_{i_n}). \qquad (1 \leq i_1 < i_2 < \ldots < i_n \leq r).$$

2. Under the conditions of the preceding problem, show that if m is even and $0 < m \leq r$ then

$$N + \sum_{n=1}^{m-1}(-1)^n N_n \leq Z \leq N + \sum_{n=1}^{m}(-1)^n N_n.$$

3. Given that $t > 0$ and that $a_1, a_2, \ldots, a_t$ are given integers no two of which are equal. Let $P(\xi)$ denote the number of $n \leq \xi$ such that $n + a_1, n + a_2, \ldots, n + a_t$ are all prime numbers. By the method used in proving Theorem 119 show that for $\xi \geq 3$

$$P(\xi) < \beta\xi(\log \xi)^{-t}(\log \log \xi)^t,$$

where β is a positive number depending only on t, a_1, a_2, ..., a_t.

(HINT: First show that the result is trivial if a_1, a_2, ..., a_t represent every residue class modulo some prime number. Also note that any prime dividing a_i-a_j for some i and j $(i\neq j)$ plays an exceptional role similar to that played by the prime 2 in the proof of Theorem 119.)

4. Show that Theorem 120 is still true if the general term of the series is $p^{-1}(\log p)^{\vartheta}$ instead of p^{-1}, where $\vartheta < 1$.

Exercises for Chapter III

1. If $m > 0$ and $\varkappa(m)$ is defined as in Ex. 13 of Part One, Chap. V, show that there exists a number g that belongs to the exponent $\varkappa(m)$ modulo m. Infer that the numbers that occur as exponents modulo m are precisely the divisors of $\varkappa(m)$.

2. Let $m > 1$. Show that the following five assertions are equivalent:

(a) m is 2, 4, a power of an odd prime number, or twice a power of an odd prime,

(b) $\varkappa(m) = \varphi(m)$,

(c) there exists a number g such that every integer relatively prime to m is congruent modulo m to a power of g,

(d) if a belongs to the exponent 2 modulo m, then $a \equiv -1 \pmod{m}$,

(e) the product of the elements in a reduced residue system modulo m is congruent to -1 modulo m.

3. If $k_1 > 0$, $\chi_1(a)$ is a character modulo k_1, $k_2 > 0$, and $\chi_2(a)$ is a character modulo k_2, then $\chi_1(a)\chi_2(a)$ is a character modulo the least common multiple of k_1 and k_2.

4. If $k_1 > 0$, $k_2 > 0$, $(k_1, k_2) = 1$, and $\chi(a)$ is a character modulo $k_1 k_2$, then $\chi(a)$ is expressible uniquely in the form $\chi_1(a)\chi_2(a)$, where $\chi_1(a)$ is a character modulo k_1 and $\chi_2(a)$ is a character modulo k_2.

(HINT: Let $u_1 \equiv 1 \pmod{k_1}$, $u_1 \equiv 0 \pmod{k_2}$, $u_2 \equiv 0 \pmod{k_1}$, $u_2 \equiv 1 \pmod{k_2}$. Then $\chi(a) = \chi(u_1 a + u_2)\chi(u_1 + u_2 a)$.)

5. Let $\chi(a)$ be a character modulo k and $\chi_0(a)$ the principal character modulo k. Let k_1 and k_2 be divisors of k, $\chi_1(a)$ a character modulo k_1, and $\chi_2(a)$ a character modulo k_2 such that

$$\chi(a)=\chi_0(a)\chi_1(a)=\chi_0(a)\chi_2(a).$$

Show that there exists a character $\chi_3(a)$ modulo (k_1, k_2) such that

$$\chi(a)=\chi_0(a)\chi_3(a).$$

6. Let $k>0$, where k has r distinct odd prime factors. Show that the number of real characters (characters of the first and second kinds) is 2^r if $4\nmid k$, 2^{r+1} if $4|k$ but $8\nmid k$, and 2^{r+2} if $8|k$.

7. Let $\chi(a)$ be a non-principal character modulo k (character of the second or third kind) and

$$S(m)=\sum_{a=1}^{m}\chi(a).$$

If d is a number such that $d\geq|S(m)|$ for every $m\geq1$, show that

$$|L(1,\chi)|<1+\frac{1}{2}+\frac{1}{3}+\cdots+\frac{1}{d}$$

Infer that $|L(1,\chi)|<\log k$.

(HINT: $L(1,\chi)=\sum_{m=1}^{\infty}S(m)\{m(m+1)\}^{-1}$.)

8. Show that the series (71) and (73) actually converge uniformly for $s\geq\varepsilon$, provided $\varepsilon>0$.

9. If $\chi(a)$ is a character put $g=g(s,\chi)=\sum_{a=2}^{\infty}\chi(a)\Lambda(a)(a^s\log a)^{-1}$ for $s>1$. Show that $e^g=L(s,\chi)$ for $s>1$.

(HINT: Show that the derivative of $e^{-g}L(s,\chi)$ is zero.)

10. Show that if $0<\eta<1$ and ν and λ are real then

$$(1-\eta)^{2\lambda^2+1}|1-\eta e^{\nu i}|^{4\lambda}|1-\eta e^{2\nu i}|<1.$$

(HINT: Use the relation

$$\log|1-\eta e^{\nu i}|=-\sum_{n=1}^{\infty}\eta^n(\cos n\nu)n^{-1}.)$$

Also show that if $\sqrt{2}|\lambda-1|<1$, the above inequality can be used in place of Theorem 149 for the purpose of proving Theorem 151. (Theorem 149 is the special case $\lambda=\frac{1}{2}$. The case $\lambda=1$ is also sometimes used.)

11. If $k>0$ use Ex. 9 to show that

$$\prod_\chi L(s, \chi) > 1$$

for real $s>1$, where the product is extended over all the characters modulo k. Show that this inequality can be used to give another proof of Theorem 151.

(Hint: The conjugate of a character of the third kind is itself a character of the third kind.)

12. Given that $k>0$ and χ_0 is the principal character modulo k. Show that as $s \to 1$ from the right

$$\frac{L'(s, \chi_0)}{L(s, \chi_0)} + \frac{1}{s-1}$$

has a finite limit. Infer from this fact and equation (82) that if $(l, k)=1$ then

$$\sum_{p \equiv l} \frac{1}{p^s} \log p - \frac{1}{h(s-1)}$$

has a finite limit as $s \to 1$ from the right.

13. a) Let $k>0$. If $\chi_0(a)$ is the principal character modulo k, show that (in the notation of Ex. 9) $g(s, \chi_0)+\log(s-1)$ has a finite limit as $s \to 1$ from the right. If $\chi(a)$ is a non-principal character modulo k, show that $g(s, \chi)$ has a finite limit as $s \to 1$ from the right.

b) Let $(l, k)=1$, $l>0$. Show that for $s>1$ (with the summations as in Theorem 154)

$$\frac{1}{h} \sum_\chi \frac{1}{\chi(l)} g(s, \chi) = \sum_{a \equiv l} \frac{\Lambda(a)}{a^s \log a}.$$

c) Prove Theorem 155 by using b) and the functions $g(s, \chi)$ instead of (82) and the functions $-\dfrac{L'(s, \chi)}{L(s, \chi)}$. In fact show that

$$\sum_{p \equiv l} \frac{1}{p^s} + \frac{1}{h} \log(s-1)$$

has a finite limit as $s \to 1$ from the right.

(d) Show that $\sum_{p \equiv l} \dfrac{1}{p}$ diverges.

14. Using Theorem 155 and Exercise 9 of Part I, Chap. V, show that, given any positive number r, however large, there exist an infinite number of primes q such that the difference between q and any other prime is greater than r in absolute value.

EXERCISES FOR PART THREE

Exercises for Chapter I

1. If $b>0$, $b'>0$, and $ba'-ab'=\pm1$, show that $\dfrac{a}{b}$ and $\dfrac{a'}{b'}$ are neighbors in the Farey series of order n for any n such that $b+b'>n\geq\max(b,b')$. (*Cf.* the proof of Theorem 156.)

2. If $\dfrac{a}{b}$ and $\dfrac{a'}{b'}$ are neighbors in the Farey series of some order, then $\dfrac{a+a'}{b+b'}$ is the only fraction between them in the Farey series of order $b+b'$.

3. Suppose that for each fraction $\dfrac{a}{b}$ with $(a,b)=1$ and $b>0$ we construct the circle with radius $(2b^2)^{-1}$ and center at $\dfrac{a}{b}+i(2b^2)^{-1}$ in the complex plane. Show that no two of these circles intersect and that two such circles are tangent if and only if the corresponding fractions are neighbors in the Farey series of some order.

4. If ξ is a given irrational number, show that there are an infinite number of fractions $\dfrac{a}{b}$ with $(a,b)=1$, $b>0$, and $\left|\xi-\dfrac{a}{b}\right|<(2b^2)^{-1}$.

Exercises for Chapter II

1. Show directly (that is, without using any of the results of this chapter) that if

$$n=x^2+y^2,\ x>0,\ y>0,\ 2|x$$

has more than one solution, then n is composite.

2. Show directly that if some $p\equiv3\pmod 4$ divides n with exactly odd multiplicity, then n is not expressible as a sum of two squares.

3. By using the identity $2(x^2+y^2)=(x+y)^2+(x-y)^2$ but using none of the results of this chapter, show that $U(2n)=U(n)$.

4. Prove that every $p\equiv1$ (mod 4) is expressible as a sum of two squares by use of Exercise 8 of Part One, Chapter V instead of the methods of this chapter.

(HINT: In the notation of the problem mentioned, take $r=s=[\sqrt{p}]+1$ and choose a so that $a^2+1\equiv0$ (mod p).)

5. By using only the result of the preceding problem and the identity

$$(x_1^2+y_1^2)(x_2^2+y_2^2)=(x_1x_2+y_1y_2)^2+(x_1y_2-y_1x_2)^2,$$

show that a positive n is expressible as a sum of two squares if no $p\equiv3$ (mod 4) divides n with exactly odd multiplicity.

6. If $n>0$, if no $p\equiv3$ (mod 4) divides n with exactly odd multiplicity, and if m is defined as in Theorem 164, show that the number of solutions of

$$n=x^2+y^2,\ x\geq y\geq0$$

is equal to the number of solutions of

$$m=xy,\ x\geq y>0.$$

(HINT: Show that both quantities are equal to $\left[\dfrac{1}{2}T(m)+\dfrac{1}{2}\right]$.

Cf. Exercise 2 of Part One, Chap. II.)

7. For $n>0$ put $b_n=1$ if $U(n)>0$ and $b_n=0$ if $U(n)=0$. Show that $\sum\limits_{n=1}^{\infty}b_nn^{-a}$ converges if $a>1$ and diverges if $a\leq1$.

8. If $x>0$ show that

$$\pi x-4\sqrt{x}-4<\sum_{n=1}^{x}U(n)<\pi x+4\sqrt{x}.$$

Exercises for Chapter III

1. Show that in the proof of Theorem 168 it is possible to dispense with the preliminary proof that m is odd. (If this is done, the inequality $|y_k|<\dfrac{m}{2}$ must be replaced by $|y_k|\leq\dfrac{m}{2}$, and later the possibility that $n=m$ must be excluded by a separate argument.)

2. Show that if $n_1>0$, $n_2>0$, and $(n_1,n_2)=1$, then

$$\frac{Q(n_1n_2)}{8}=\frac{Q(n_1)}{8}\cdot\frac{Q(n_2)}{8}.$$

3. Let $R(n)$ be the number of solutions of

$$x_1^2 + x_2^2 + x_3^2 + x_4^2 = n, \quad (x_1, x_2, x_3, x_4) = 1.$$

If $n > 0$ show that

$$Q(n) = \sum_{d^2 \mid n} R\left(\frac{n}{d^2}\right), \qquad R(n) = \sum_{d^2 \mid n} \mu(d) Q\left(\frac{n}{d^2}\right).$$

(*Cf.* Theorems 38 and 162.)

4. Use the results of the two preceding exercises to show that if $n_1 > 0$, $n_2 > 0$, and $(n_1, n_2) = 1$, then

$$\frac{R(n_1 n_2)}{8} = \frac{R(n_1)}{8} \cdot \frac{R(n_2)}{8}.$$

5. Let u be a positive odd number and v the largest square-free divisor of u. Using the results of the preceding two exercises, show that

$$R(u) = 8u\, S(v) v^{-1},$$
$$R(2u) = 24u\, S(v) v^{-1},$$
$$R(4u) = 16u\, S(v) v^{-1},$$
$$R(2^l u) = 0 \quad \text{if} \quad l > 2.$$

6. Show that there are infinitely many positive n for which

$$x_1^2 + x_2^2 + x_3^2 + x_4^2 = n, \quad x_1^2 > x_2^2 > x_3^2 > x_4^2$$

has no solutions.

7. Show that if n is sufficiently large then

$$x_1^2 + x_2^2 + x_3^2 + x_4^2 + x_5^2 = n, \quad x_1^2 > x_2^2 > x_3^2 > x_4^2 > x_5^2$$

has solutions.

Exercises for Chapter IV

1. Use Theorem 181 to give another proof that if $n > 0$ and no $p \equiv 3$ (mod 4) divides n with exactly odd multiplicity, then n is expressible as a sum of two squares.

(Hint: Without loss of generality it may be assumed that n is square-free. Then there exist integers b and c such that $b^2 = -1 + cn$. Hence the definite binary form $nx_1^2 + 2bx_1 x_2 + cx_2^2$ is equivalent to $x_1^2 + x_2^2$.)

2. If each of two positive integers is expressible as a sum of two squares, their product is also. Show that the analogous assertion for three squares is false.

3. Show that if $p \equiv 5$ (mod 12) and $p > 17$, then p is expressible as a sum of three distinct positive squares.

(HINT: Show that $p = a^2 + b^2$, where $a + b \equiv 0$ (mod 3). Then use the identity

$$9(a^2 + b^2) = (2a - b)^2 + (2a + 2b)^2 + (2b - a)^2.)$$

4. Using only the results of this chapter show that for $n > 0$ there exist solutions of

$$x_1^2 + x_2^2 + x_3^2 + x_4^2 = n, \qquad (x_1, x_2, x_3, x_4) = 1$$

if and only if $8 \nmid n$.

5. Show that for given m and n the system

$$x_1^2 + x_2^2 + x_3^2 + x_4^2 = n, \qquad x_1 + x_2 + x_3 + x_4 = m$$

has a solution if and only if either

(i) $4n - m^2 = 0$ and $4 \mid m$ or

(ii) $4n - m^2 > 0$, $m \equiv n$ (mod 2), and $4n - m^2$ is not of the form $4^a(8b + 7)$, $a \geq 0$, $b \geq 0$.

6. If $x > 0$ let $N(x)$ be the number of positive integers not exceeding x and not expressible as a sum of three squares. Show that

$$N(x) = \sum_{a=0}^{r} \left[\frac{1}{8}(4^{-a}x + 1) \right],$$

where $r = [(\log x - \log 7) \log^{-1} 4]$, and infer that

$$\frac{x}{6} - \frac{7 \log x}{8 \log 4} - 1 < N(x) < \frac{x}{6} + \frac{\log x}{8 \log 4}.$$

7. Use the arguments of this chapter to show that if $n > 0$ and $n \equiv 1, 2, 3, 5,$ or 6 (mod 8), there exist solutions of

$$x_1^2 + x_2^2 + x_3^2 = n, \qquad (x_1, x_2, x_3) = 1.$$

Also show that if $n \equiv 0, 4,$ or 7 (mod 8) no such solutions exist.

INDEX

INDEX OF CONVENTIONS

INDEX OF DEFINITIONS

INDEX OF SYMBOLS

INDEX